9.99

G000139038

**R.L. Timings**

# Manufacturing technology volume 1

# Manufacturing technology volume 1

**R L Timings**

Longman
Scientific &
Technical

**Longman Scientific & Technical,**
Longman Group UK Limited,
Longman House, Burnt Mill, Harlow,
Essex CM20 2JE, England
*and Associated Companies throughout the world.*

© Longman Group UK Limited 1990

All rights reserved; no part of this publication
may be reproduced, stored in a retrieval system,
or transmitted in any form or by any means, electronic,
mechanical, photocopying, recording, or otherwise without
either the prior written permission of the Publishers
or a licence permitting restricted copying in the United
Kingdom issued by the Copyright Licensing Agency Ltd,
33–34 Alfred Place, London, WC1E 7DP.

First published 1990

**British Library Cataloguing in Publication Data**
Timings, R. L. (Roger Leslie), *1927–*
  Manufacturing technology.
  Vol. 1
  1. Manufacturing industries. Technological development
  I. Title
  670.427

**ISBN 0-582-03039-0**

Produced by Longman Group (FE) Limited
Printed in Hong Kong

# Contents

# Foreword

*Manufacturing Technology: volume one* has been written to satisfy the requirements of the Business and Technician Education Council (BTEC) standard unit 1667C: Manufacturing Technology — level 'N' and, therefore, the requirements of students studying for an engineering qualification at the ONC/OND level. This text follows on naturally from *Engineering Fundamentals — level 'F'* and leads into *Manufacturing Technology: volume 2*. This latter text expands the topic areas of volume 1 in both depth and breadth as well as introducing further essential topic areas for students studying manufacturing engineering at the HNC/HND level.

The broad coverage of *Manufacturing Technology: volumes 1 and 2* not only satisfies the requirements of Technician Engineers, but also provides an excellent technical background for undergraduates studying for a degree in Production Engineering, Mechanical Engineering or Combined Engineering.

The author wishes to thank Mr. D.W.G. Hall for his assistance in the preparation of Chapter 5: Part Programming, and Mr. Tony May for reading the manuscript and providing many helpful comments and suggestions.

R.L. Timings
12 April 1989

# Acknowledgements

We are indebted to the following for permission to reproduce copyright material:

A.A. Jones & Shipman, Ltd. for our Figs. 1.46, 3.34 and 10.17; B. & S. Massey Ltd. for our Fig. 1.21; Cincinatti Milacron Ltd. for our Fig. 2.17; Colchester Lathe Co. for our Fig. 4.5; Dany-Loewy Ltd. for our Fig. 1.24; Kenrick Hardware Ltd. for our Fig. 1.9; T. Norton & Co. Ltd. for our Fig. 1.33; Sir James Farmer Norton & Co. (International) Ltd. for our Fig. 1.27; PMG Ballscrews Ltd. for our Fig 4.23; Rabone Chesterman Ltd. for our Fig. 10.8; Rank Taylor-Hobson Ltd. for our Fig. 10.35; Rushworth & Co. (Sowerby Bridge) Ltd. for our Figs. 7.4 and 7.5; Tucker Fasteners Ltd. for our Fig. 7.16; Windley Bros. Ltd. for our Fig. 10.16.

# 1 Alteration of shape

## 1.1 Factors affecting the selection of manufacturing processes

There are many factors which affect the selection of a suitable manufacturing process for a component or an assembly of components. Some of these factors are commercial, such as the unit cost of production and whether the existing plant is to be used, or whether there is to be investment in new and more economical plant. Other factors are of a more technical nature.

### Design specification

This is fundamental to the choice of manufacturing processes to be used as it specifies:

- (a)  the shape of the component;
- (b)  the material from which the component is going to be made;
- (c)  the quality of the component; that is, the dimensional accuracy, the geometrical accuracy, and the surface finish;
- (d)  any heat-treatment processes, and any corrosion-resistant, wear-resistant, or decorative finishing processes.

### Geometry

Cylindrical, conical and plain surfaces, where they form shaft ends, shoulders, etc., are most easily produced on a lathe. Screw threads may also be produced on a lathe. However, mutually parallel and perpendicular plain surfaces and slots are generally produced by shaping, planing, milling or surface broaching. More complex components may need to be cast, forged, or moulded to shape before machining. Thus the shape of a component will dictate the processes which must be used to produce that component.

## Quality

Quality control has become increasingly important in modern manufacturing industry. Until comparatively recently it was only necessary to specify the linear dimensional tolerances on a component and the appropriate machining process was expected to provide suitable geometrical accuracy and surface finish. This is no longer the case and as well as dimensional tolerances, the component drawing will also specify geometrical tolerances and surface roughness (finish). The manufacturing process will need to be carefully chosen not only to enable the quality specification to be met quickly and cheaply, but to achieve a level of repeatability which is economical, for example, keeping reject parts to a minimum. Generally, it can be assumed that the closer the tolerances, the greater will be the unit cost of production.

Modern production techniques involving automation and the computer control of processing (including automatic gauging built into the machining process) have substantially reduced the production costs for high-quality components. The relationship between linear dimensional tolerance and typical manufacturing processes is considered in section 6.6, whilst the relationship between surface finish and typical manufacturing processes is considered in section 10.8.

## Quantity

The quantity, or batch size, dictates the economics of process selection. Single components are generally produced (expensively) by hand, or by manually controlled machining processes. For example, the cost of producing a single component during the restoration of a veteran motor car is very much greater than the original cost, when the same component was manufactured in batches. Generally, the cost falls as the batch size increases and more productive techniques can be employed. For example, it is quicker (and cheaper) to drill all the holes in a component using a drill-jig than it is to mark out and drill each hole individually. However, when a drill-jig is used, the cost of such a jig has to be allowed for in the overall cost of the component. To determine whether the use of a jig is economical, a *break-even diagram* can be used.

Figure 1.1 shows an example of a simple break-even diagram which is based on the following data.

(a) When a batch of components is made by individually marking out the holes and then drilling them, the cost of material is £4.00 for

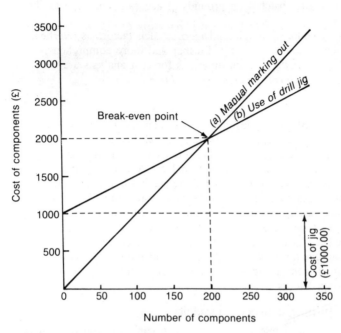

**Fig. 1.1** Break-even diagram

each component, and the labour cost is £6.00 for each component, giving a total cost of £10.00 for each component.

(b) When a batch of the same components is made using a drilling jig to position the drilled holes, the material cost is again £4.00 for each component, but the labour cost is reduced to £1.00 for each component, giving a total cost of £5.00 for each component. However in this instance £1000 for the cost of the jig has to be allowed for and this is a fixed cost irrespective of the number of components made.

Plotting these two sets of data on the same axes produces the results shown in Fig. 1.1. It can be seen that the lines, representing each batch size plotted against cost, cross each other for a batch of 200 components. This is the *break-even point* and the production cost is the same for both methods. For smaller quantities, (for example 50 components), the cost of production by method (*a*) would be £500 for the batch. Production by method (*b*) would be £1250. Thus for quantities less than 200 components the jig is not justified. However, for batches larger than 200 components (for example 500 components) the cost of production by method (*a*) would be £5000 for the batch, whilst the cost of production by method (*b*) would be £3500. Thus for batches larger than 200 components the jig is justified on grounds of cost. However the jig might be justified for smaller batches on grounds of accuracy and repeatability of quality.

This is a very simple example and ignores such factors as overhead expenses and depreciation of the jig. Further and more comprehensive examples of the use of break-even diagrams for cost analysis are considered in *Manufacturing Technology: volume 2*.

## Material

The material specified by the designer also influences the method of production. For example, a thermoplastic material would usually be injection-moulded to shape, whilst a thermosetting plastic material would be pressure-moulded in a press (see section 1.5). Again, a zinc based alloy such as 'Mazak' would be ideal for die-casting but unsuitable for sand-casting. However cast-iron would be ideal for sand-casting but unsuitable for die-casting because of its high melting temperature. Even within a selected process the material can influence the tooling chosen. For example, turned components in free-cutting low-carbon steels can be economically manufactured using high-speed steel tools. The same components turned from a high-tensile alloy steel would require more costly carbide-tipped tools.

## Machine or equipment process capacity

Figure 1.2(*a*) shows a simple component which can be stamped out of strip metal using a power press. The second operation would punch the holes in the blanks. The production cost for each component can be substantially reduced by combining the two operations in a *progression tool* as shown in Fig. 1.2(*b*). This tool produces the pierced blanks in a single operation. The cost of the more complex progression tool will be approximately the same or even slightly less than the cost of two separate tools. The decision as to which method of production is adopted will depend upon the capacity of the press available. If the press available is

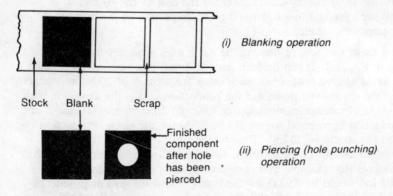

(i) *Blanking operation*

Stock    Blank    Scrap

Finished component after hole has been pierced

(ii) *Piercing (hole punching) operation*

(a) *Separate operations*

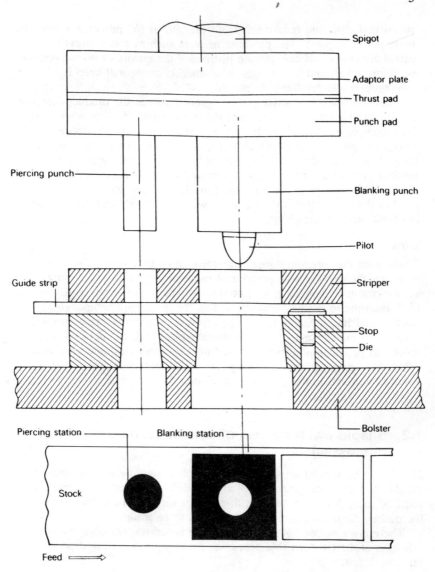

Spigot

Adaptor plate

Thrust pad

Punch pad

Piercing punch

Blanking punch

Pilot

Guide strip

Stripper

Stop

Die

Bolster

Piercing station

Blanking station

Stock

Feed

*(b) Combined operations (follow-on tool)*

**Fig. 1.2** Process capacity

capable of producing enough force to enable the progression tool to be used, then this would be the obvious choice. However, if the press available is not capable of producing the force required by the progression tool there are two possibilities: (*a*) use the existing press and make the component in two operations — which would increase the production costs and reduce the profit margin; or (*b*) purchase a new and more powerful press. The purchase of plant such as a new press is extremely costly and can only be justified if the quantities of components being produced, and the savings in production costs, will keep it continuously and profitably employed.

Sometimes a compromise can be agreed between the product designer and the production engineer so that the components are kept within the limitations of existing plant. However, market forces often dictate changes in product design which necessitate major changes in production methods and the purchase of new plant becomes unavoidable. If the producer cannot afford, or cannot borrow, the funds necessary to purchase the new plant, or does not consider that the profit margin justifies the investment, then the work will be lost to a competitor who has suitable plant capacity.

## Cost

Throughout the foregoing arguments the cost of production has been a recurring theme. The sole purpose of production is to produce goods to satisfy customer demand at a price the customer is prepared to pay and at the same time to produce a profit so that the producing company can flourish and invest for its future. To this end, a manufacturing concern must be constantly updating its production plant and techniques so as to reduce its production costs below that of its competitors, and ensure that it has the capacity to produce the goods its customers require, when they require them and to the quality specification they require.

## 1.2 Shaping with no loss of volume (sand-casting processes)

Metals can be formed directly from the molten state by pouring them into moulds and allowing them to cool and solidify. Obviously, the mould must be made from a material with a higher melting point than that of the molten metal from which the casting is to be made.

There are a number of different casting processes available and the selection of the most suitable processes for any given casting depends upon such factors as:

(*a*)   the size of the casting;
(*b*)   the complexity and section thickness of the casting;
(*c*)   the quantity of castings required;
(*d*)   the quality of the castings (e.g. dimensional accuracy and surface finish);
(*e*)   the metal from which the casting is to be made (melting temperature);
(*f*)   the mechanical properties of the casting;
(*g*)   the unit cost of production.

One of the most versatile casting techniques is sand casting which gets its name from the fact that the mould is made from a sand and clay mixture which is self-supporting when rammed to shape. This process can be used for large, medium or small castings ranging from simple shapes to highly complex ones. It is used for metals with medium and high melting points such as copper alloys and cast-irons. The mould contains a cavity in the form of the finished product into which the molten metal is poured. In the case of sand moulding, the form of this cavity is determined by ramming sand round a wooden pattern. The pattern is the same shape as the finished casting but has slightly larger dimensions to allow for volumetric shrinkage of the molten metal as it cools and solidifies. After ramming, the mould is opened so that the pattern can be removed from the cavity. The mould is then re-assembled ready for pouring. Such moulds are made by hand where small quantities are required, or by semi- or fully-automated processes where they are required for quantity production.

Figure 1.3 shows a section through a typical two part sand mould for a simple component. The molten metal is poured from a ladle into the *runner* and the air displaced from the cavity by the molten metal escapes through the *risers*. There must be a riser above each high point in the cavity to prevent air locks. Pouring continues until the molten metal appears at the top of each riser. This ensures that the mould cavity is full and also provides surplus metal which can be drawn back into the mould as shrinkage takes place during cooling. This avoids *shrinkage cavities* occurring in the casting. The mould must also contain *vents*. These are fine holes made with a wire after the mould is complete. These vent holes stop just short of the mould cavity. The purpose of the vents is to release steam and other gases which are generated when the hot metal comes into contact with the moist moulding sand. (Moisture is required in moulding sand so that it will bind together and keep its shape.) If the mould is not vented, then the release of steam and gases causes bubbles to collect in the casting. Such bubbles are referred to as 'blow-holes' if large, or 'porosity' is small. The mechanism of solidification and the defects which can occur in castings are covered in *Engineering Materials: volume 1*. When the metal has solidified to form the casting the mould is broken open and the casting is removed. The runners and risers are cut off and melted down again. The casting is now ready for machining.

It has already been stated that the pattern has to be made oversize to allow for shrinkage as the metal cools. This is called the *shrinkage allowance*. Table 1.1 lists some common metals and the magnitude of the shrinkage allowance required. The pattern must also be made oversize wherever the casting is to be machined, that is, a *machining allowance* has to be superimposed on top of the shrinkage allowance. Not only does sufficient machining allowance have to be provided to ensure that the casting 'cleans-up', but sufficient metal must be present to allow the tip of the cutting tool to operate well below the hard and abrasive skin of the casting. This is shown in Fig. 1.4.

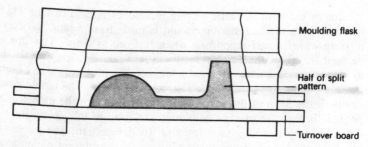

Moulding flask

Half of split pattern

Turnover board

**(a) Half pattern in position**

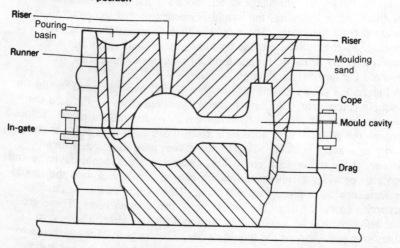

Riser

Pouring basin

Runner

In-gate

Riser

Moulding sand

Cope

Mould cavity

Drag

**(b) Complete mould — pattern removed**

**Fig. 1.3** Two-part sand mould

**Table 1.1** Shrinkage allowance

| Material | Shrinkage allowance |
|----------|---------------------|
| Aluminium | 21·3 mm/m |
| Brass | 16·0 mm/m |
| Cast iron | 10·5 mm/m |
| Steel | 16·0 mm/m |

Hollow castings require an additional part to the mould called a *core*. This is made from a mixture of moulding sand and a 'binder' which, nowadays, is usually a synthetic resin. Consider the component shown in Fig. 1.5. The inside shape is indicated by broken lines. The core, which is the same as the inside shape of the component, is made in a core box.

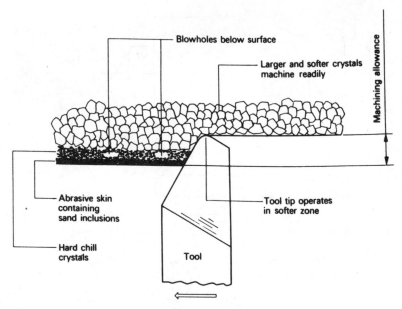

**Fig. 1.4** Need for machining allowance

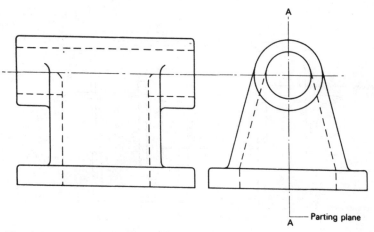

**Fig. 1.5** Cored component

The mould is then made as previously described in two parts (drag and cope). This time, however, the pattern is designed to leave locations for the core as shown in Fig. 1.6(a). These locations are called 'core-prints'. When the mould is opened to remove the pattern, the core is inserted and located in the core prints. Figure 1.6(b) shows the core in position in the lower half of the mould (the drag).

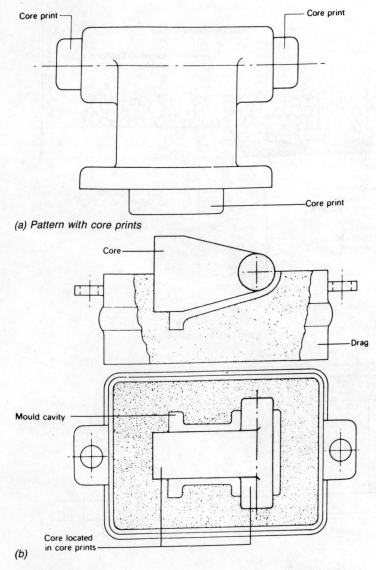

Core print

Core print

Core print

*(a) Pattern with core prints*

Core

Drag

Mould cavity

Core located
in core prints

*(b)*

**Fig. 1.6** Use of cores

## 1.3 Shaping with no loss of volume (die casting)

### Gravity die-casting

The molten metal is poured into dies from a ladle in exactly the same way as for sand-casting except, in this instance, the mould is made of metal. In gravity die-casting the parting line is usually made vertical instead of horizontal and a simple mould is shown in Fig. 1.7. Unlike the

components and up to 200 'shots' per hour for larger and more complex components. When small components are being produced multiple impression dies are frequently employed so that the machine can be operated at its optimum capacity. Figure 1.9(a) shows components as ejected from a multiple impression die. Figure 1.9(b) shows the clipped spray which can be melted down again. Figure 1.9(c) shows a set of components produced at one shot from a multiple impression die.

Figure 1.10 shows the sequence of operations for a typical pressure die-casting machine cycle.

(a)  The injection ram rises to allow molten metal to flow into the injection chamber and the dies are closed.

(b)  The injection ram descends and forces the molten metal into the die and maintains it under pressure to make good the contraction losses on cooling. This also consolidates the metal and improves the mechanical properties of the casting.

(c)  The dies open and, at the same time, separate themselves from the injection nozzle. A positive 'knock-out' ejects the casting from the dies.

(d)  The cycle is repeated.

The die-casting machine and its dies represent a very costly capital investment which can only be warranted where large quantities of components are involved. Minimum economic quantities are usually considered to be about 20 000 components for pressure die-casting, compared with 5000 components for gravity die-casting. The advantages of this process include high accuracy and good surface finish which minimises machining costs; high production rates; low material consumption rates (clipped sprays can be re-cycled without loss and without contamination), and the faithful reproduction of complex shapes and decorative motifs.

The principle of *cold-chamber* pressure die-casting is shown in Fig. 1.11. It can be seen that the process gets its name from the fact that the injection chamber is not immersed in the molten metal. This allows the higher melting point aluminium-based alloys to be cast successfully. Apart from aluminium-based alloys, the cold-chamber process can also be used with magnesium-based alloys and some brass alloys.

## 1.4  Shaping with no loss of volume (compression moulding)

Thermosetting plastic materials, such as those based on phenol formaldehyde (bakelite), urea formaldehyde, or melamine formaldehyde, are usually moulded by a compression moulding technique. The most widely used compression moulding techniques are: positive moulding, flash moulding, and transfer moulding. During moulding *curing* takes place. This is a chemical change in the moulding powder which makes it

(a) 'Spray' of
    castings ready
    for clipping
Note: Peripheral web
that improves metal
flow during casting
and gives the rigidity
essential during flash
clipping operation

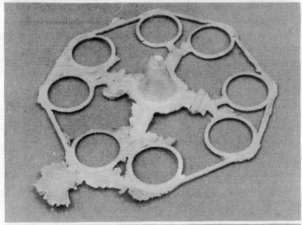

(b) The flash after
    clipping. (This is
    melted down and
    used again)

(c) The eight
    components
    after clipping
    them from the
    spray

**Fig. 1.9** Multiple impression casting

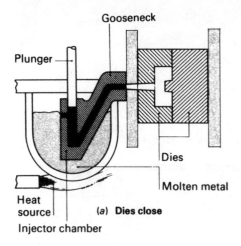

(a) **Dies close**

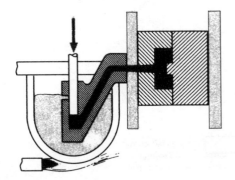

(b) **Metal is injected**

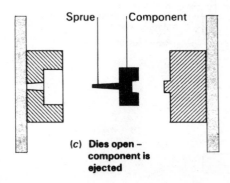

(c) **Dies open –
component is
ejected**

**Fig. 1.10** Pressure die-casting sequence

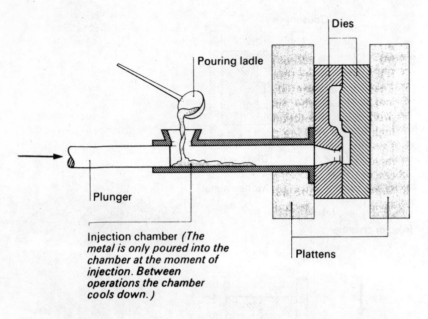

**Fig. 1.11** Cold-chamber pressure die-casting

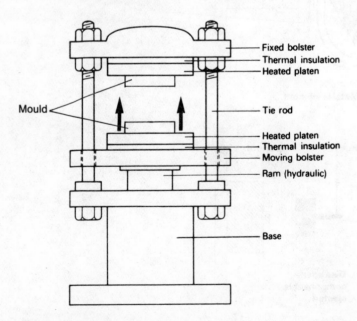

**Fig. 1.12** Up-stroke hydraulic press

hard and strong and prevents it being softened by re-heating. Since curing is accompanied by the release of water vapour (steam), the moulds have to be designed to allow for this water vapour to escape and for volumetric shrinkage to take place.

The moulds are fitted into a hydraulic press as shown in Fig. 1.12. The plattens are provided with steam or electrical heating elements so that the moulds can be raised to the curing temperature of the material being processed. Modern presses are automatic in operation to ensure that mouldings of consistent quality are produced. The three factors which have to be pre-set are: the pressure, the time for which the mould is closed, the temperature of the mould.

## Positive mould

Figure 1.13 shows a section through a typical positive mould. A pre-determined amount of thermosetting plastic moulding material in powder or granular form is placed in the heated mould cavity. The mould is

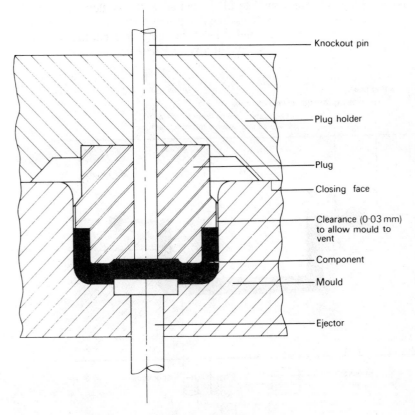

**Fig. 1.13** Positive type compression mould

closed by a hydraulic press. The moulding powder becomes plastic and is forced to flow to the shape of the mould, and the mould remains closed whilst the moulding material cures. The mould is then opened, and the moulding is ejected. Positive moulding allows the two parts of the mould to close completely so that the thickness of the moulding is accurately controlled. The disadvantages of this technique are, first, that the amount of moulding powder has to be very accurately controlled and, second, any gases liberated during curing tend to be trapped in the mould, causing porosity in the moulding. For this reason a venting clearance of 0.01 mm to 0.03 mm per side is left between the plug and the mould.

## Flash mould

This is the commonest type of mould, and it is suitable for a wide range of components. A slight excess of moulding powder is placed in the mould cavity to ensure complete filling. The excess powder is forced out horizontally into the flash gutter as the moulds close. The flash-land restricts the flow of the moulding powder and tends to hold it back in the mould cavity ensuring complete filling and adequate moulding pressure. The flash produced by the excess moulding powder has to be removed from the finished moulding after it has been removed from the press. Figure 1.14 shows a section through a typical flash mould.

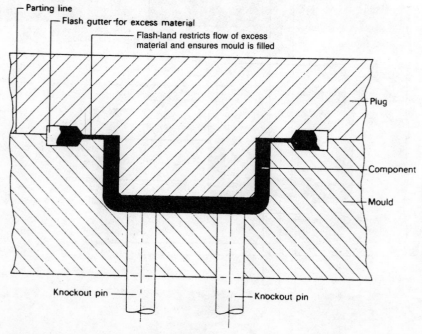

**Fig. 1.14** Flash type compression mould

## Transfer mould

This technique uses a more complex and costly three-part mould, as shown in Fig. 1.15, and is only resorted to where:

(a) the moulding is of complex shape with many changes of wall thickness which would make it difficult to ensure uniform filling of the cavity in a simple positive or flash mould;

(b) a number of components are to be made at each stroke in a multi-cavity mould. This ensures that the press is used to its maximum capacity and therefore, economically.

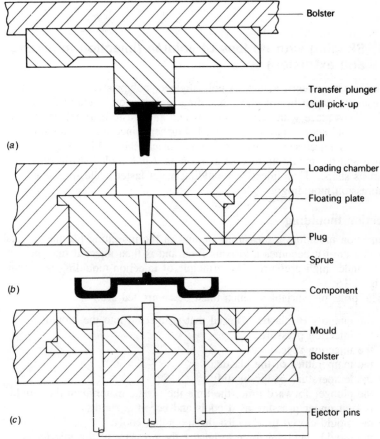

(a) Die shown open ready for removal of component and cull.

(b) Floating plate closes on mould and moulding powder is loaded into chamber.

(c) Transfer plunger descends and forces plasticised moulding powder through sprue into mould.

**Fig. 1.15** Transfer type compression mould

The moulding powder is placed in the loading chamber and becomes pre-heated and plasticised as the press closes the mould. The plasticised material is forced under pressure into the mould cavity or cavities via the *sprue*. The sprue is removed after the mould has been opened and the moulding has been ejected. The sprue is not part of the moulding, and since cured thermosetting plastic materials cannot be re-cycled, this represents waste material. Since the plasticised moulding powder is forced into the closed mould under very high pressure, complete filling of the mould is ensured, shrinkage is reduced, and improved mechanical properties are obtained from the moulding material because of the consolidation that takes place.

## 1.5 Shaping with no loss of volume (injection moulding and extrusion)

Thermoplastic materials such as polyethylene, polypropylene and nylon, are usually shaped by injection moulding or extrusion techniques. No curing takes place with these materials and any waste material, such as the flash and sprue, may be re-cycled. Further, since the moulds do not have to remain closed whilst curing takes place, the moulds may be opened and the moulding ejected as soon as it has cooled sufficiently to retain its shape. Thus injection moulding has a faster cycle time than compression moulding.

### Injection moulding

In injection moulding a measured amount of thermosetting plastic material is heated until it becomes a viscous fluid and is then injected into the mould under high pressure. The principle of injection moulding is shown in Fig. 1.16.

The principle variables which must be controlled are:

(a) the quantity of plastic material that is injected into the mould;
(b) the injection pressure;
(c) the injection speed;
(d) the temperature of the plastic;
(e) the temperature of the mould;
(f) the plunger forward time (the time the plastic material in the mould is kept under pressure as it cools and becomes rigid);
(g) the mould-closed time whilst the moulding cools;
(h) the mould clamping force to ensure the pressure of the injected moulding material does not separate the moulds;
(i) the mould open time whilst the moulding is ejected and the moulds are cleaned and sprayed with a release agent before commencing the next cycle.

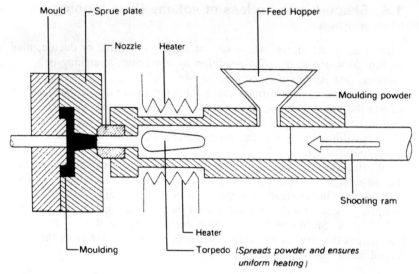

**Fig. 1.16**  Injection moulding

## Extrusion

The extrusion of thermoplastic materials is, in principle, a continuous injection-moulding process. Any thermoplastic material can be extruded to produce lengths of uniform cross-section such as rods, tubes, filaments and sections. The principle of this process is shown in Fig. 1.17 where it can be seen that, in order to obtain a continuous flow of plastic material through the die, the plunger of the injection moulding machine has been replaced by a feed screw. The plastic is still soft and lacking rigidity as it leaves the die and it must be carefully supported to prevent distortion. Cooling is provided by a water trough, mist spray, or air blast. Except for rigid plastics such as unplasticised vinyl chloride, a conveyor carries the extruded material away from the die ready for coiling or cutting to length.

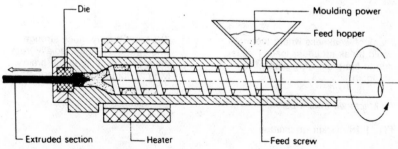

**Fig. 1.17**  Extrusion moulding

## 1.6 Shaping with no loss of volume (flow forming metals)

Many metals and alloys, which are sufficiently malleable or ductile, may be formed whilst in the solid condition by squeezing, stretching or bending, that is, they may be *flow formed*.

If the metal is flow formed above the temperature of recrystallisation, so that the grains can reform as fast as they are distorted, the metal is said to be *hot-worked*. If the metal is flow formed below the temperature of recrystallisation, so that the grains remain distorted, the metal is said to be *cold-worked*.

When metals are flow formed to shape, their grain structure flows to the shape of the component and this greatly increases the strength of the component. This orientation of the grain is shown in Fig. 1.18 which compares a gear blank machined from a bar with one machined from a forged blank. Since metals break more easily along the 'lay' of the grain than across the 'lay' of the grain, the teeth of the gear cut from the forged blank will be the stronger.

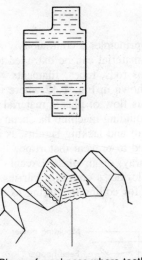

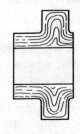

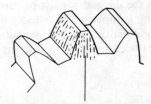

Plane of weakness where tooth could break off under load. This is due to the grain lying parallel to the tooth

The tooth is very much stronger when the grain flows radially from the blank, resulting in the grain lying at right angles to the tooth

*(a) Machined from a bar*

*(b) Machined from a forging*

**Fig. 1.18** Grain orientation

The advantages and limitations of hot-working and cold-working processes are compared in Tables 1.2 and 1.3. Some examples of typical hot-forming and cold-forming processes will now be considered.

**Table 1.2** Hot-working processes

| Advantages | Limitations |
| --- | --- |
| 1. Low cost | 1. Poor surface finish — rough and scaly |
| 2. Grain refinement from cast structure | 2. Due to shrinkage on cooling the dimensional accuracy of hot-worked components is of a low order |
| 3. Materials are left in the fully annealed condition and are suitable for cold-working (heading, bending, etc.) | 3. Due to distortion on cooling and to the processes involved, hot-working generally leads to geometrical inaccuracy |
| 4. Scale gives some protection against corrosion during storage | 4. Fully annealed condition of the material coupled with a relatively coarse grain leads to: (a) a poor finish when machined; (b) low strength and rigidity for the metal considered |
| 5. Availability as sections (girders) and forgings as well as the more usual bars, rods, sheets and strip and tube | 5. Damage to tooling from abrasive scale on metal surface |

**Table 1.3** Cold-working processes

| Advantages | Limitations |
| --- | --- |
| 1. Good surface finish | 1. Higher cost than for hot-worked materials. It is only a finishing process for material previously hot-worked. Therefore, the processing cost is added to the hot-worked cost. |
| 2. Relatively high dimensional accuracy | 2. Materials lack ductility due to work hardening and are less suitable for bending, etc. |
| 3. Relatively high geometrical accuracy | 3. Clean surface is easily corroded |
| 4. Work hardening caused during the cold-working processes: (a) increases strength and rigidity (b) improves the machining characteristics of the metal so that a good finish is more easily achieved | 4. Availability limited to rods and bars also sheets and strip, solid drawn tubes |

## Hot forging

Basic forging operations such as *drawing down, upsetting, piercing, drifting* and *swaging*, as performed manually by the blacksmith on the anvil, are shown in principle in Fig. 1.19. These same operations can be applied to larger components by substituting pneumatic and steam hammers for the blacksmith's hand tools. The hot-working temperature ranges for a number of engineering materials are shown in Fig. 1.20.

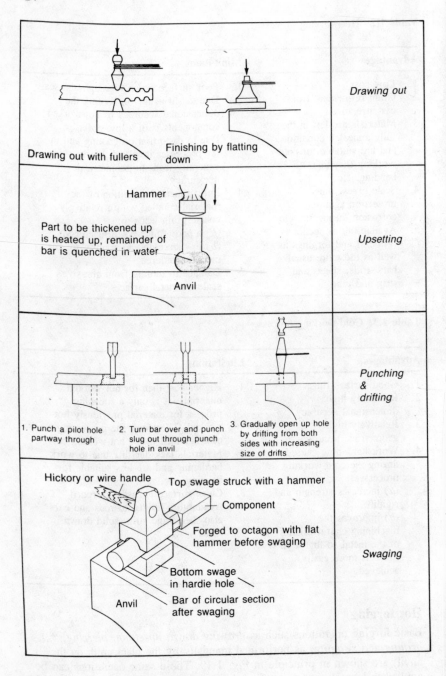

**Fig. 1.19** Summary of forging processes

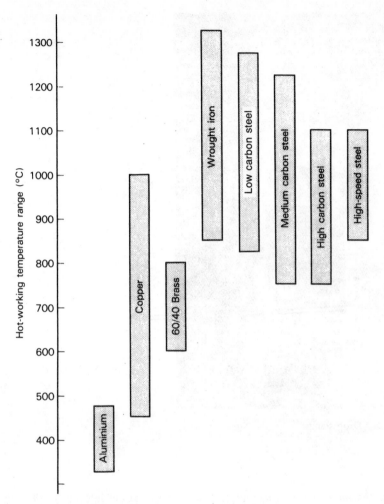

**Fig. 1.20** Forging temperatures

Where large batches of components need to be forged, as in the motor car industry, closed-die forging is used. In place of the general smithying tools previously described, formed dies are used to produce the finished component. The dies may be closed by a hydraulic or mechanical press or, more usually for small components, by a *drop-stamp* or *drop-hammer*. Figure 1.21 shows a typical drop-stamp being used for closed-die forging and Fig. 1.22 shows a section through forging dies in the closed position. To ensure complete filling of the die cavity, the hot blank is made slightly larger in volume than the volume of the finished

**Fig. 1.21**  Drop stamp

forging. As the dies close, the surplus metal is forced out into the *flash-gutter* through the *flash-land*. The flash-land offers a constriction to the flow of surplus metal and holds it back in the die cavity to ensure complete filling. It also ensures that the flash is thinnest adjacent to the component being forged. This results in a neat, thin flash line being left after the flash has been trimmed off. The flash-land should be kept as short as possible, otherwise the dies may fail to close. The *rapping faces* are provided to ensure that the component is the correct thickness when the dies are closed. The sharp 'rap' of the hardened surfaces coming into contact tells the operator that the operation is complete. The vertical walls of the die cavity are given a 7° taper, or draught, so that the forging can be easily removed.

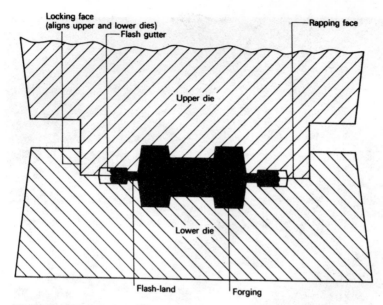

Locking face
(aligns upper and lower dies)
Flash gutter

Rapping face

Upper die

Lower die

Flash-land    Forging

**Fig. 1.22** Closed forging dies

## Hot rolling

The effect of hot rolling on the grain structure of a metal ingot is shown in Fig. 1.23, and the hot rolling of an ingot into a slab is shown in Fig. 1.24. The white-hot slab is seen to be just leaving the rolls and is supported on a motorised roller bed (conveyor).

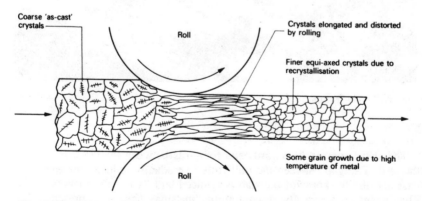

Coarse 'as-cast' crystals

Roll

Crystals elongated and distorted by rolling

Finer equi-axed crystals due to recrystallisation

Some grain growth due to high temperature of metal

Roll

**Fig. 1.23** Effect of hot rolling on the grain structure of a metal

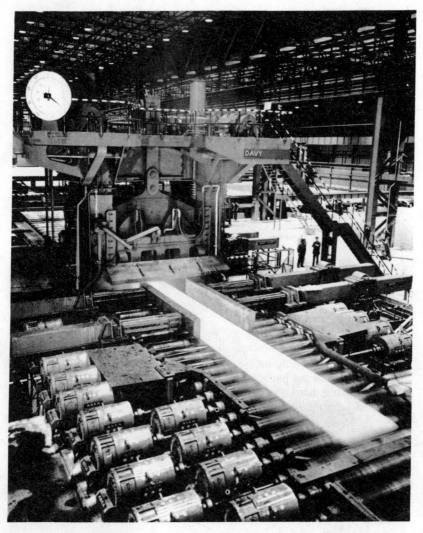

**Fig. 1.24** Hot rolling

The slab is passed backwards and forwards between the work rolss of the mill. The gap between the mill rolls is gradually reduced for each pass and the thickness of the slab is reduced and its length is increased. This process removes any discontinuities that may have been present in the ingot and also refines the grain structure and improves the mechanical properties of the metal.

## Hot extrusion

The principle of hot-extrusion is shown in Fig. 1.26. A hydraulic ram squeezes a billet of metal, which has been pre-heated to above the temperature of recrystallisation, through a die in a similar manner to tooth-paste being squeezed out of the end of a tooth-paste tube. The hole in the die is shaped to produce the required section and long lengths of material are produced by this process. Materials which are commonly extruded in this way are copper, brass alloys, aluminium and aluminium alloys. After hot-extrusion the sections are often finished by cold-drawing to improve the surface texture, dimensional accuracy and stiffness.

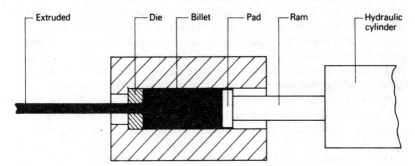

*(a) Commencement of extrusion stroke*

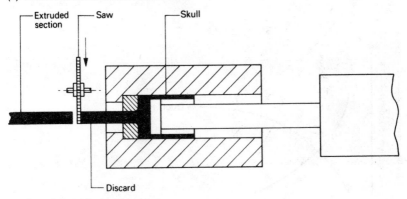

*(b) Completion of extrusion stroke*

**Fig. 1.25** Hot extrusion

## Cold-rolling

Cold-working processes are essentially finishing processes. The forces required to produce quite modest reductions in cross-sectional area are very much higher than those for hot-working, so the amount of reduction is kept to a minimum. However, the finish and dimensional accuracy produced by cold-working is much superior to that produced by hot-working. Since cold-working results in some work-hardening of the metal, there is a corresponding improvement in its mechanical properties. The metal is usually broken down by hot-working until there is only a finishing allowance left. The oxide film (scale) on the surface of the hot-worked metal is removed by pickling the metal in acid, after which it is passed through a neutralising bath and oiled to prevent corrosion before being passed to the cold-working process. Figure 1.26 shows the effect of cold-rolling on the properties of the metal, and Fig. 1.27 shows a typical cold strip rolling mill. The pickled and oiled strip is unwound from the de-coiler situated to the extreme left of the figure. This strip is straightened and flattened in the pinch rolls and leveller and passed to the mill rolls themselves for reduction in thickness. The mill shown is classified as a *four-high, single-stand, reversing mill*, that is, in addition to the reducing rolls there are a pair of backing rolls to help support the forces imposed by cold rolling, and there is only one mill stand. The metal is passed back and forth until it is reduced to the required thickness. The lower rolls in this mill are loaded hydraulically. (In earlier mills the top rolls were screwed down mechanically.) After passing through the mill, the strip, now reduced in thickness, is recoiled on the right-hand coiler. After the first pass the mill is reversed and the strip is returned through the mill for further reduction and is finally recoiled on the left-hand middle coiler.

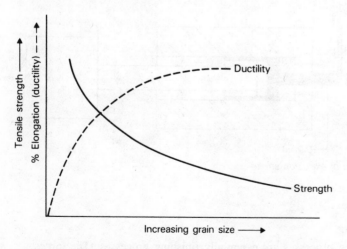

**Fig. 1.26** Effect of cold rolling on the properties of a metal

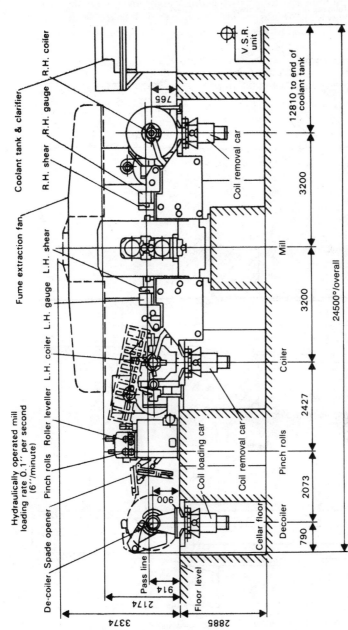

The typical line shown above consists of coil storage, coil car, undriven de-coiler with de-bender rolls. 4-high reversing hydraulic mill. Reversing coilers, coil car and storage station. Separate high and low pressure hydraulic packs provide the mill loading system and the operations of the ancillary equipment. A high capacity soluable oil system supplies strip lubrication and roll cooling.

**Fig. 1.27** Cold rolling mill

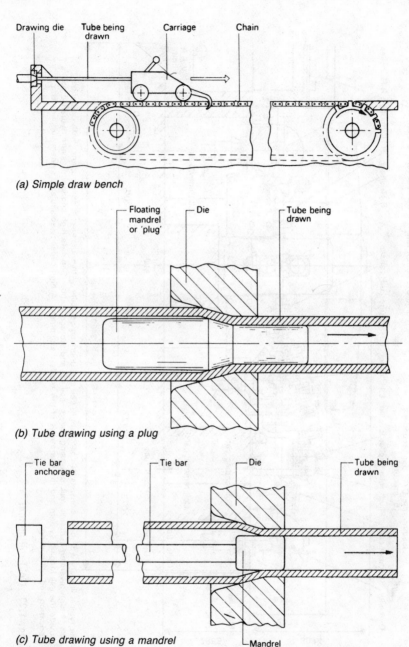

(a) Simple draw bench

(b) Tube drawing using a plug

(c) Tube drawing using a mandrel

**Fig. 1.28** Tube drawing

## Tube drawing

In this process a pickled and oiled hot-drawn tube is further reduced and finished by cold-drawing it through a die on a draw bench as shown in Fig. 1.28(a). In order to control the wall thickness and internal finish of the tube, a 'plug' mandrel is used as shown in Fig. 1.28(b). The floating mandrel, or 'plug' is drawn forward with the tube but cannot pass through the die. This technique is used for long thin-walled tube, but is of limited accuracy. Alternatively a fixed mandrel can be used as shown in Fig. 1.28(c). Obviously there are limitations to the length of tube which can be drawn with a fixed mandrel. However, it is widely used for thick walled tubes and where greater accuracy is required.

## Wire drawing

This process is shown in Fig. 1.29. It is similar in principle to tube drawing but, since a longer length of material is involved, the wire is pulled through the die by a capstan or 'bull-block'. The drawn wire may be coiled on the capstan or passed to a separate coiler after taking only one or two turns round the capstan. Fine wire, as used for electrical conductors, is produced on multiple head machines as shown in Fig. 1.30.

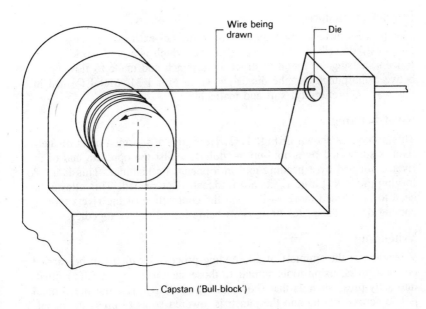

**Fig. 1.29** Single-die wire drawing

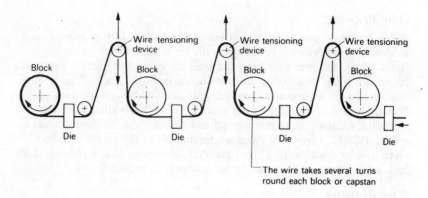

**Fig. 1.30** Multiple-die wire drawing

As the wire becomes thinner it becomes progressively longer. Thus each successive capstan has to run faster than the preceding one. The speed is controlled by the pull of the wire on the tension arm which is coupled to the capstan motor speed control. If the tension on the arm increases, the capstan motor is slowed slightly but if the tension on the arm decreases, the capstan motor is speeded up.

## Impact extrusion

This process differs fundamentally from the hot-extrusion process previously described. In impact extrusion, which is a cold-working process, a 'slug' of metal is struck by a punch and made to flow up between the punch and the die as shown in Fig. 1.31. Metal formed in this way is, preferably, soft and malleable.

## Rivet heading

This process is shown in Fig. 1.32. Here, the pre-formed head of the rivet is supported by a hold-up or 'dolly', whilst the opposite end of the rivet is formed by a heading tool in a pneumatic hammer. This is a cold-forging process. Large rivets are frequently hot-riveted. This allows the head to be formed more easily, and the contraction of the rivets on cooling draws the plates or sections being joined tightly together.

## V-bending

V-bending is the simplest of all bending processes which can be carried out in a press, using tools similar to those shown in Fig. 1.33(a) fitted into a fly-press such as that shown in Fig. 1.33(b). The flat metal blank is laid across the die and the punch is lowered so as to press the metal into the 'Vee' of the die. As the bending pressure is increased, the stress

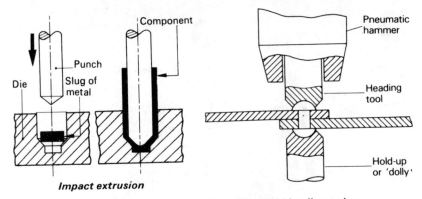

**Fig. 1.31** Impact extrusion

**Fig. 1.32** Cold-heading a rivet

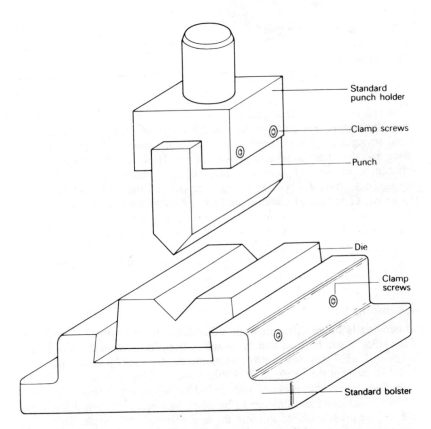

**Fig. 1.33(a)** Simple vee-bend tool

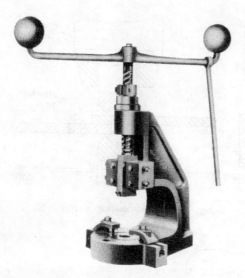

**Fig. 1.33(b)** Fly press

produced in the outermost grains of the metal (on both the tension and the compression sides) eventually exceeds its yield strength. Once the yield strength has been exceeded, plastic deformation of the grains takes place and the material takes a permanent set. However, the grains adjacent to the *neutral plane* are only subject to elastic strain and try to spring back straight when the punch is raised and the bending force removed. (The neutral plane is the layer of metal towards the centre of the section where there is no change of length as shown in Fig. 1.34.) This results in some 'spring back' of the bent metal and has to be allowed for in the design of the tools by bending the metal beyond the angle required (over-bend). For larger components and thicker material a power press or a press brake would be used.

## U-bending

U-bending is rather different from V-bending and an example is shown in Fig. 1.35. It can be seen that the blank is trapped between the punch and a spring-loaded pad which also acts as the ejector. This pressure pad helps to prevent the blank from skidding and bowing as it is bent. The spring loading of the pressure pad should be substantial if these objectives are to be achieved and this has to be taken into account when determining the size of press required to close the tool and bend the blank. To prevent skidding completely, the pressure pad may be fitted with pilot pegs positioned to locate in holes in the blank. If no convenient holes are

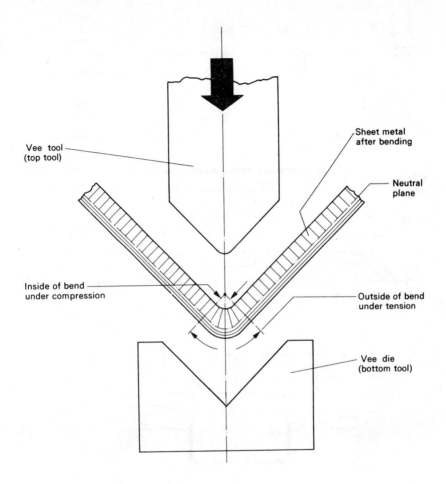

**Fig. 1.34** V-bending

available, additional holes are sometimes pierced in the blank specially
for location purposes. These are called *tooling holes*. Bending tools
should always be designed to balance the bending forces as far as
possible. When strip or sheet metal is bent, and especially when it is bent
after cold-rolling, particular attention has to be taken of the orientation or
'lay' of the grain since the orientation of the grain will be parallel to the
direction of rolling, there will be a tendency for the metal to tear and
crack if the line of the bend is parallel to the orientation of the grain.
Therefore, metal should always be bent perpendicular to the orientation
of the grain.

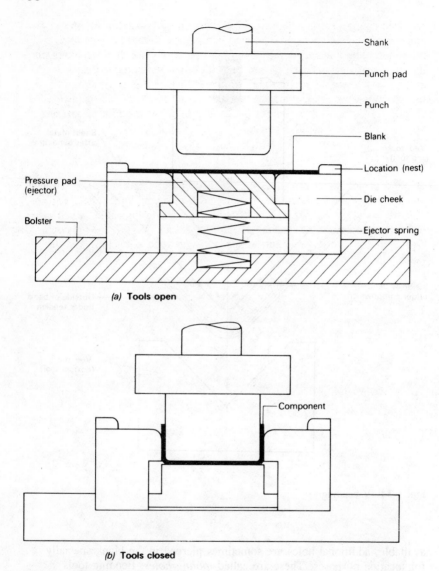

*(a)* **Tools open**

*(b)* **Tools closed**

**Fig. 1.35** U-bending

## 1.7 Shaping materials with loss of volume (machining)

During the machining of metallic and non-metallic materials, surplus material is cut away from the blank until the finished shape of the required component is achieved. This is obviously wasteful and the amount of machining to produce any component should be kept to a minimum. The advantages of machining operations are their accuracy and the high surface finish which can be achieved when compared with casting or forging. Since tooling, workholding and the kinematics of manufacturing equipment will be considered in detail in subsequent chapters, only a brief outline of the more important machining operations will be considered in this chapter.

## Drilling

Drilling and reaming processes are used for producing cylindrical holes, and for countersinking, counterboring and spot-facing such holes. Figure 1.36 shows a typical heavy-duty column type drilling machine suitable for the batch production of medium-sized components. Figure 1.37 shows typical drills, reamers and cutters for use with such a machine and the holes and surfaces they produce.

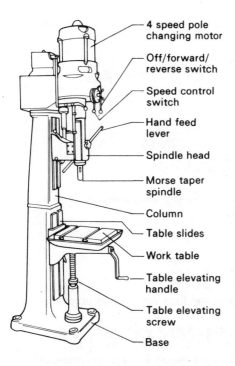

4 speed pole changing motor

Off/forward/reverse switch

Speed control switch

Hand feed lever

Spindle head

Morse taper spindle

Column

Table slides

Work table

Table elevating handle

Table elevating screw

Base

**Fig. 1.36** Column drilling machine

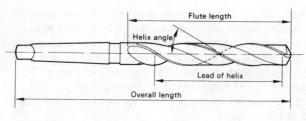

(i) Twist drill

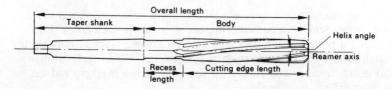

(ii) Long fluted machine reamer with Morse taper shank,
right-hand cutting with left-hand helical flutes

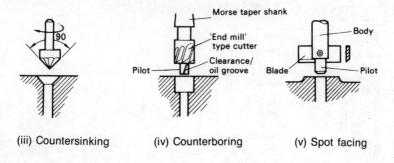

(iii) Countersinking    (iv) Counterboring    (v) Spot facing

**Fig. 1.37**  Drills, reamers and cutters for use in a drilling machine

## Turning

Figure 1.38 shows a typical centre lathe.

Typical single-point turning tools and their applications are shown in
Fig. 1.39.

Turned components are produced on such a lathe and the more
common cylindrical, conical and plain surfaces so produced are
summarised in Fig. 1.40. It can be seen that in turning operations the
workpiece is rotated and that the shape of the workpiece is determined by
the path of the tool relative to the axis of the work piece.

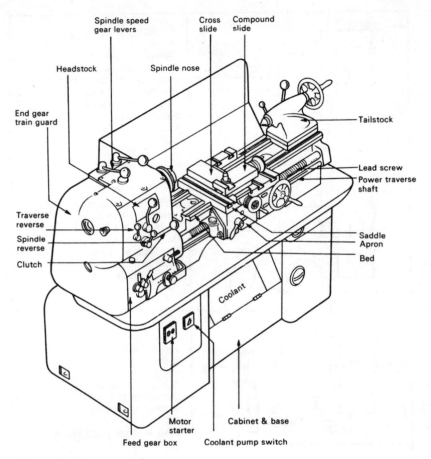

**Fig. 1.38** The centre lathe

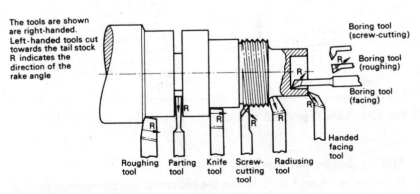

**Fig. 1.39** Lathe tool profiles

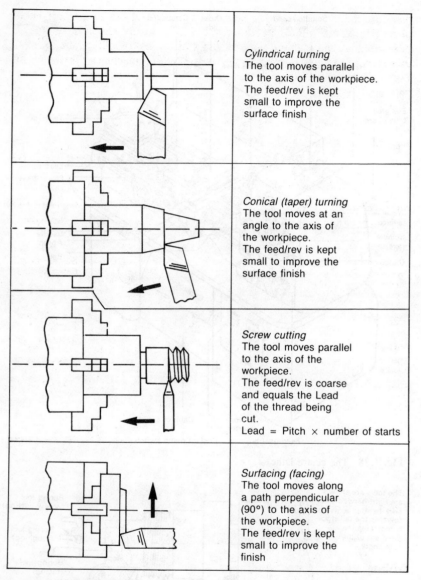

**Fig. 1.40** Surfaces produced on a lathe

## Milling (horizontal machine)

It can be seen from Fig. 1.41 that the horizontal milling machine gets its name from the fact that the axis of the spindle of the machine, and therefore the axis of the arbor supporting the cutter, lies in the horizontal plane. Horizontal milling operations produce mutually parallel, perpendicular and inclined plain surfaces using multi-tooth cutters. Some examples of the cutters used on horizontal milling machines are shown in Fig. 1.42 together with some typical examples of the shapes and surfaces produced.

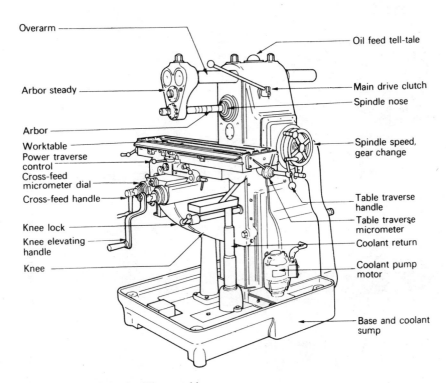

**Fig. 1.41** Horizontal milling machine

## Milling (vertical machine)

It can be seen from Fig. 1.43 that the vertical milling machine gets its name from the fact that the axis of the spindle of the machine, and therefore the axis of the cutter, lies in the vertical plane. Vertical milling operations also produce mutually parallel, perpendicular and inclined plain surfaces. They can also produce pockets and islands. Some examples of vertical milling cutters are shown in Fig. 1.44 together with some typical examples of the shapes and surfaces produced.

44

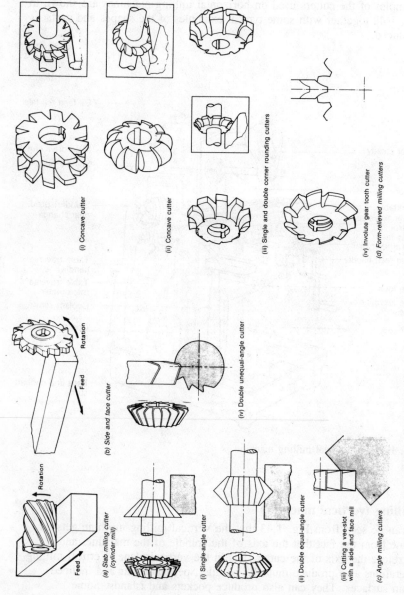

(a) Slab milling cutter (cylinder mill)

(b) Side and face cutter

(c) Angle milling cutters
(i) Single-angle cutter
(ii) Double equal-angle cutter
(iii) Cutting a vee-slot with a side and face mill
(iv) Double unequal-angle cutter

(d) Form-relieved milling cutters
(i) Concave cutter
(ii) Concave cutter
(iii) Single and double corner rounding cutters
(iv) Involute gear tooth cutter

Rotation

Feed

**Fig. 1.42** Horizontal milling machine cutters and the surfaces they produce

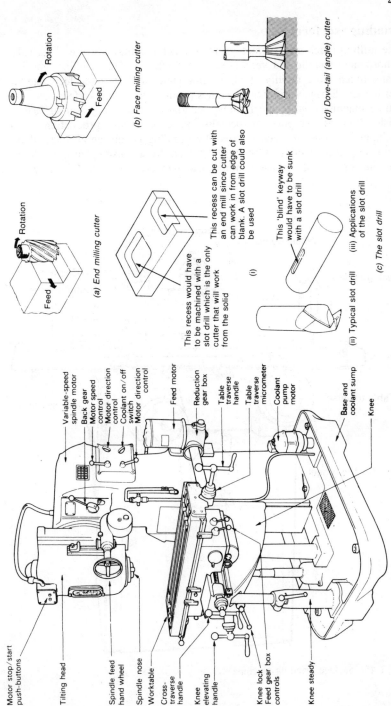

Rotation

Feed

(b) Face milling cutter

(d) Dove-tail (angle) cutter

Rotation

Feed

(a) End milling cutter

This recess would have to be machined with a slot drill which is the only cutter that will work from the solid

This recess can be cut with an end mill since cutter can work in from edge of blank. A slot drill could also be used

(i)

This 'blind' keyway would have to be sunk with a slot drill

(ii) Typical slot drill

(iii) Applications of the slot drill

(c) The slot drill

**Fig. 1.44** Vertical milling machine cutters and the surfaces they produce

Motor stop/start push-buttons

Variable-speed spindle motor

Back gear Motor speed control

Motor direction control

Coolant on/off switch Motor direction control

Feed motor

Reduction gear box

Table traverse handle

Table traverse micrometer

Coolant pump motor

Base and coolant sump

Knee

Tilting head

Spindle feed hand wheel

Spindle nose

Worktable

Cross-traverse handle

Knee elevating handle

Knee lock Feed gear box controls

Knee steady

**Fig. 1.43** Vertical milling machine

## Grinding (surface)

Like milling machines, surface grinding machines may also be classified as horizontal spindle and vertical spindle machines. The grinding wheel rotates much more rapidly than a milling cutter and the table feed rate is also higher. Surface grinding machines produce the same surfaces as milling machines but to much higher standards of accuracy and surface finish. With the exception of specialist and experimental production machines, the rate of metal removal by grinding is substantially less than that achieved by milling. Grinding is essentially a finishing process. Some examples of typical surface grinding machines are shown in Fig. 1.45.

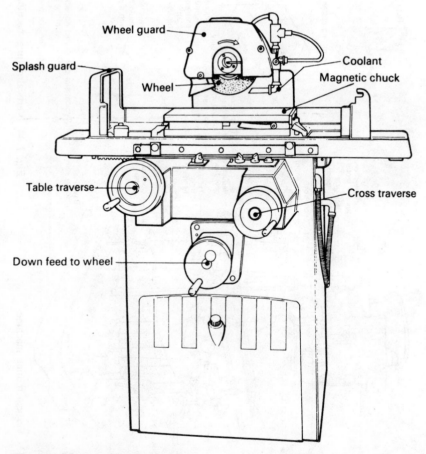

**Fig. 1.45** Surface grinding machine

## Grinding (cylindrical)

In cylindrical grinding the slowly rotating workpiece is brought into contact with the edge of a rapidly rotating grinding wheel. Again, the rate of metal removal is limited and the process is essentially a finishing process, producing work of high dimensional and geometrical accuracy with a high surface finish. A typical cylindrical grinding machine is shown in Fig. 1.46 and some examples of cylindrical grinding operations are shown in Fig. 1.47.

**Fig. 1.46** Cylindrical grinding machine

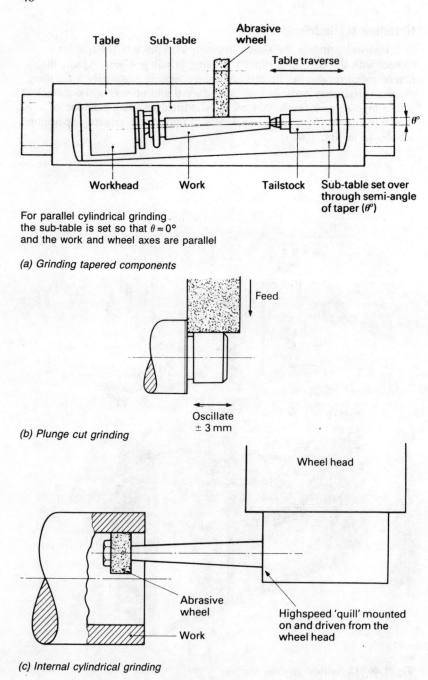

Table  Sub-table  **Abrasive wheel**

Table traverse

$\theta°$

Workhead  Work  Tailstock  Sub-table set over through semi-angle of taper ($\theta°$)

For parallel cylindrical grinding
the sub-table is set so that $\theta = 0°$
and the work and wheel axes are parallel

*(a) Grinding tapered components*

Feed

Oscillate
± 3 mm

*(b) Plunge cut grinding*

Wheel head

Abrasive wheel

Highspeed 'quill' mounted on and driven from the wheel head

Work

*(c) Internal cylindrical grinding*

**Fig. 1.47** Some cylindrical grinding operations

## Chemical machining (etching)

This technique is used to produce printed circuit boards and similar components. The metal is removed by allowing it to react with a chemical reagent, for example ferric chloride solution is used to remove copper. The solution is either sprayed on to the surface to be attacked, or the whole component is immersed in the solution.

(a) The circuit to be transcribed onto copper-faced tufnol or fibre glass board is produced as a large scale drawing. This is reduced photographically to an actual-size transparency.

(b) The copper-faced board is pre-treated with a *photo-resist* coating which is sensitive to ultra-violet light. The transparency of the circuit is placed tightly in contact with the treated circuit board material and exposed to ultra-violet light.

(c) The exposed board is placed in a developer solution which removes the photo-resist where it has been exposed to the ultra-violet light and hardens the photo-resist wherever it was masked by the transparency making such areas immune to the reagent.

(d) The board is now exposed to the reagent and the copper is stripped away wherever it was unprotected by the transparency of the circuit. The chemically machined (etched) circuit board is then washed to remove all traces of the reagent and any residual coating of photo-resist. The printed circuit is then tinned ready for drilling and for the mounting and soldering of the components.

## 1.8 Shaping with loss of volume (shearing)

Blanks cut from sheet or strip metal are produced by shearing processes. The principle of cutting a material by shearing is shown in Fig. 1.48.

*Stage 1* As the top cutting blade is moved downwards and brought to bear on the material with continuing pressure, the top and bottom surfaces of the material are deformed.

*Stage 2* As the pressure increases, the cutting blades close together and *plastic deformation* of the material occurs.

*Stage 3* After a certain amount of plastic deformation has occurred, the cutting blades start to cut into the material. The remaining uncut material commences to work-harden and become brittle in the zone indicated.

*Stage 4* Fractures start to run into the work-hardened zone from the point of contact with the cutting blades. When the fractures meet, the material being cut fails in shear and the two portions separate.

It is a popular misconception that, in order to get a clean cut blank free from 'burr', the edges of the cutting blades should be set close together. In fact, there should be a carefully controlled clearance between

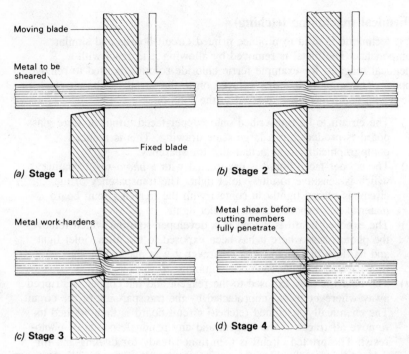

**Fig. 1.48** The shearing action

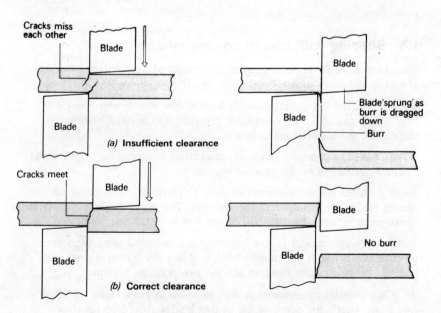

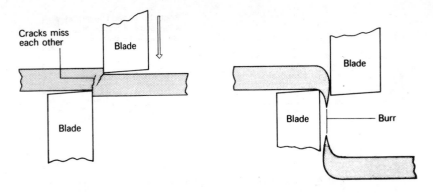

*(c)* **Excessive clearance**

**Fig. 1.49** Need for correct clearance

the cutting blades. The reason for this is shown in Fig. 1.49. If the blades are set too close together the cracks, which run out from the points of contact with the cutting edges, miss each other and a clean shear does not take place. The excess metal tends to spring the blades apart and is dragged down between them to form a 'burr' on the cut edge. This also causes excessive wear of the blades which soon become blunt. Where correct clearance is applied, as shown in Fig. 1.49(*b*), the cracks coincide and a clean shear occurs leaving minimum 'burr'. Wear on the shear blades is also reduced to a minimum. Excessive clearance, as shown in Fig. 1.49(*c*), again causes the cracks to miss each other. There is also sufficient clearance through which the material may be dragged. This results in a radius on the outer edge of the material being cut and a heavy 'burr' on the inner edge of the material. For correct shearing, the correct clearance must be carefully chosen to suit the type of material and its thickness. The cutting edges of the shear blades must be kept sharp. A correctly sheared edge is shown in Fig. 1.50.

Where a large number of sheet metal blanks of complex shape are required it is usual to stamp them out in a press using a *blanking tool*. Figure 1.51(*a*) shows a simple blanking tool for use in a press whilst Fig. 1.51(*b*) shows the strip and the blank stamped from it. Blanking is a very rapid process with up to several hundred components being produced each minute. In principle, it is a shearing process and the force to cut the blank from the strip can be calculated as shown in Example 1.1.

Since the cutting action of a blanking tool is the same as for the shearing process previously described, it is equally important that the

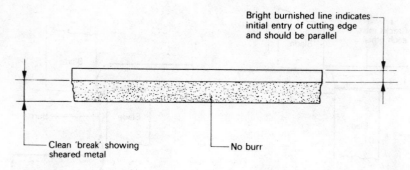

Bright burnished line indicates initial entry of cutting edge and should be parallel

Clean 'break' showing sheared metal

No burr

*(a)* **Appearance of sheared edge when clearance is correct**

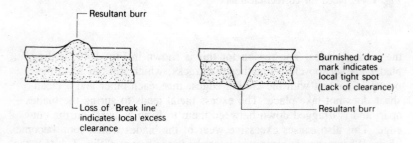

Resultant burr

Loss of 'Break line' indicates local excess clearance

Burnished 'drag' mark indicates local tight spot (Lack of clearance)

Resultant burr

*(b)* **Appearance of sheared edge when clearance is incorrect**

**Fig. 1.50** Correctly sheared edge

correct clearance exists between the punch and the die. Some typical examples of clearances are given in Table 1.4, and the calculation of suitable punch and die diameters for cutting blanks from low-carbon steel strip is given in Example 1.2. Note that for blanking, the die is made the required size and the clearance is deducted from the punch. For piercing (hole punching) the punch is made the required size and the clearance is added to the die.

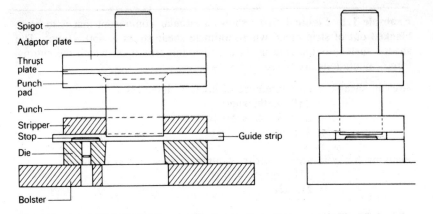

Spigot
Adaptor plate
Thrust plate
Punch pad
Punch
Stripper
Stop
Die
Bolster

Guide strip

*(a) Blanking tool*

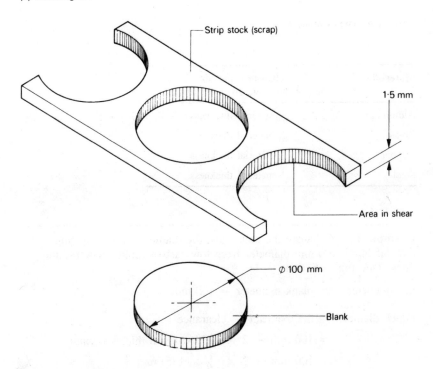

Strip stock (scrap)

1·5 mm

Area in shear

Ø 100 mm

Blank

*(b) Circular blank produced by tool (a)*

**Fig. 1.51** Blanking

**Example 1.1** Figure 1.51($b$) shows a circular component that is to be blanked out of strip metal whose ultimate shear stress is 450 N/mm$^2$. The shaded surface is the area in shear and is the area upon which the cutting force calculations are based ($\pi = 3 \cdot 14$).

Area in shear = circumference of hole × thickness
= 2$\pi$R × thickness
= 2 × 3·14 × 50 × 1·5
= 471 mm$^2$

Blanking force = area in shear × ultimate shear stress of metal
= 471 mm$^2$ × 450 N
= 212 kN

**Table 1.4**  Die clearances

| Material | clearance per side (double the value given for diameters) |
|---|---|
| Aluminium | $\frac{1}{60}$ material thickness |
| Brass | $\frac{1}{40}$ material thickness |
| Copper | $\frac{1}{50}$ material thickness |
| Steel | $\frac{1}{20}$ material thickness |

**Example 1.2**  Calculate the punch and die diameters for producing a circular blank 100 mm diameter from low carbon (mild) steel 1·5 mm thick. (see Fig. 1.51($b$)).

Die diameter = blank diameter = 100 mm

Punch diameter = die diameter − clearance
= 100 mm − 2 × ($\frac{1}{20}$* × metal thickness) mm
= 100 mm − 2 × ($\frac{1}{20}$ × 1·5) mm
= 100 mm − 2 × 0·075 mm
= 100 mm − 0·15 mm
= 99·85 mm

*See Table 1.4

## 1.9 Blank layout

In order to avoid waste, the positioning of the blank in the strip material is very important. Figure 1.52 shows some examples of alternative blank layouts. For instance, the 'L'-shaped bracket may be cut from the strip as shown in Fig. 1.52(a) or as in Fig. 1.52(b). It is apparent that in the latter case greater economy of material is obtained. Alternatively, the strip may be passed through the tools twice, as shown in Fig. 1.52(c) and 1.52(d).

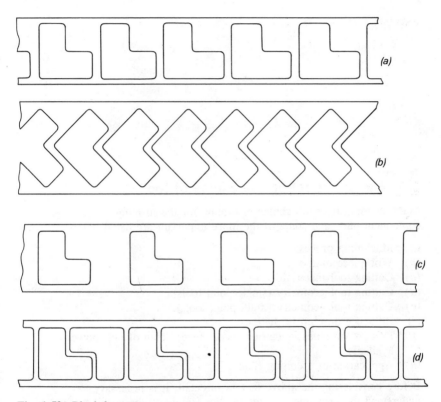

**Fig. 1.52**  Blank layout

# 2 Tooling

## 2.1 Factors affecting the choice of tooling

Many factors affect the choice of tooling for the manufacture of a given component part, and some of the more important are listed below.

(*a*) Machining process.
(*b*) Workpiece material.
(*c*) Cutting tool materials.
(*d*) Cutting tool geometry (single-point tools).
(*e*) Cutting tool geometry (multi-point tools).
(*f*) Influence on chip formation.
(*g*) Process variables — cutting speed, feed, depth of cut, power available.
(*h*) Application of a cutting fluid.

Before considering the above factors in detail, it is necessary to understand the principles of cutting. For simplicity these will be applied to single-point cutting tools as used on lathes, shaping and planing machines. The same principles apply, in general, to multi-point cutting tools such as milling cutters.

## 2.2 Basic principles of cutting tools

All cutting tools used for machining metals and non-metals require a basic wedge shape. Figure 2.1(*a*) shows a cutting tool ground so that it

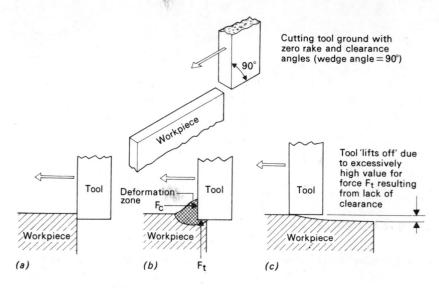

**Fig. 2.1** The need for clearance

has a zero rake angle and a zero clearance angle. The work piece, which is slightly narrower than the width of the cutting tool, is a low strength ductile material such as low-carbon (mild) steel. Figure 2.1(*b*) shows what happens when the tool starts to cut. The metal just ahead of the tool is compressed until it starts to shear away from the workpiece and piles up ahead of the cutting tool. This deformation of the metal ahead of the cutting tool sets up reaction forces to the movement of the cutting tool. The most important of these, as shown in Fig. 2.1(*b*), are:

$F_c$ which is the cutting reaction force;
$F_t$ which is the thrust reaction force.

Assuming that the machine tool in which cutting is taking place is strong enough to keep cutting without mechanical failure, the thrust force ($F_t$) would gradually push the tool off the workpiece, by springing the tool and workpiece apart, as shown in Fig. 2.1(*c*). The underside of the tool would be heavily worn and scored, the cutting edge would be destroyed, and the newly cut surface of the workpiece would be very rough and uneven.

The situation can be greatly improved by grinding a *clearance angle* of about 7° on the tool as shown in Fig. 2.2(*a*). This allows the tool to 'bite' into the workpiece and also prevents the underside of the tool from rubbing on the newly cut surface, thus reducing the thrust force ($F_t$). The tool can now cut relatively freely without lifting off the workpiece. The chip produced by workpiece material shearing ahead of the cutting tool has the shape shown in Fig. 2.2(*b*). The chip parts from the workpiece along a path called a *shear plane*. In Fig. 2.2(*c*), the chip has been

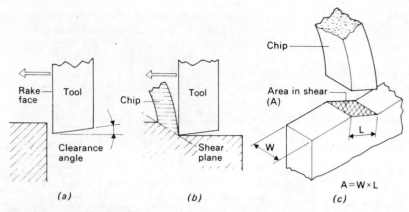

**Fig. 2.2** The shear plane

'lifted away' from the workpiece to expose the area in shear. It can be seen that the length of the shear plane (L) multiplied by the width of the cut (W) gives the area (A) in shear for the material being cut.

For any given material the smaller the area in shear can be made, the smaller will be the cutting force ($F_c$) and the greater will be the cutting efficiency. Since any reduction in the width of cut would cause a corresponding reduction in the rate of metal removal, the most effective way of reducing the shear area is to reduce the length of the shear plane (L). It has been shown by experimentation that if the rake face of the tool is inclined away from the perpendicular by giving the tool a *positive rake angle*, the length of the shear plane is reduced as shown in Fig. 2.3. Furthermore, a rake face with a positive rake angle enables the chip to

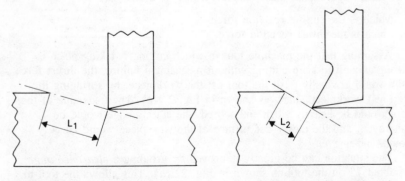

$L_1$ = Shear plane with zero rake          $L_2$ = Shear plane with positive rake

Comparing $L_1$ with $L_2$, it is apparent that the shear plane is shortened by increasing the rake angle from zero to a positive value.

**Fig. 2.3** The effect of rake on the shear plane

peel away from the parent material without having to turn through such an acute angle. Thus, a high positive rake angle reduces the cutting force ($F_c$) by reducing the cutting area, and it also reduces the pressure of the chip on the rake face of the tool. Both these factors lead to increased cutting efficiency and reduced tool wear.

Unfortunately, there is a limit to how much the rake angle can be increased. Figure 2.4 shows the metal cutting *wedge*. It can be seen that three angles are involved: clearance angle, rake angle and tool or wedge angle. The clearance angle is generally fixed at the following angles by the surface being cut.

(*a*)  External cylindrical surfaces 5° to 7°.
(*b*)  Flat surfaces 6° to 8°.
(*c*)  Internal cylindrical surfaces 8° to 10° plus secondary clearance.

Clearance angles less than the above values can lead to rubbing, whilst angles greater than the above can lead to 'chatter' and a tendency for the tool to 'dig-in'. Further, any increase in the clearance angle leads to a corresponding reduction in the wedge angle and reduction in the strength of the tool at the cutting edge.

Thus with the clearance angle fixed within narrow limits, the rake angle and wedge angle have to be balanced to form a compromise between cutting efficiency (high value of rake angle) and tool strength (high value of wedge angle). A low value of wedge angle not only reduces the strength of the tool at the cutting edge, it also reduces the mass of metal behind the cutting edge which is available to conduct away the heat generated by the cutting process. This can lead to overheating of the tool, resulting in softening and early failure of the cutting edge.

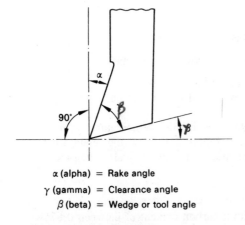

α (alpha)  = Rake angle
γ (gamma) = Clearance angle
β (beta)  = Wedge or tool angle

| Some typical rake angles for high speed steel tools | |
| --- | --- |
| Material being cut | Rake |
| Cast iron | 0° |
| Free-cutting brass | 0° |
| Ductile brass | 14° |
| Tin bronze | 8° |
| Aluminium alloy | 30° |
| Mild steel | 25° |
| Medium carbon steel | 20° |
| High carbon steel | 12° |
| 'Tufnol' plastic | 0° |

**Fig. 2.4**  Cutting tool angles

## 2.3 Workpiece materials

The material from which the workpiece is made has a considerable
influence upon the choice of cutting tool geometry and cutting tool
material. Generally, when using high-speed steel cutting tools, low-
strength ductile materials are cut with high-rake angle tools to take
advantage of the increased cutting efficiency and to leave a good surface
finish. High-strength materials are cut with low-rake angle tools to give
the cutting edge a large wedge angle to provide adequate strength and
heat dissipation capability. Typical rake angles for high-speed steel single-
point cutting tools are listed in Fig. 2.4. The values given are for
roughing cuts and may be increased slightly, with advantage, for finishing
cuts.

So far, only ductile metals have been considered and the only factor
influencing the choice of rake angle has been the shear strength of the
workpiece. However, other materials often have to be machined. For
example, sand castings and thermoset plastic mouldings are highly
abrasive and carbide tooling is used for these materials to give an
adequate tool life, despite the fact that the shear strength of these
materials is relatively low. Carbide tooling is also required when
machining high-strength alloys. Such tooling is also used where the
economics of manufacture demand high rates of metal removal and where
machine tools are available with sufficient power to exploit such tooling.
Non-ductile materials such as grey cast iron and free-cutting brass do not
form the continuous, ribbon-like chip associated with the ductile metals,
but form a granular, discontinuous chip (see section 2.8). For such non-
ductile materials the rake angle of the cutting tool can be reduced to
very low values (see Fig. 2.4) and advantage can be taken of the
corresponding increase in tool strength.

## 2.4 Cutting tool materials

Cutting tool materials must have the following properties:

(a) sufficient strength to resist the cutting forces;
(b) sufficient hardness to resist wear and give an adequate life between
regrinds;
(c) the ability to retain its hardness at the high temperatures generated
at the tool point when cutting. Figure 2.5 shows the relationship
between hardness and temperature for some typical cutting-tool
materials.

### High-carbon steels

These are plain carbon steels with a carbon content of between 0.87%
and 1.2%. As can be seen from Fig. 2.5, although such steels can have
an initial hardness greater than high-speed steel, its hardness is rapidly

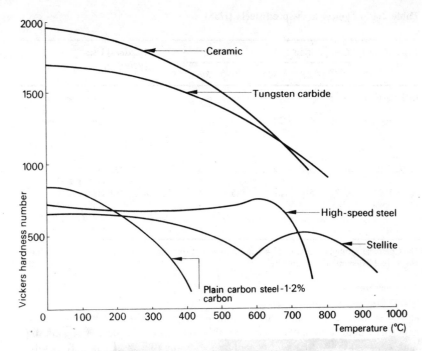

**Fig. 2.5** Hardness-temperature curves for cutting-tool materials

reduced when the temperature rises. Therefore such steels are unsuitable for production machining and are mainly used for hand tools.

## High-speed steels

These are amongst the most widely used cutting-tool materials for such applications as drills, reamers, milling cutters, turning tools, thread-cutting tools, planing and shaping tools. In the annealed condition high-speed steels can be forged and machined with relative ease yet, when hardened, they retain sufficient strength to work unsupported with high positive rake angles whilst retaining their hardness almost up to red-heat. Table 2.1 lists the composition of some typical high speed steels. The more costly 'super-high-speed steels' contain an appreciable amount of cobalt. This has the effect of substantially raising the temperature at which the steel can retain its hardness, as well as increasing its strength and toughness so that it can resist the cutting forces met with when machining modern high strength alloys.

## Stellite

This is a cobalt based alloy containing little or no iron. It can only be cast to shape or deposited as a hard facing. It requires no heat treatment

**Table 2.1**  Typical high-speed steels (HSS)

| Type of steel | Composition (%) | | | | | | Hardness (VNP) | Uses |
|---|---|---|---|---|---|---|---|---|
| | C | Cr | W | V | Mo | Co | | |
| 18% tungsten | 0·68 | 4·0 | 19·0 | 1·5 | | | 800−850 | Low quality alloy, not much used |
| 30% tungsten | 0·75 | 4·7 | 22·0 | 1·4 | | | 850−950 | General-purpose cutting tools for jobbing work shops |
| 6% Cobalt | 0·8 | 5·0 | 19·0 | 1·5 | 0·5 | 6·0 | 800−900 | Heavy-duty cutting tools |
| Super HSS 12% cobalt | 0·8 | 5·0 | 21·0 | 1·5 | 0·5 | 11·5 | 850−950 | Heavy-duty cutting tools for machining high-tensile materials |

The Chemical symbols used are: $C$ = Carbon, $Cr$ = chromium, $W$ = tungsten, $V$ = vanadium, $Mo$ = molybdenum, $Co$ = cobalt.

Remainder iron

and is so hard that it can only be machined by grinding. It is much more expensive than high-speed steel and although slightly softer, it retains its hardness even when the cutting edge is glowing red-hot. It is sufficiently strong and tough to be used in standard tool-holders at high values of positive rake angles. A typical composition is: cobalt 50%; tungsten 33%; carbon 3%; various 14%.

## Cemented carbides

Preformed tool tips made from metallic carbides are harder and cheaper than stellite, and capable of operating at the same temperatures. Carbides can only be machined by grinding, using silicon carbide (green grit) abrasive wheels. Carbide cutting tools fall into three categories.

*Tungsten carbide* is very hard and brittle and is used to machine such materials as grey cast iron and cast bronzes. These metals have a relatively low tensile strength and form a discontinuous chip. However they have a hard and abrasive skin as a result of the casting process. Tool tips made from tungsten carbide tend to be porous and particles of metal from the workpiece material tend to become embedded in the tool tip. Although the metal being cut will not chip-weld directly to the carbide, it will adhere to the embedded particles to form a built up edge (see section 2.8). Therefore, owing to its brittleness and low strength coupled with the tendency for a built up edge to form on the tool tip, straight tungsten carbide inserts are unsuitable for machining ductile materials.

*Mixed carbides* are mixtures of tungsten and titanium carbides. They are less hard and abrasion resistant than straight tungsten carbide, but are very much stronger and tougher and are used for cutting high strength materials. They are also less porous than straight tungsten carbide and are, therefore, less prone to form a built-up edge.

*Coated carbides* are more expensive than tungsten or mixed carbides but can be run at cutting speeds up to 30% greater than those recommended for tungsten or mixed carbides without any reduction in tool life.

Table 2.2 lists the standard grades of carbide together with some typical applications.

Since carbides are very brittle compared with metallic cutting tool materials they have to be securely supported by the tool shank to which

**Table 2.2** Carbide grades for metal cutting tools

| ISO Code | ISO Grades | General Applications |
|---|---|---|
| **P** (Blue) | P01 → P50 | Ductile materials such as plain carbon and low alloy steels, stainless steel, long-chipping malleable cast iron, ductile non-ferrous metals and alloys |
| **M** (Yellow) | M10 → M40 | Tough and 'difficult' materials such as: high carbon steels and high duty alloy steels, manganese steels, cast steels, alloy cast irons, austenitic stainless steel castings, malleable cast iron, heat-resistant alloys |
| **K** (Red) | K01 → K30 | Materials lacking in ductility and components which cause intermittent cutting. Cast iron, chill-cast iron, short-chipping malleable cast iron, hardened steel, non-ferrous free-cutting alloys, free-cutting steels, plastics, wood, titanium alloys |

*CUTTING PROPERTIES*

PO1 ◄———————————————— K30

Increasing hardness and ability to withstand wear — high cutting speeds and fine feeds

P01 ————————————————► K30

Increasing toughness and ability to withstand interrupted cutting with coarse feeds — rough machining high strength materials

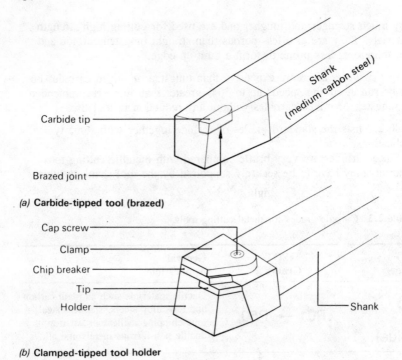

*(a)* **Carbide-tipped tool (brazed)**

*(b)* **Clamped-tipped tool holder**

**Fig. 2.6** Carbide tipped single point tools

they may be brazed or clamped as shown in Fig. 2.6. Modern practice favours the use of clamped, indexable tips so that they can be simply turned around to expose a new cutting edge when blunt and finally throwing the tip away when all the edges have been used, that is, 'throwaway' tooling. This results in more consistent machining performance since standard replacement tips are manufactured to a high degree of accuracy.

## Ceramics

Ceramic tips are even harder than those made from carbides and are even more brittle. The ceramic material most commonly used is aluminium oxide, either commercially pure or mixed with other metallic oxides such as chromic oxide. Ceramic tips cannot be brazed to their shanks and can only be used with clamped-tip holders. Ceramic tips are weak in tension and susceptible to edge chipping. They are used for high speed finishing cuts with fine feed rates where high standards of surface finish are required.

Machines used with ceramic tooling must be very powerful and rigid to exploit this material's special properties. Cutting speeds of 150 to 300 m/min are common when using ceramic tooling, but any vibration or chatter will cause immediate failure of the cutting edge. Because of its low transverse strength, ceramic tooling is normally used with a negative rake angle of $-5°$ to $-7°$ and the chips are frequently seen to be red-hot as they leave the tool. (This is another proof of the high power necessary when using ceramic tooling.)

## 2.5 Cutting tool geometry (single-point tools)

The tools illustrated so far are concerned only with establishing the principle of the metal cutting wedge, together with the corresponding rake and clearance angles in a single plane. The plan profile of the tool is also important as it has a significant effect upon the tool geometry and cutting efficiency. The lathe tool shown in Fig. 2.7(a) is performing a parallel (cylindrical) turning operation. Since the cutting edge is perpendicular to the direction of feed the tool is said to be cutting *orthogonally*. The shaded area represents the cross-sectional area (shear area) of the chip. The area is calculated by multiplying the feed per revolution by the depth of cut (d × f). Figure 2.7(b) shows the same turning operation using a tool in which the cutting edge is inclined to the direction of feed. Such a tool is said to be cutting *obliquely*. The cross-sectional area of the chip is the same as when cutting orthogonally since it is again equal to d × f.

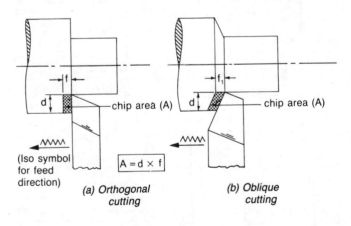

(a) Orthogonal cutting

(b) Oblique cutting

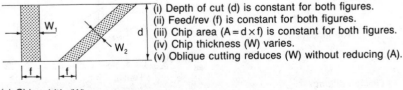

(i) Depth of cut (d) is constant for both figures.
(ii) Feed/rev (f) is constant for both figures.
(iii) Chip area (A = d × f) is constant for both figures.
(iv) Chip thickness (W) varies.
(v) Oblique cutting reduces (W) without reducing (A).

(c) Chip width (W)

**Fig. 2.7** Feed and depth of cut for parallel (cylindrical) turning

However, when cutting obliquely, the chip thickness (W) is reduced as shown in Fig. 2.7(c), where it can be seen that:

(a) the depth of cut d is constant for each example;
(b) the feed/rev f is constant for each example;
(c) the chip area (d × f) is constant for each example (parallelogram theory);
(d) the chip thickness W varies so that $W_1 > W_2$.

Therefore, when cutting obliquely, the rate of metal removal is the same as when cutting orthogonally but the chip is thinner. This thinner chip is more easily deflected over the rake face of the tool and the tangential cutting force on the tool is reduced as is the frictional wear on the rake face of the tool. Figure 2.8 shows the main forces acting upon orthogonal

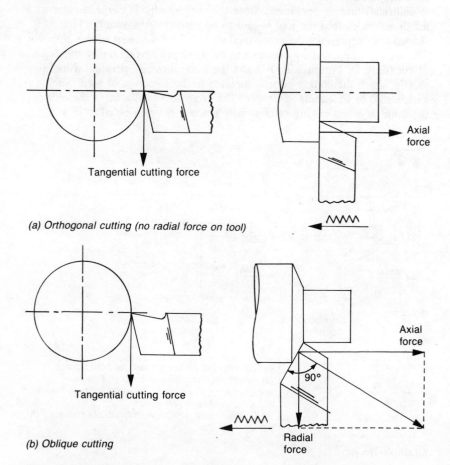

(a) Orthogonal cutting (no radial force on tool)

Tangential cutting force

Axial force

(b) Oblique cutting

Tangential cutting force

Axial force

90°

Radial force

**Fig. 2.8** Forces acting on turning tools

and oblique turning tools. It can be seen that when cutting obliquely there is also a radial component of the feed force acting on the tool. Since this radial force keeps the flanks of the cross-slide traverse screw and nut in contact, any backlash that may be present is taken up, thus preventing the tool being drawn into the work when taking a heavy cut. Care must be taken when cutting obliquely that the plan approach angle of the tool is not made excessive or chatter will occur. Figure 2.9 shows how the principles of orthogonal and oblique cutting are applied during a perpendicular (surfacing) operation on a lathe. The area of cut is again d × f.

So far only tools with positive rake angles have been considered. Such tools have to be made from materials with a high transverse strength such as high-speed steel or stellite. Carbide tools are more brittle and are only used with small positive rake angles or, more usually, negative rake angles. Negative rake geometry provides greater support for the brittle carbide tool tip as shown in Fig. 2.10. Previously it has been stated that a positive rake angle is necessary for efficient cutting and to ease the path of the chip over the rake face of the tool. Therefore it may appear strange that a tool with negative geometry can cut effectively. However negative rake geometry transfers the greater part of the work done in cutting to the chip. This, together with the high cutting speeds possible with carbide and ceramic tipped tools, causes considerable heating at the

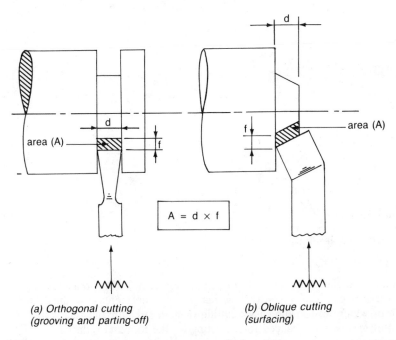

$$A = d \times f$$

(a) Orthogonal cutting
(grooving and parting-off)

(b) Oblique cutting
(surfacing)

**Fig. 2.9**  Feed and depth of cut for perpendicular turning

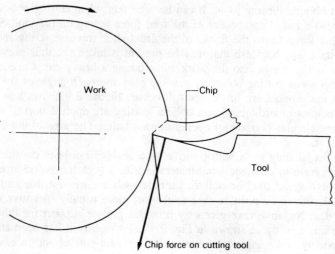

(a) **Positive rake**

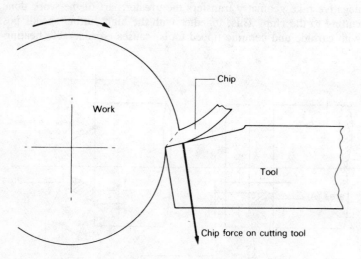

(b) **Negative rake**

**Fig. 2.10** Negative rake geometry

cutting zone and in the chip. In turn, this results in a local reduction of the shear strength of the workpiece material and an increase in ductility, both of which lead to the easier cutting of high strength and relatively hard materials with reduced forces acting on the tool and reduced abrasive wear of the rake face.

## 2.6  Cutting tool geometry (multi-point tools)

The fundamental metal cutting wedge is equally applicable to multi-point cutting tools but is sometimes less obvious to see. The cutting geometry of a number of commonly used multi-point tools will now be considered.

### Twist drill

The application of the basic cutting angles to a twist drill is shown in Fig. 2.11. It can be seen that the helix angle of the drill flutes provides the rake angle at the outer edge of the lip of the drill. This angle is not constant and becomes reduced towards the centre of the drill, with a corresponding reduction in cutting efficiency. It is not possible to vary the rake angle of a twist drill to any great extent during regrinding since the helix angle of the flutes is fixed at the time of manufacture. However, drills of various helix and point angles can be purchased for drilling different materials, as shown in Fig. 2.12.

The d:f ratio and area of cut for a drill is determined as shown in Fig. 2.13. The depth of cut is fixed and equal to the radius of the drill, whilst the feed is variable and equal to the axial movement of the drill per revolution. The cutting speed and feed rate depend upon the workpiece material properties. For any given workpiece material, the feed rate also depends upon the drill diameter as this influences the strength of the drill.

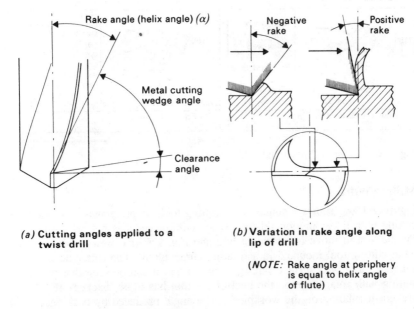

*(a)* **Cutting angles applied to a twist drill**

*(b)* **Variation in rake angle along lip of drill**

(*NOTE:* Rake angle at periphery is equal to helix angle of flute)

**Fig. 2.11**  Twist drill cutting angles

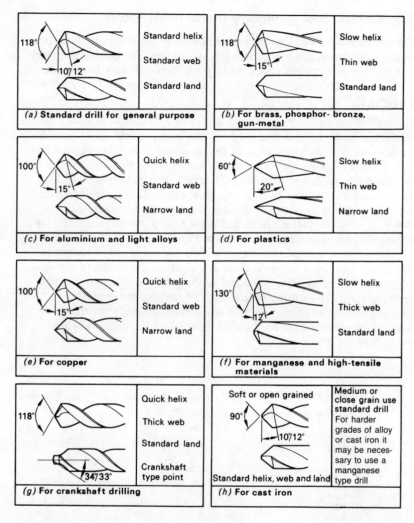

**Fig. 2.12** Twist drill point and helix angles

## Milling cutters

Figure 2.14(a) shows a single-point cutting tool, as previously described, cutting with linear motion relative to the workpiece. It is not necessary for the tool to move in a straight line and Fig. 2.14(b) shows a single-point cutting tool mounted in a rotating cutter block. The cutter now generates a curved surface (arc of a circle) and it can be seen that when cutting with rotary motion the heel of the tool has to be 'backed-off' to prevent it rubbing on the workpiece. The angle produced by backing-off the heel of the cutting tool is called the *secondary clearance angle*.

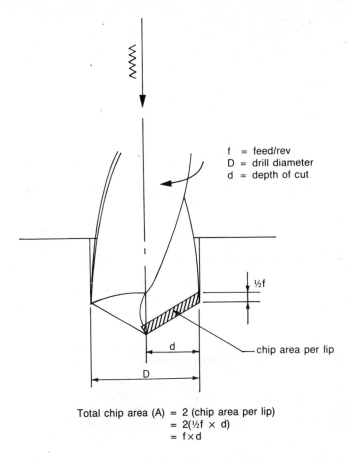

Total chip area (A) = 2 (chip area per lip)
               = 2(½f × d)
               = f × d

**Fig. 2.13**  Feed and depth of cut for a twist drill

If the axis of the rotating cutter is moved parallel to the workpiece as shown in Fig. 2.14(c), then a surface approaching a plain surface will be generated. The finer the feed per revolution of the cutting tool, the closer the surface generated will approach a plain surface since successive cuts will overlap. Unfortunately, reducing the feed per revolution also reduces the rate of material removal.

The performance of the rotating cutter can be greatly improved by inserting a number of single-point tools in the cutter block as shown in Fig. 2.15(a). The feed per revolution of the cutter block is shared between the individual cutting tools, thus reducing the feed per tool without reducing the rate of material removal. This is shown in Fig. 2.15(b). The forces acting on each tool tip are also correspondingly reduced. The basic cutting geometry of a milling cutter tooth is compared with that of a single-point tool in Fig. 2.16.

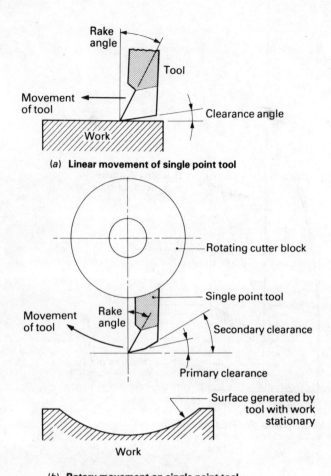

Rake angle

Tool

Movement of tool

Clearance angle

Work

(a) **Linear movement of single point tool**

Rotating cutter block

Single point tool

Rake angle

Movement of tool

Secondary clearance

Primary clearance

Surface generated by tool with work stationary

Work

(b) **Rotary movement on single point tool**

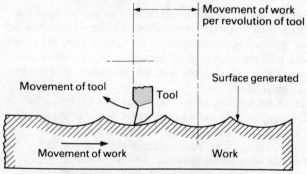

Movement of work per revolution of tool

Movement of tool

Tool

Surface generated

Movement of work

Work

(c) **Effect of traversing work under a rotating cutter**

**Fig. 2.14** Rotary cutting action

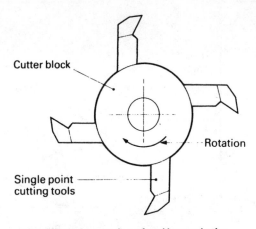

Cutter block

Rotation

Single point cutting tools

(a) **Increasing number of tool inserts in the cutter block**

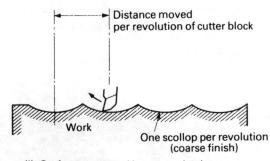

Distance moved per revolution of cutter block

Work

One scollop per revolution (coarse finish)

(i) Surface generated by one tool point

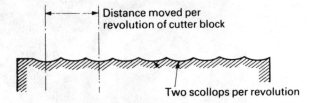

Distance moved per revolution of cutter block

Two scollops per revolution

(ii) Surface generated by two tool points

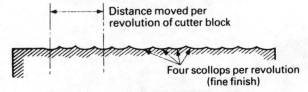

Distance moved per revolution of cutter block

Four scollops per revolution (fine finish)

(iii) Surface generated by four tool points

(b) **Improvement in surface finish using four tool inserts**

**Fig. 2.15** Effect of using multiple cutting tools on surface generation

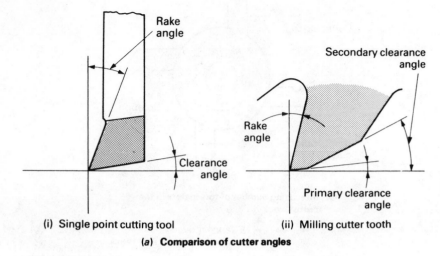

(i) Single point cutting tool    (ii) Milling cutter tooth

(a) **Comparison of cutter angles**

**Fig. 2.16** Basic tooth geometry

(a) Orthogonal cutting (straight-tooth cutter)

*(b) Oblique cutting (30° helical tooth cutter)*

**Fig. 2.17**  Orthogonal and oblique tooth form

Like single-point cutting tools, milling cutters can also be selected to provide orthogonal or oblique cutting actions. Figure 2.17(*a*) shows a straight-tooth cutter cutting orthogonally, whilst Fig. 2.17(*b*) shows a helical-tooth cutter cutting obliquely. The helical tooth cutter not only reduces the chip thickness but ensures that each successive tooth commences to cut before the preceding tooth ceases to cut. This not only maintains uniform torque loads on the machine drive, but less chatter occurs and an improved surface finish is given to the workpiece.

The 'hand' of the helix should be chosen so that the axial force produced acts towards the machine spindle and *not* away from it. This results in greater rigidity and stability, particularly when using 'high-power' cutters with helix angles as high as 70° for rapid stock removal.

Unlike the drilling machine and the lathe, the longitudinal traverse rate of a milling machine table is not related to the rotational speed of the spindle but is stated independently as the distance travelled by the worktable per minute. This is limited by the optimum 'feed per tooth' which will give a satisfactory cutter life between regrinds for a given application. A typical example of the calculation of the rate of material removal when milling is given in Example 2.1.

**Example 2.1** Calculate the time taken to complete a cut using a slab mill under the conditions set out in the following table.

Diameter of cutter     125 mm
Number of teeth     6
Feed/tooth     0·05 mm
Cutting speed     45 m/min
Length of cut     270 mm
(take $\pi$ as 3)

Spindle speed, $N$    $= \dfrac{1000\,S}{\pi D}$     where: $N$ = spindle speed

$= \dfrac{1000 \times 45}{3 \times 125}$     $S$ = 45 m/min

$\pi$ = 3

$D$ = 125 mm

$= 120$ rev/min

Feed/rev     = Feed/tooth $\times$ number of teeth
= $0·05 \times 6$
= $0·3$ mm/rev

Table feed/min     = Feed/rev $\times$ rev/min
= $0·3 \times 120$
= 36 mm/min

Time to complete     $= \dfrac{\text{length of cut}}{\text{table feed/min}}$

$= \dfrac{270}{36}$

$= 7·5$ min

## Abrasive wheels

The grinding process removes material by the use of rapidly rotating abrasive wheels. Abrasive wheels consist of a large number of abrasive particles called *grains*, held together by a *bond* to form a multi-tooth cutter which cuts in a similar manner to a milling cutter as shown in Fig. 2.18. The grains at the surface of the wheel are called *active grains* because they actually perform the cutting operation. In peripheral grinding each active grain removes a short chip of workpiece material and these can be seen in Fig. 2.19 which shows grinding wheel dross highly magnified. It can be seen that the dross consists of particles of

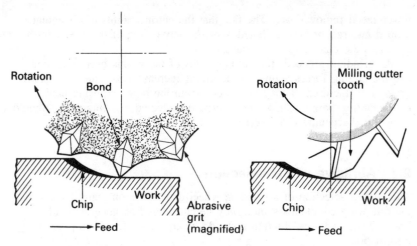

**Fig. 2.18** Cutting action of abrasive wheel grains

**Fig. 2.19** Grinding wheel dross

abrasive material stripped from the grinding wheel together with metallic chips which are remarkably similar to the chips produced by the milling process.

Since the abrasive wheels used in grinding processes have many more 'teeth' than a milling cutter, and because this reduces the chip clearance, the abrasive wheel produces a superior surface finish at the expense of a lower metal removal rate. The fact that the cutting points are irregularly shaped and randomly distributed over the active face of the wheel further enhances the quality of the surface finish.

As grinding proceeds the cutting edges of the grains become dulled and the cutting forces acting on the grains increase until either the blunt grains are fractured or they are ripped from the bond exposing new active cutting points. Therefore a correctly selected grinding wheel should have self-sharpening characteristics.

## 2.7 Abrasive wheel selection

The correct selection of a grinding wheel depends upon many factors and the following comments should only be considered as general 'guide lines'. Manufacturers' literature should be consulted for more precise information.

### Material to be ground

(a) Aluminium oxide abrasives should only be used on materials with relatively high tensile strengths.

(b) Silicon carbide abrasives should only be used on hard, brittle materials with relatively low tensile strengths.

(c) A fine grain wheel can be used on hard, brittle materials.

(d) A coarser grain wheel should be used on soft, ductile materials.

(e) When considering the *grade*, a general guide is to use a soft grade of wheel with a hard workpiece, and a hard grade of wheel with a soft workpiece.

(f) When considering the *structure*, it is permissible to use a close structured wheel on hard, brittle materials, but a more open structured wheel should be used on soft, ductile materials.

(g) The *bond* is chosen for a particular application and is rarely influenced by the material being ground.

### Rate of stock removal

(a) A coarse grain wheel should be used for rapid stock removal, but it will give a comparatively rough finish. A fine grain wheel should be used for finishing operations requiring low rates of stock removal.

(b) The structure of the wheel has a major effect on the rate of stock removal, an open structured wheel with a wide grain spacing being used for maximum stock removal and cool cutting conditions.

(c) It should be noted that the performance of a grinding wheel can be appreciably modified by the method of dressing, the operating speed, and the workpiece traverse rate.

### Arc of contact

Figure 2.20 explains the meaning of *arc of contact*. Generally, for efficient grinding of cylindrical work, the arc of contact should be kept as small as possible, that is, the abrasive wheel diameter should be large compared with the workpiece diameter.

(*a*)  For a small arc of contact, a fine-grained wheel should be used, whereas for a large arc of contact a coarser grained wheel should be used to prevent overheating.

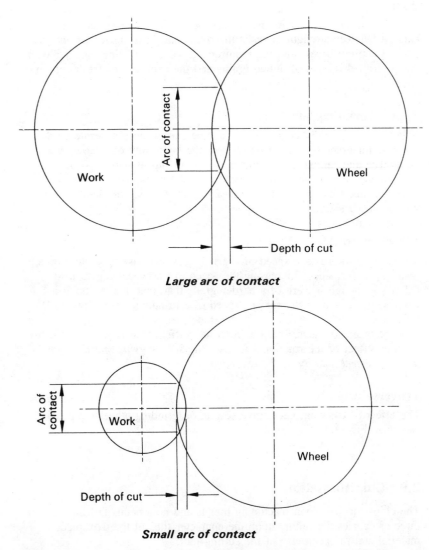

**Large arc of contact**

**Small arc of contact**

**Fig. 2.20**  Arc of contact

(*b*) For a small arc of contact, a 'hard' wheel may be used, whereas for a large arc of contact a 'soft' wheel should be used as the cutting edges will become dulled more quickly.

(*c*) For a small arc of contact a close structured wheel may be used, with the advantage of improved surface finish and closer dimensional control. For a large arc of contact an open structured wheel should be used to maintain free cutting conditions.

## Bond

The bond is selected for its mechanical properties. It must achieve a balance between strength to resist the rotational, bursting forces and the applied cutting forces, and the requirements of cool cutting together with the controlled release of dulled grains and the exposure of fresh cutting edges.

## Type of grinding machine

A heavy duty, rigidly constructed machine can produce accurate work using softer grade wheels. This reduces the possibility of overheating the workpiece and 'drawing' its temper (i.e. reducing its hardness) or, in extreme cases, causing surface cracking of the workpiece. Furthermore, broader wheels can be used and this increases the rate of metal removal without loss of accuracy.

## Wheel speed

Variation in the surface speed of a grinding wheel has a profound effect upon its performance. Increasing the speed of the wheel causes it to behave as though it were of a harder grade than that marked upon it. Conversely, reducing the surface speed of a grinding wheel causes it to behave as though it were of a softer grade than that marked upon it. Care must be taken to ensure that the bond has sufficient strength to resist the bursting effect of the rotational forces. *The safe working speed of an abrasive wheel must never be exceeded.*

## Traverse rate

The effect of the workpiece traverse rate on grinding wheel wear is shown in Fig. 2.21.

## 2.8 Chip formation

The chips formed when machining metals and non-metals fall into one of three categories depending upon the characteristics of the workpiece material and the geometry of the cutting tool.

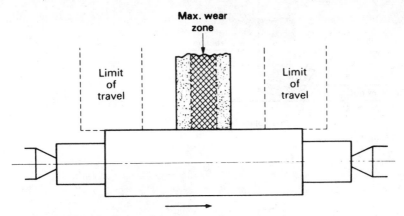

*(a) Wear conditions when work traverses 2/3 of wheel width per revolution of work*

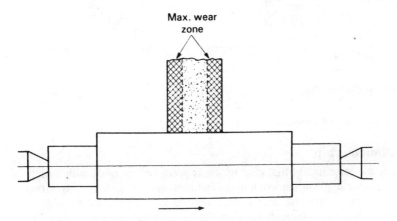

*(b) Wear conditions when work traverses 1/3 of wheel width per revolution of work*

**Fig. 2.21** Abrasive wheel wear

## Discontinuous chip

The shearing of the chip from the workpiece material has already been discussed in section 2.2. In forming the chip, as shown in Fig. 2.22(a), the workpiece material is severely strained and, if it is a brittle, non-ductile material, it may completely fracture along the shear planes in the primary deformation zone to give rise to a *discontinuous* or granular chip as shown in Fig. 2.22(b). Discontinuous chips are associated with non-ductile materials such as grey cast iron, free-cutting brass and thermosetting plastics.

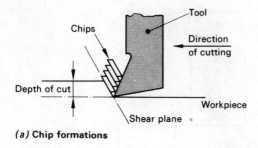

(a) **Chip formations**

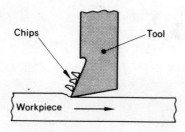

(b) **Discontinuous chip**

**Fig. 2.22** Discontinuous chip

## Continuous chip

This is the long ribbon-like chip which is produced by tools with a high positive rake angle when machining ductile materials such as low-carbon (mild) steels, copper and aluminium. The workpiece material behaves as a rigid plastic but, although the chip shears from the workpiece material along shear planes as previously described, the chip does not separate into completely separate plates as shown in Fig. 2.22(a). Instead, only partial separation occurs and a *continuous* chip is produced as shown in Fig. 2.23(a). The inside of the curvature of the chip is usually rough and the slip planes are visible even to the unaided eye in the large chips produced by heavy machining. The outer surface of the chip is burnished smooth as it flows over the rake face of the cutting tool. Chips produced from some very soft and ductile materials, with a low strength, tend to tear away from the parent workpiece material just ahead of the cutting tool instead of shearing cleanly. This can be overcome to some extent by reducing the rate of feed and increasing the cutting speed. Some materials such as aluminium and copper have to be finish machined using diamond tipped tools and very high cutting speeds. Under these conditions the material behaves as though it were very much stiffer and harder and very good surface finishes can be obtained.

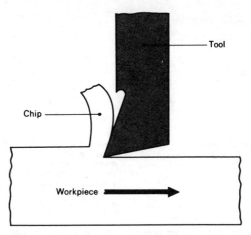

*(a)* **Continuous chip**

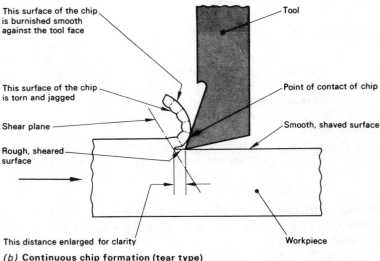

*(b)* **Continuous chip formation (tear type)
for soft, ductile, low strength metals**

**Fig. 2.23** Continuous chip

## Continuous chip with built-up edge

Under some conditions the friction between the chip and the rake face of the tool becomes very great. This results in particles of metal from the chip becoming pressure-welded to the rake face of the tool making it rough, masking the cutting edge, and changing its geometry. This leads to increased friction and heat at the cutting edge and layer after layer of

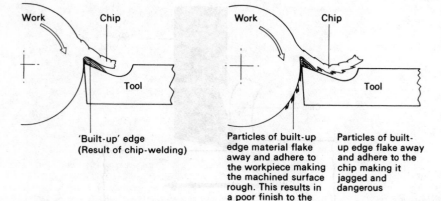

(a) **Layering of chip material on rake face of tool during chip-welding**

(b) **Instability of built up edge if chip-welding becomes excessive**

**Fig. 2.24** Chip welding (built-up edge)

chip material is built up as shown in Fig. 2.24. This is referred to as a *built-up edge* and the mechanism by which it is produced is referred to as *chip welding*. Eventually the amount of built-up material becomes unstable and it breaks down. The particles of built-up material which flake away weld themselves to the chip and to the surface of the workpiece. This leaves a rough surface on the workpiece and a dangerously jagged chip.

Since chip welding has a considerable and adverse influence on tool life, power consumption and surface finish, every attempt must be made to prevent it occurring. This is achieved by reversing one or more of the causes of chip-welding as follows.

(a) **Reducing friction**. This can be achieved by increasing the rake angle, polishing the rake face, and introducing a lubricant between the chip and the tool.

(b) **Reducing the temperature**. The temperature at the cutting zone can be lowered by reducing the friction between the chip and the tool and by using a coolant.

(c) **Reducing the pressure**. The pressure between the chip and the tool can be reduced by increasing the rake angle, reducing the feed rate, and/or using oblique instead of orthogonal cutting.

(d) **Preventing metal-to-metal contact**. This can be achieved by introducing a high-pressure lubricant between the chip and tool interface. Such lubricants contain chlorine or sulphur additives which build up a thin non-metallic film on the tool rake-face which has a high lubricity. This reduces the friction between the chip and the tool and prevents metal-to-metal contact. Alternatively non-metallic cutting tool materials such as metallic carbides and ceramics may be used.

Continuous chips have razor sharp and ragged edges which are extremely dangerous. Further, these long ribbon-like chips tend to tangle with the cutter and workpiece and are difficult to dispose of. Swarf removal is particularly important in high production automatic and computer-controlled machine tools. To remove the dangers and difficulties associated with continuous chips the cutting tools should be fitted with a *chip-breaker* as shown in Fig. 2.25(*a*). The action of the chip-breaker is shown in Fig. 2.25(*b*). It can be seen that the chip-breaker forces the chip to curl up into a tight spiral. This work-hardens the chip making it brittle so that it breaks up into short lengths which are safely and easily disposable.

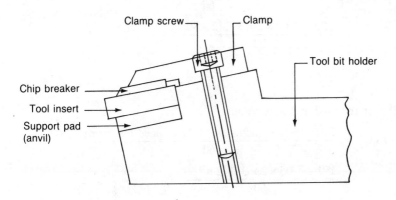

*(a) Inserted tip tool with chip breaker*

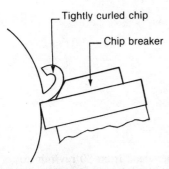

*(b) Action of chip-breaker*

**Fig. 2.25** Chip breaker

## 2.9 Process variables

These are the factors immediately under the control of the machine operator and are largely concerned with achieving a compromise between maximum metal removal rate and tool life.

### Cutting speed

Cutting speed influences the power required for the cutting process and the tool life. It does not influence the forces acting on the cutting tool.

---

**Example 2.2** Compare the power required to turn a 100 mm diameter bar at 80 rev/min with the power required at 160 rev/min. The tangential force is constant at 350 N in both cases.

(i) Power required at 80 rev/min.

$$\text{Power (W)} = \frac{\text{force } (N) \times \text{radius } (m) \times 2\pi \times \text{speed (rev/min)}}{60}$$

$$= \frac{350 \times 0 \cdot 05 \times 2 \times 3 \cdot 142 \times 80}{60}$$

$$= \underline{\underline{146 \cdot 6 \text{ W}}}$$

(ii) Power required at 160 rev/min.

$$\text{Power (W)} = \frac{\text{force } (N) \times \text{radius } (m) \times 2\pi \times \text{speed (rev/min)}}{60}$$

$$= \frac{350 \times 0 \cdot 05 \times 2 \times 3 \cdot 142 \times 160}{60}$$

$$= \underline{\underline{293 \cdot 2 \text{ W}}}$$

Expressed algebraically,

$$P = \frac{2\pi R F_t N}{60}$$

where $\dfrac{2\pi R F_t}{60}$ is constant

thus $\underline{\underline{P \propto N}}$

Therefore it will be seen that doubling the speed from 80 rev/min to 160 rev/min results in doubling the power required from 146·6 W to 293·2 W.

---

The forces acting on the cutting tool are solely dependent upon the properties of the workpiece material, the cutting tool geometry, and the depth of cut and rate of feed. Example 2.2 shows the effect on the power required for a given process of increasing the cutting speed. The upper limit is set by the rigidity of the machine tool being used and the power available at its spindle.

The cutting speed also influences the tool life. It has just been shown that increasing the cutting speed increases the power required. Since power can be defined as the rate of doing work or using up energy, it is apparent that increasing the cutting speed leads to the rate at which energy is dissipated at the cutting zone. Since energy cannot be created or destroyed, (law of conservation of energy), the mechanical energy of cutting is converted into heat energy at the cutting edge. This results in an increase of temperature at the tool tip and a reduction in tool life. The relationship between cutting speed and tool life is logarithmic, and an empirical relationship for calculating the effect on tool life of changing the cutting speed has been derived experimentally. This relationship can be expressed as:

$$Vt^n = C$$

where: $V$ = cutting speed in m/min;
$t$ = tool life in minutes;
$n$ = tool life index (see Table 2.3);
$C$ = a constant for a given set of cutting conditions.

**Table 2.3**  Tool-life index

| Material and conditions | Tool material | n |
| --- | --- | --- |
| $3\frac{1}{2}$% nickel steel | Cemented carbide | 0·2 |
| $3\frac{1}{2}$% nickel steel (roughing) | High-speed steel | 0·14 |
| $3\frac{1}{2}$% nickel steel (finishing) | High-speed steel | 0·125 |
| High carbon, high chromium die steel | Cemented carbide | 0·15 |
| High carbon steel | High-speed steel | 0·2 |
| Medium carbon steel | High-speed steel | 0·15 |
| Mild steel | High-speed steel | 0·125 |
| Cast iron | Cemented carbide | 0·1 |

It can be seen from Example 2.3 (page 88) that a reduction of cutting speed of only 8.3 per cent results in doubling the tool life. Similarly it was shown that an increase in cutting speed of only 8.3 per cent resulted

**Example 2.3** The life of a lathe tool is 4 hours when operating at a cutting speed of 40 m/min. Given that $Vt^n = C$, find the highest cutting speed that will give a tool life of 8 hours. The value of n is $0 \cdot 125$.

(i) determine the value of $\log_{10} C$ from the initial conditions:

$$C = Vt_1^n$$

where: $V = 40$ m/min
$t_1 = 240$ minutes
$n = 0 \cdot 125$

$$
\begin{aligned}
\log_{10} C &= \log_{10} V + n \log_{10} T_1 \\
&= \log 40 + (0 \cdot 125 \log 240) \\
&= 1 \cdot 6021 + (0 \cdot 125 \times 2 \cdot 3802) \\
&= 1 \cdot 6021 + 0 \cdot 2975 \\
&= \underline{\underline{1 \cdot 8996}}
\end{aligned}
$$

(ii) determine $V_{max}$ for the revised conditions:

$$V_{max} = \frac{C}{t_2^n}$$

where: $t_2 = 480$ minutes

$$
\begin{aligned}
\log_{10} V_{max} &= \log_{10} C - n \log_{10} t_2 \\
&= 1 \cdot 8996 - (0 \cdot 125 \times 2 \cdot 6812) \\
&= 1 \cdot 8996 - 0 \cdot 3352 \\
&= 1 \cdot 5644
\end{aligned}
$$

$$V_{max} = \underline{\underline{36 \cdot 68 \text{ m/min}}}$$

in almost halving the tool life, hence the need always to select a lower rather than higher cutting speed if the machine controls do not give the optimum value.

## Depth of cut and rate of feed

The depth of cut, feed rate and area of cut have already been described for a number of machining operations. The same area of cut and thus the same rate of metal removal can be achieved in two ways:

(a) using a shallow depth of cut and a coarse feed;
(b) using a deep cut and a fine feed.

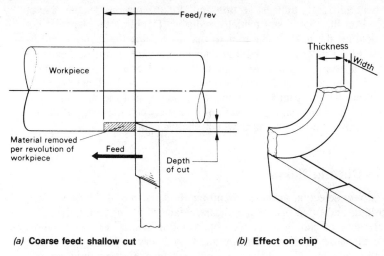

*(a)* **Coarse feed: shallow cut**     *(b)* **Effect on chip**

**Fig. 2.26**   Effect of high feed rates

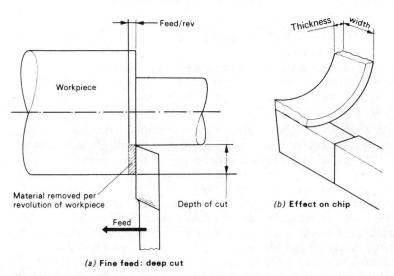

*(a)* **Fine feed: deep cut**

*(b)* **Effect on chip**

**Fig. 2.27**   Effect of deep cuts

Figure 2.26 shows the effect of using a shallow cut and a coarse feed. It can be seen that the chip is bent across its thickest section and, since the bending force increases as the cube of the thickness of the chip, doubling the rate of feed increases the load on the tool resulting from the deflection of the chip by eight times, $(2^3 = 8)$. Figure 2.27 shows the alternative effect of using a deep cut and a fine rate of feed. The chip is now bent across its thinnest section and, for the reasons set out above, the load on the tool is substantially reduced. Doubling the depth of cut only doubles the load on the tool so that increasing the depth of cut has far less effect on the cutting force than increasing the rate of feed. Further, a deep cut with a fine rate of feed will produce a better surface finish without reducing the rate of metal removal. Unfortunately, an excessively deep cut tends to promote vibration, and the ratio of depth of cut to rate of feed has to be a compromise between the load on the tool, surface finish, and the point at which chatter commences.

## 2.10 Cutting fluids

The correct selection and use of cutting fluids is one of the most important, and often one of the cheapest factors in enhancing the performance of cutting tools. To obtain optimum rates of metal removal and at the same time, maintain optimum tool service life, it is necessary to both lubricate and cool the chip/tool interface. Cutting fluids are designed to fulfil one or more of the following functions:

(a) to cool the tool and workpiece;
(b) to lubricate the chip/tool interface and reduce tool wear due to friction and abrasion;
(c) to prevent chip welding (formation of a built-up edge);
(d) to improve the finish of the machined surface;
(e) to flush away the chips from the cutting zone;
(f) to prevent corrosion of the work and machine.

Experiments have shown that for the majority of machining operations, the cooling and flushing action of the cutting fluid is most important, as the tool wear-rate is extremely sensitive to small temperature changes at the chip/tool interface. For this reason emulsified cutting fluids are used for the majority of workship applications, since the high water content improves the cooling action and reduces the cost.

However, the lubricating action of the cutting fluid becomes of prime importance in reducing the wear-rate of the tool in such operations as tapping, broaching and gear cutting, where expensive form tools are used. Such lubricants often contain an extreme pressure additive.

Mineral lubricating oils are unsuitable as cutting fluids. Their viscosity is too high and their specific heat capacity is too low to make them effective coolants; their lack of lubricity renders them unsuitable to withstand the high contact pressure between the chip and the tool and they give off noxious fumes when raised to the cutting temperature. They also represent a fire hazard.

### Soluble oils

High cutting temperatures cause tool softening, chip welding, and can promote corrosive chemical reactions between the chip and the tool. In some instances a reduction in temperature of only 14°C at the cutting zone can increase tool life by 150 per cent. Control of the cutting temperature leading to a reduction of thermal expansion can also help in maintaining cutting accuracy and preventing distortion of the workpiece.

When water and oil are added together they refuse to mix, but if an emulsifier, in the form of a detergent is added, the oil will break up into droplets and spread throughout the water to form an emulsion. This is what happens when the so-called 'soluble' oils are added to water. The milky appearance of these emulsions is due to the light being refracted by the oil droplets. It is from this milky appearance that the emulsion gets the popular name of 'suds'.

The dilution with water reduces the lubricating properties of the oil and soluble oils are unsuitable for very severe machining conditions. Further, the high water content tends to cause corrosion of the workpiece and the machine. Therefore soluble oils must contain a rust inhibitor.

## Compounded or blended oils

These are mixtures of mineral and fatty oils. The film strength of the fatty oils is retained, even when diluted with 75 per cent mineral oil. As a result they are much cheaper, more fluid and more chemically stable than neat fatty oils, whilst retaining the superior high pressure lubricating properties of fatty oils. Blended oils are very versatile and are suitable for a wide range of machining operations.

## Synthetic cutting fluids

In this group of cutting fluids, the mineral and fatty oil base of conventional cutting oils is replaced by aqueous solutions of inorganic chemicals together with corrosion inhibitors and extreme pressure lubricating additives. These solutions are transparent, but colouring agents are added to differentiate them from water and from soda-ash solutions. Having a high water content, synthetic chemical cutting fluids possess excellent cooling properties. Other benefits include a high level of cleanliness in the cooling system and on the machine slideways with lack of sludging, long term stability, easily removable residual films and no tendency to foaming. Being transparent they give improved visual control of intricate machining operations. Other advantages are:

(a) an absence of fire risk (some oil-based cutting fluids are highly flammable);
(b) improved long-term stability over soluble oils, particularly in hard water areas;
(c) reduced health hazards for operators;
(d) disposal of spent fluids as a normal trade effluent without first having to render them safe environmentally by complex and expensive chemical treatment.

## Extreme pressure additives

It has already been stated that the very high pressures that exist at the chip/tool interface during machining under severe cutting conditions do not allow conventional fluid film and boundary layer lubrication to be achieved to any significant extent. Where extreme pressure lubrication properties are required, chlorine and sulphur compounds are added to the cutting oil. These compounds react chemically with the tool and chip material at the chip/tool interface to produce a coating of high lubricity even when subjected to extreme pressures.

**Sulphurised oils** are probably the most useful and widely used group of extreme pressure cutting fluids, available either as 'straight' oils or as soluble oils. They are compounded so that no free sulphur is present which would attack and stain copper and high-nickel alloys. Sulphurised oils are used for such processes as gear cutting, broaching, thread grinding, thread cutting and automatic lathe work.

**Sulphured oils** contain free or elemented sulphur which is completely dissolved in a mineral or compounded oil. The sulphur is in a very active state and although exhibiting the ultimate in extreme pressure characteristics, will attack and stain copper and high-nickel content alloys.

# 3 Toolholding and workholding

## 3.1 Principles of location and restraint

It can be seen from Fig. 3.1 that a body in space, free of all restraints, has *six degrees of freedom*. That is, it is able to

(i)   move back and forth along the $X$ axis;
(ii)  move from side to side along the $Y$ axis;
(iii) move up and down along the $Z$ axis;
(iv) rotate in either direction about the $X$ axis;
(v)  rotate in either direction about the $Y$ axis;
(vi) rotate in either direction about the $Z$ axis.

In order that the metal block shown in Fig. 3.1 can be worked upon by hand or machine tools it must be located in a given position by restraining its freedom of movement.

Figure 3.2 shows how a metal block similar to that shown in Fig. 3.1 can be located in a given position by the application of suitable restraints. The base plate supports the block and locates it in the vertical plane by restraining its downward movement. At the same time it restrains rotation about the $X$ and $Y$ axes of the block. The addition of three location pegs adds restraint along the $X$ and $Y$ axes and positions the block on the plate. Finally screw clamps are provided to complete the restraint of the block by ensuring its contact with the plate and the location pegs at all times. The use of screw clamps also provides for variation in size of the block due to manufacturing tolerances. Since, in this example, the block

94

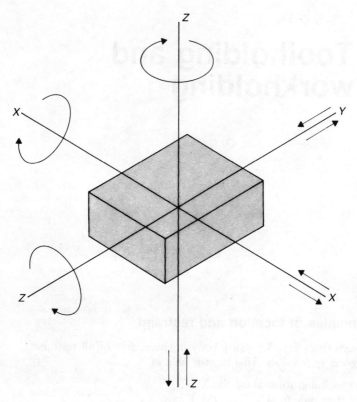

**Fig. 3.1** Six degrees of freedom

is restrained in every direction by contact with solid metal abutments, it is said to be subjected to *positive* restraint. Thus *locations* position the tool or workpiece relative to the machine, whilst *restraints* prevent unwanted movement of the tool or workpiece and ensure its contact with the locations.

Restraints may be *positive* or *frictional* as shown in Fig. 3.3. Wherever possible, cutting forces should be resisted by positive restraints (solid abutments) and not by frictional restraint alone. Figure 3.3(*a*) shows the workpiece restrained by clamps alone (frictional restraint). This is not good practice and should be avoided if possible. The use of multiple clamps leads to distortion of the workpiece and is also time wasting when setting-up. Figure 3.3(*b*) shows better work-holding practice. The main cutting force is resisted by a solid abutment (positive restraint) which also provides location of the workpiece in a longitudinal direction. This enables the frictional restraint to be reduced to only two clamps.

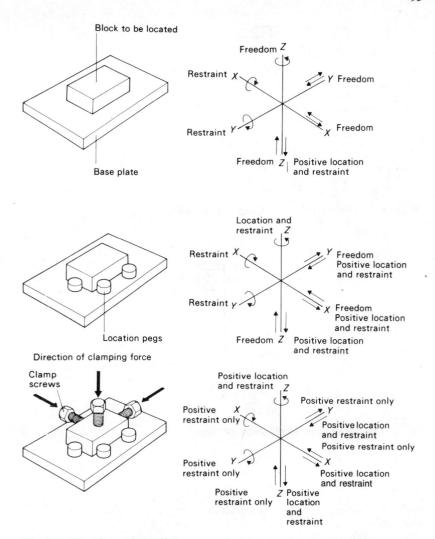

**Fig. 3.2** Location and restraint

## 3.2 Practical locations

During the continuous or batch production of large numbers of components by repetitive machining it is essential that each successive component is located in exactly the same position on the machine. The choice of location will depend upon whether the locating or datum surface of the component is a flat or curved external surface or a hole. Simple cylindrical location pegs were shown in Fig. 3.2. Some additional location devices are shown in Fig. 3.4. Where positive locations are

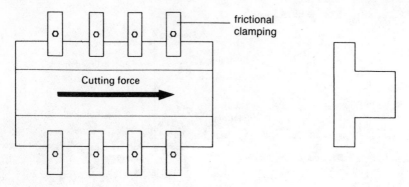

*(a) Excessive clamping is time wasting and bad practice*

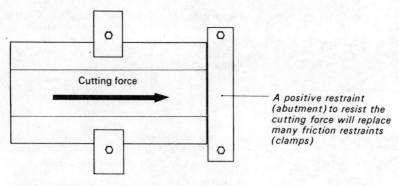

*(b) Correctly placed clamps and abutment (stop)*

**Fig. 3.3** Positive and frictional restraints (abutments and clamps)

used, they should be kept to a minimum to prevent distortion and interaction.

An example of the care needed when using multiple locations is shown in Fig. 3.5. The flat plate link is to be located from the two previously machined holes. However, the centre distance between the holes can vary because of the manufacturing tolerance allowed by the designer. It would be impossible, therefore, for all the components to be located over two cylindrical location spigots fixed in position on the base plate. Only a component whose hole centre distance was exactly the same as the centre distance of the location spigots would fit. Thus only one cylindrical location spigot should be used and the second hole is located on a location spigot which has been *form relieved* to allow for the variation in hole centre distance.

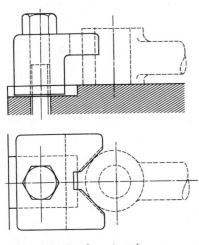

(a) Vee location for external
curved surfaces

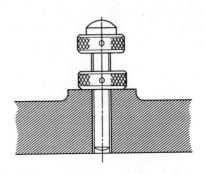

(d) Screw jack adjustable location

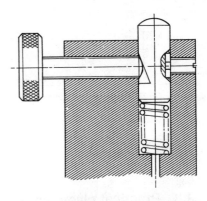

(e) Spring loaded adjustable location

(d) and (e) are for locating irregular
external flat surfaces

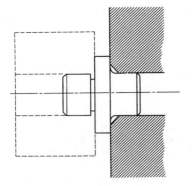

(b) Spigot location for
datum hole

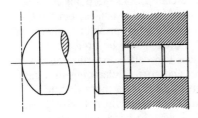

(c) Plain button location for
external flat surface

**Fig. 3.4** Locations for jigs and fixtures

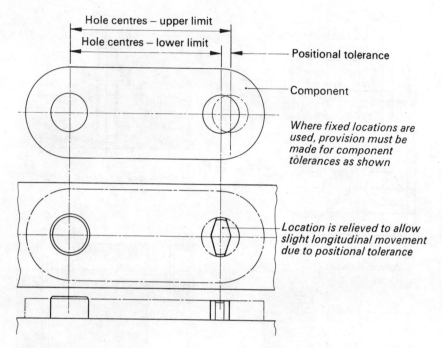

**Fig. 3.5** Use of locations

## 3.3 Practical clamping

Whilst offering adequate restraint, clamping devices should be designed to prevent damage to previously machined surfaces and to avoid distortion or damage to the workpiece. Figure 3.6 shows the difference between clamps and locations suitable for unfinished and finished surfaces. The arrangement shown in Fig. 3.6(*a*) would be satisfactory for a rough casting or forging. The line contact of the clamp, and the point contact of the location pad are suitable for a rough and uneven surface, but would mark a previously machined surface. For holding on previously machined surfaces the arrangement shown in Fig. 3.6(*b*) would be preferable.

Clamping on thin, unsupported surfaces can cause distortion and even breakage. Figure 3.7 shows the incorrect and correct clamping of a cast iron workpiece. Had the workpiece been made from a more ductile material, clamping on a thin, unsupported section would not have caused breakage, but would have caused the workpiece to bend and distort leading to loss of accuracy and even permanent distortion.

It has already been stated that the main cutting force should be supported by a solid abutment. This abutment must be proportioned to support the workpiece as close to the point of cutting as possible or, again, distortion or breakage can occur as shown in Fig. 3.8.

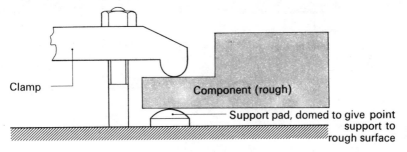

*(a) Restraint and location for unfinished surfaces*

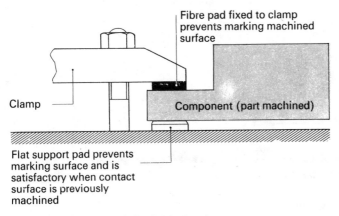

*(b) Restraint and location for finished surfaces*

**Fig. 3.6** Selection of restraints and locations

Clamps should be quick and easy to apply in order to keep set-up time to a minimum. Some typical clamping devices are shown in Figs 3.9 (screw-type) and 3.10 (toggle and cam types). These latter types are generally associated with jigs and fixtures (sections 3.4 and 3.5) which are used for batch and continuous production. The clamping force on the component should be maximised by ensuring that the bolt and nut securing the clamp are nearer to the workpiece than they are to the heel of the clamp or packing (moments of forces).

Clamping can also be applied by the use of compressed air operating through pistons and cylinders. Figure 3.11(*a*) shows a section through a typical double-acting piston and cylinder, whilst Fig. 3.11(*b*) shows a suitable pneumatic circuit for use with such a piston and cylinder. The incoming air is first passed through a filter to remove dust and moisture, which would cause rapid wear and early failure of the valves and cylinder bores. It is then passed through a pressure regulator to reduce the pressure from the workshop air line to a suitable value for holding

100

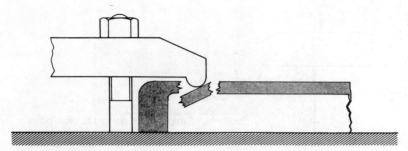

*(a) INCORRECT – breakage caused by clamping on thin, unsupported section*

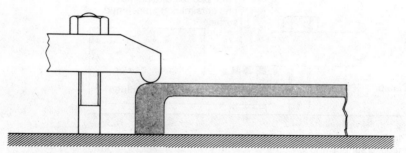

*(b) CORRECT – clamping applied where the clamping force is adequately supported*

**Fig. 3.7**  Avoiding damage

the workpiece securely but without damage. The air then passes through
a lubricator and then to the control valve before finally passing to the
cylinder. As shown, compressed air would pass into the valve at A and
then to the cylinder via port B. This would move the piston to the right
of the figure. Air already in the cylinder would be exhausted to the
atmosphere through ports C and D. Reversing the valve, as shown in the
inset diagram, feeds the compressed air to the cylinder via ports A and D
thus moving the piston in the reverse direction to the left of the figure.
Air already in the cylinder would be exhausted to the atmosphere via
ports B and C.

The piston and cylinder may be used for direct clamping as shown in
Fig. 3.12(a) or indirect clamping as shown in Fig. 3.12(b). The
arrangement in Fig. 3.12(a) has the advantage that variations in
component size can be accommodated and that the clamping pressure is
constant for a given air pressure. The clamping pressure is easily
adjustable by altering the air pressure at the regulator (Fig. 3.11).
Unfortunately if the air pressure fails then, with direct clamping, the

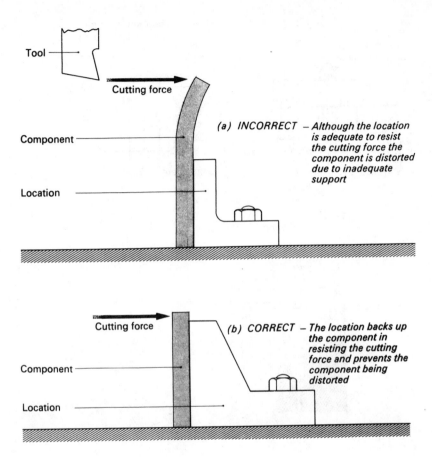

**Fig. 3.8** Resisting the cutting force

clamping pressure is lost and if this happens during machining a serious accident could occur. To overcome this danger, indirect clamping can be used as shown in Fig. 3.12(*b*). Here, the clamping pressure is provided by the toggle clamp and the air cylinder is only used to open and close the toggle. In the event of loss of air pressure the toggle would remain closed and the clamping force on the workpiece would not be lost. Unfortunately, as with all toggle clamps, variation in component size cannot be tolerated. Although costly compared with manually operated mechanical clamps, pneumatic clamps have the advantage that the clamping pressure can be accurately controlled, they are quick to operate and in the case of large and complex work-holding devices, many clamps can be operated simultaneously or sequentially by a single lever.

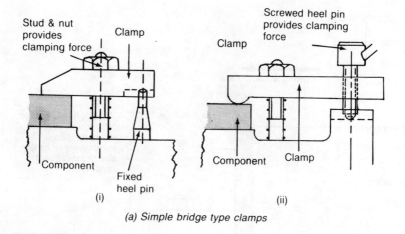

*(a) Simple bridge type clamps*

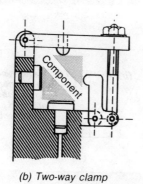

*(b) Two-way clamp*

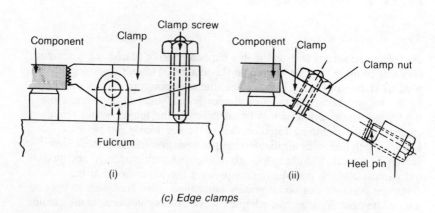

*(c) Edge clamps*

**Fig. 3.9**  Screw type clamping devices

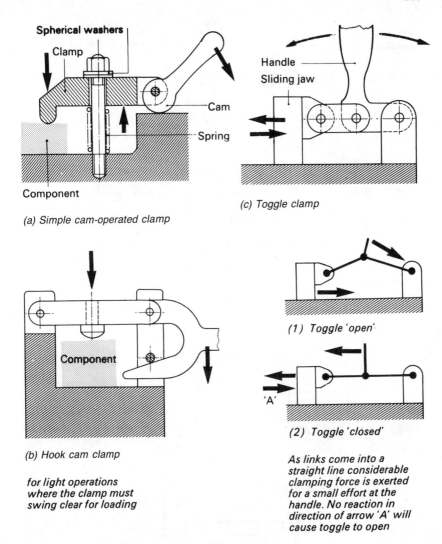

(a) Simple cam-operated clamp

(c) Toggle clamp

(b) Hook cam clamp

*for light operations where the clamp must swing clear for loading*

(1) Toggle 'open'

(2) Toggle 'closed'

*As links come into a straight line considerable clamping force is exerted for a small effort at the handle. No reaction in direction of arrow 'A' will cause toggle to open*

**Fig. 3.10** Toggle and cam operated clamping devices

## 3.4 Tool-holding and work-holding in a drilling machine

To drill a hole in a drilling machine so that it is correctly sized and positioned, four basic conditions must be satisfied:

(i) The drill must be located in the drilling machine spindle so that the axis of the drill is coincident with the axis of the machine spindle.

(ii) The drill and spindle must rotate together without slippage

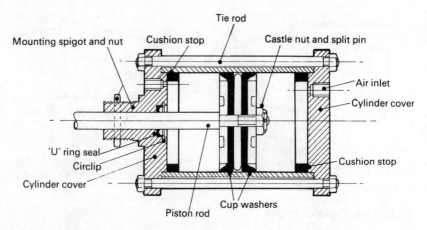

*(a) Typical double acting piston and cylinder*

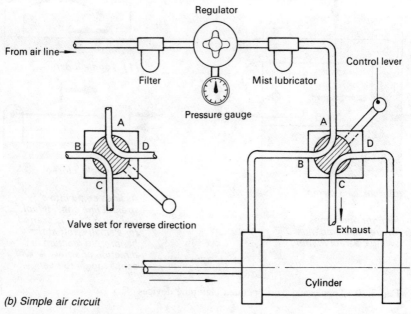

*(b) Simple air circuit*

**Fig. 3.11** Pneumatic equipment

       occurring. There must be total restraint between the drill shank and the spindle.

(iii)   The workpiece must be located so that the centre lines of the holes are in alignment with the spindle axis as shown in Fig. 3.13.

(iv)   The workpiece must be restrained so that it resists the cutting forces and is not dragged round by the drill.

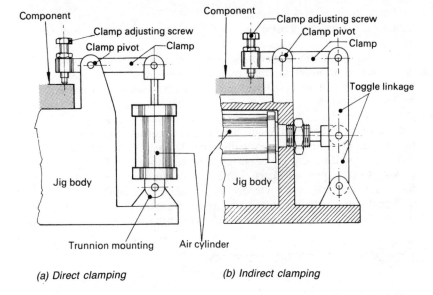

**Fig. 3.12** Pneumatic clamping

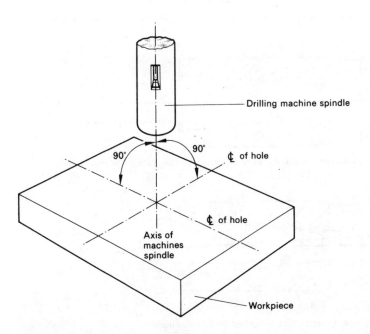

**Fig. 3.13** Basic drilling alignments

106

Large twist drills are normally held in the spindle nose directly by means of a taper shank as shown in Fig. 3.14. Axial alignment of the drill in the spindle is assured and also maintained despite variations in the size of the tapers due to manufacturing tolerances and wear. However it is essential that the internal and external tapers are carefully cleaned before the drill shank is inserted into the machine spindle to prevent damage to the tapers, to ensure correct alignment, and to ensure that the drill does not slip. The narrow angle of taper ensures that the drill does not drop out of the spindle and that there is adequate frictional restraint to drive the drill under normal cutting conditions. However, should the drill be allowed to 'dig-in' or seize in the hole then it will slip and damage to the tapers will occur. The tang on the drill is provided solely for its removal and is not intended to provide additional drive.

Small diameter twist drills normally have a parallel shank and are held in a drill chuck as shown in Fig. 3.15. The drill chuck and its shank rely

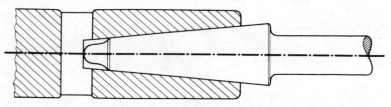

*(a)* Spindle and shank maintain axial alignment under maximum metal conditions

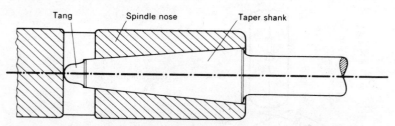

*(b)* Spindle and shank maintain axial alignment under minimum metal conditions

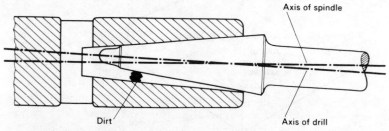

*(c)* Misalignment due to dirt between drill and spindle

**Fig. 3.14** Taper location of drill shank

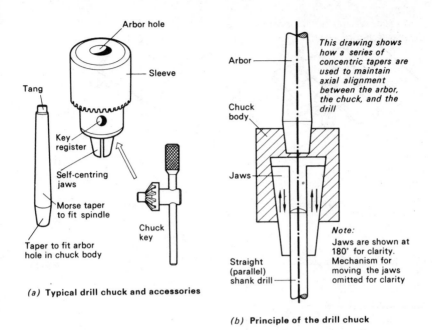

**(a) Typical drill chuck and accessories**

*This drawing shows how a series of concentric tapers are used to maintain axial alignment between the arbor, the chuck, and the drill*

*Note:*
Jaws are shown at 180° for clarity. Mechanism for moving the jaws omitted for clarity

**(b) Principle of the drill chuck**

**Fig. 3.15** The drill chuck

upon a system of concentric tapers to ensure axial alignment. The jaws are closed on the drill shank by rotation of the sleeve of the chuck.

The location and restraint of the workpiece must follow the principles previously discussed. For one-off and 'jobbing' work, small components are usually held in a machine vice bolted to the work table of the machine, whilst large components are bolted directly to the work table itself. Figure 3.16 shows the restraints and locations offered by a machine vice. To ensure that the spindle axis is perpendicular to the workpiece, the following alignments should be checked.

(a) A matched pair of parallels are used to support the work and ensure that its under-surface is parallel to the vice slideways (*a,a*).

(b) The working surfaces of the vice slideways are parallel to the machine work table (*b,b*).

(c) The fixed jaw of the vice is perpendicular to the machine work table.

The parallels provide positive restraint by resisting the axial feed force of the drill in a downward direction. The vice jaws provide positive restraint by resisting the tendency of the rotary cutting forces to rotate the workpiece. Cylindrical work is more difficult to hold. Figure 3.17 shows how a cylindrical component is held vertically in a machine vice using a V-block. To ensure that the spindle axis is parallel to the workpiece axis, the following alignments must be checked.

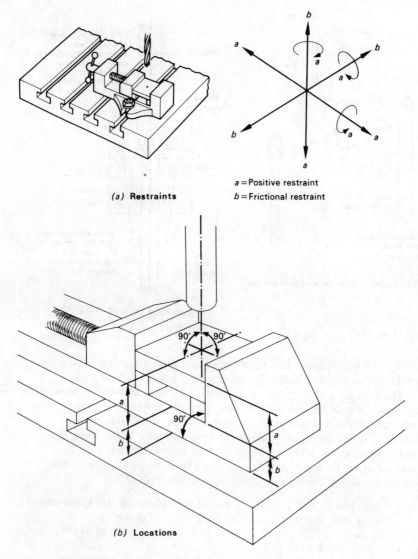

*(a)* **Restraints**

*a* = Positive restraint
*b* = Frictional restraint

*(b)* **Locations**

**Fig. 3.16** Workholding in a vice — restraints and locations

(a) The V-block must be seated on the vice slideways so that the Vee is perpendicular, that is, its end face is parallel to the vice slides in each direction (*a,a*).

(b) As previously, the vice slideways must be parallel to the machine work table (*b,b*), and the fixed jaw of the vice must be perpendicular to the work table.

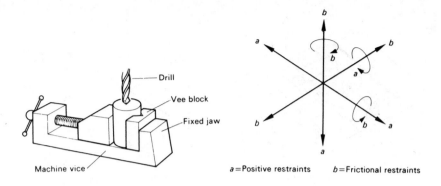

**Drill**

**Vee block**

**Fixed jaw**

Machine vice

a=Positive restraints    b=Frictional restraints

*(a)* **Restraints**

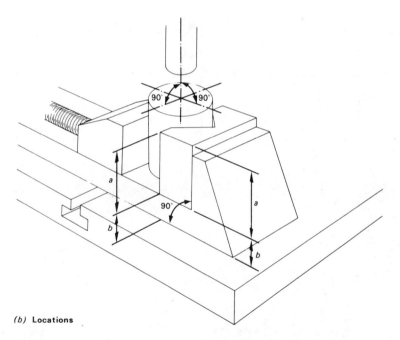

*(b)* **Locations**

**Fig. 3.17** Workholding cylindrical work in a vice

Figure 3.18 shows how a cylindrical component can be held horizontally on the drilling machine work table. To ensure that the axis of the component is parallel to the work table $(a,a)$, it is essential to use a matched pair of V-blocks as shown. It is difficult to start a drill on the curved surface of a cylindrical component and some guidance is required. Figure 3.19 shows a drill jig suitable for drilling a cross-hole through a

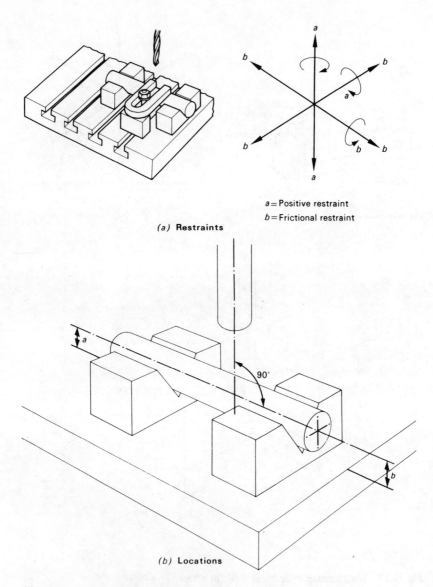

$a$ = Positive restraint
$b$ = Frictional restraint

*(a)* **Restraints**

90°

*(b)* **Locations**

**Fig. 3.18** Workholding cylindrical work on a drilling machine table

shaft end. A drill jig not only locates the workpiece in the correct place relative to the drill axis, it also guides the drill close to its point so that it cannot wander out of position. Since the bush is a close running fit on the drill, the hole cannot be reamed without first removing the bush. Figure 3.20 shows a removable bush and liner sleeve. The drill bush is placed in the liner sleeve as shown to guide the drill during the drilling

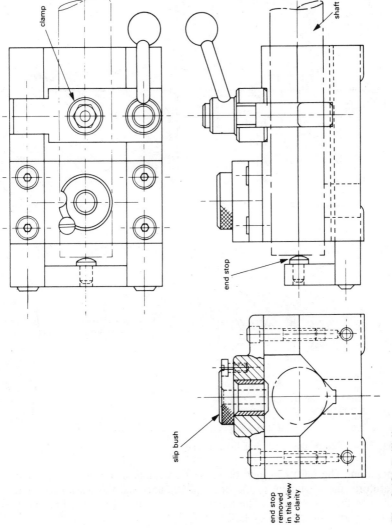

**Fig. 3.19** Drill jig

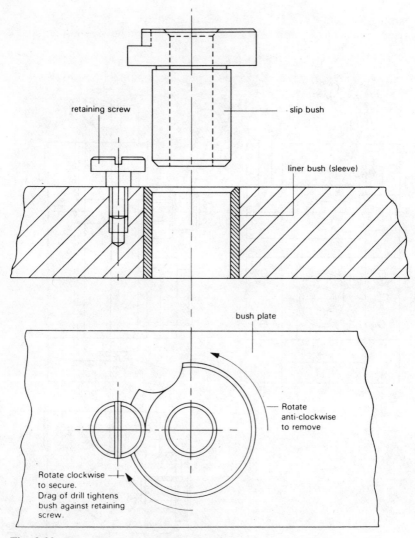

**Fig. 3.20** Removable bush and liner sleeve

operation. The bush can then be removed without disturbing the jig and, therefore, the alignment of the drill spindle axis and the workpiece. The hole can then be reamed. The reamer is a clearance fit in the liner sleeve and is guided by the drilled hole.

## 3.5 Tool-holding and work-holding in a milling machine

Milling cutters are usually mounted on an arbor which locates and drives the rotating cutter. Unlike the morse taper of the drilling machine, the milling machine taper only locates the arbor which is driven by 'dogs' fixed to the spindle nose. The arbor is held into the spindle-nose by a draw-bolt passing through the spindle of the machine.

Figure 3.21(a) shows the restraints and locations acting upon a cutter mounted on a long arbor. In the example shown the arbor is driven positively by the 'dogs' on the spindle nose, but the cutter is driven by

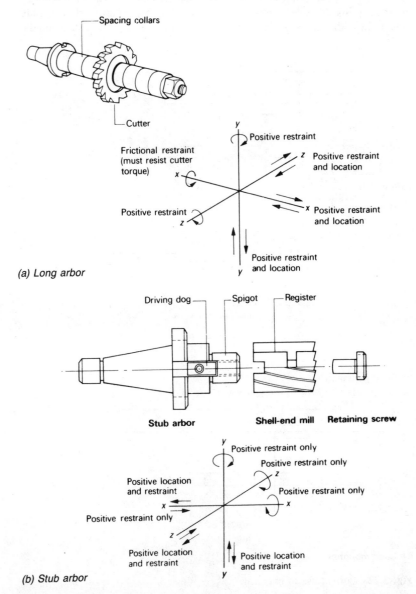

*(a) Long arbor*

*(b) Stub arbor*

**Fig. 3.21** Mounting of arbors and cutters

114

friction alone. This is adequate for the majority of jobbing applications, but for production milling where heavier cuts are likely to be taken the cutters should be keyed to the arbor to provide a positive drive. The long arbor should always be supported as a beam rather than as a cantilever to keep the deflection of the cutter to a minimum (see Fig. 3.22). Stub-arbors are also used and these are supported as a cantilever in the spindle nose alone. Figure 3.21(*b*) shows a typical stub arbor used for mounting shell-end mills. The restraints and locations for this type of arbor are also shown. In addition, large face mills may be bolted directly to the spindle

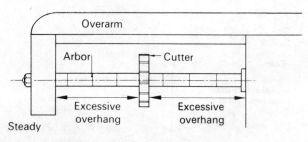

(*a*) **Bad mounting**

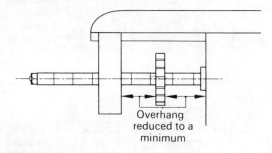

(*b*) **Good mounting**

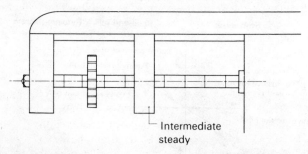

(*c*) **Good mounting**

**Fig. 3.22** Correct use of overarm

nose, and small end-mills and slot-drills may be held in a collet chuck inserted into the spindle nose.

The forces acting on a milling cutter, when removing metal rapidly, are very great. Therefore the cutter arbor must be adequately supported and the cutter correctly mounted to avoid inaccuracies and chatter. Figure 3.22(a) shows a cutter incorrectly mounted as excessive overhang from the points of support allows the arbor to flex. This leads to inaccuracy, chatter, and poor surface finish. In extreme cases the cutter teeth may be damaged. Figure 3.22(b) shows a cutter correctly mounted with the minimum of overhang and maximum rigidity. The cutter is kept as close to the spindle nose as possible, and the overarm and steady are adjusted to provide support as close to the bearing as possible. Sometimes the shape and size of the work itself prevents the cutter being mounted close to the spindle nose. Figure 3.22(c) shows how an additional, intermediate steady can be placed on the overarm to support the arbor close behind the cutter to reduce the effective overhang to a minimum.

Various methods of work-holding are available on the milling machine. Figure 3.23(a) shows a small component held in a machine vice, whilst Fig. 3.23(b) shows a large component clamped directly to the machine table. The appropriate restraints and locations are shown in both instances. The above examples show work held on a horizontal spindle milling machine. When work is held on a vertical spindle milling machine (Fig. 3.24(a)) the forces acting on the workpiece are very different. In the vertical spindle machine, the cutter will tend to rotate the work as well as push it along the table. Therefore side abutments should also be provided to prevent the work from rotating, as shown in Fig. 3.24(b). The clamp screws should be inclined as shown in Fig. 3.24(c) to prevent the component from lifting. Cylindrical components may be clamped and located using V-blocks as shown in Fig. 3.25.

To reduce setting time when large quantities of the same component are to be produced, a *fixture* is usually provided. This locates the component in the correct position relative to the milling machine table and cutter and provides the necessary restraints to resist the cutting forces. Unlike the drilling jig, described in section 3.4, which guided the drill as well as locating the work, a fixture only locates the work. Figure 3.26(a) shows a component flame cut from steel plate. The faces of the component have been ground flat and parallel, and the two holes have been bored in a previous operation. The lug is now to be milled on the face XX prior to drilling. A suitable milling fixture is shown in Fig. 3.26(b). Primary location is on the larger bore and the location spigot has been form relieved to assist loading. The secondary location is on the smaller bore, and the secondary location spigot has been form relieved to compensate for small variations in the bore centre distance due to manufacturing tolerances. Tenons are provided to locate the fixture parallel to the milling machine table T-slot, and a fouling peg is provided to prevent incorrect loading of the component, that is, to prevent the component being accidentally loaded upside down. The setting block is

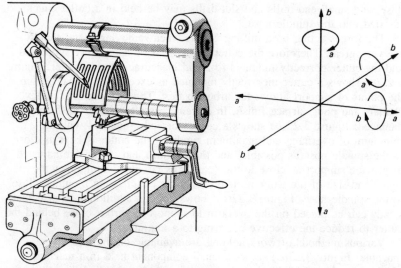

*(a)* Location of work in the milling machine vice

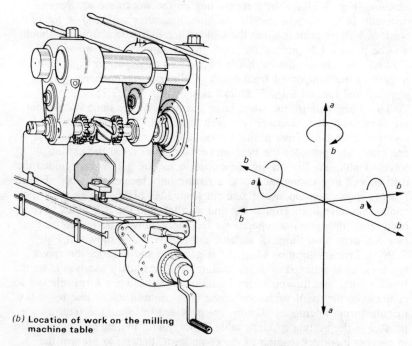

*(b)* Location of work on the milling
machine table

**Fig. 3.23** Workholding on the horizontal milling machine

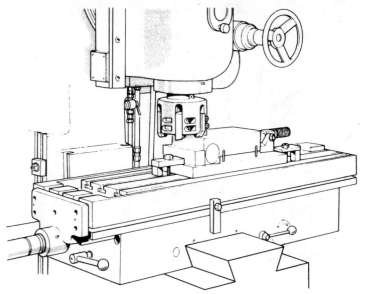

*(a)* **Typical example of vertical machine work**

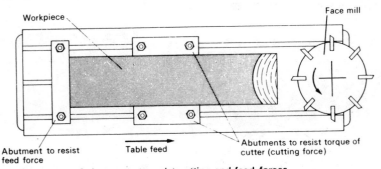

*(b)* **Positioning of abutments to resist cutting and feed forces**

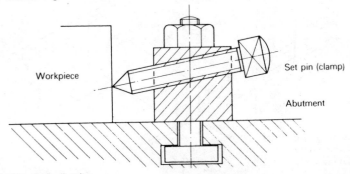

*(c)* **Set pin inclination**

**Fig. 3.24** Workholding on the vertical milling machine

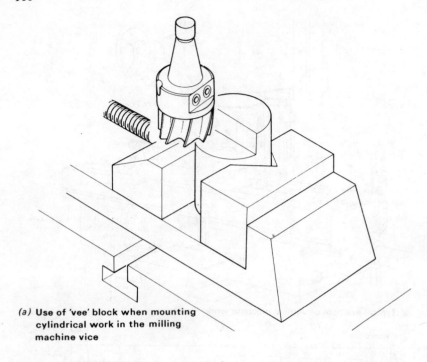

(a) Use of 'vee' block when mounting
cylindrical work in the milling
machine vice

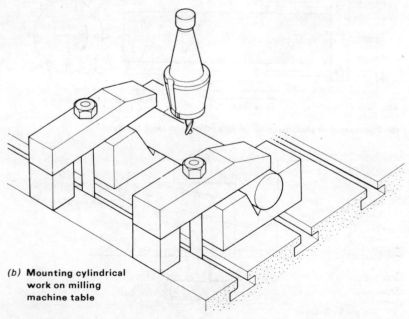

(b) Mounting cylindrical
work on milling
machine table

**Fig. 3.25** Holding cylindrical work

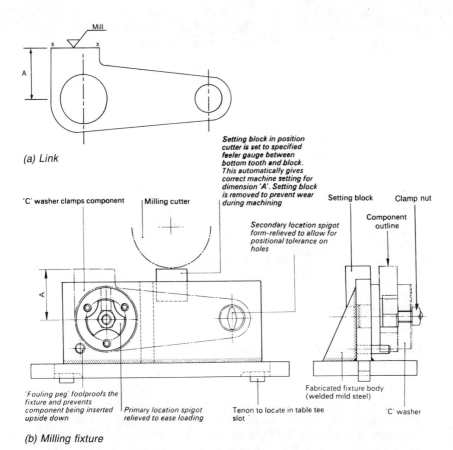

(a) Link

*Setting block in position cutter is set to specified feeler gauge between bottom tooth and block. This automatically gives correct machine setting for dimension 'A'. Setting block is removed to prevent wear during machining*

'C' washer clamps component | Milling cutter

*Secondary location spigot form-relieved to allow for positional tolerance on holes*

Setting block          Clamp nut

Component outline

'Fouling peg' foolproofs the fixture and prevents component being inserted upside down | Primary location spigot relieved to ease loading

Tenon to locate in table tee slot

Fabricated fixture body (welded mild steel)

'C' washer

(b) Milling fixture

**Fig. 3.26** Milling fixture for link

used to set the cutter. When the bottom tooth of the cutter is a prescribed distance above the setting block, as checked with a feeler gauge, the machine is set to provide the correct dimension A on the component. The component is clamped into position by means of a C-washer and nut.

## 3.6 Tool-holding and work-holding in a lathe

The single-point tools used on centre lathes are held in tool posts as shown in Fig. 3.27. The four-way turret type tool post shown in Fig. 3.27(a) enables a set of tools to be selected as required and saves on setting time where a batch of components is to be turned. Adjustment of tool height is by inserting packing under the tool which is inconvenient

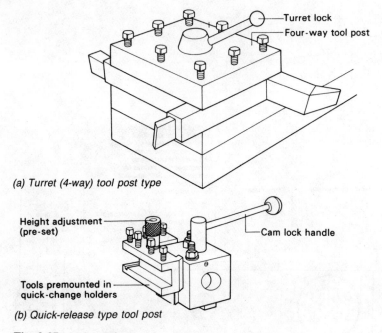

(a) Turret (4-way) tool post type

(b) Quick-release type tool post

**Fig. 3.27** Lathe tool posts

and can lack rigidity. The quick-release tool post shown in Fig. 3.27(*b*) has the advantage of quick tool changing and easy, pre-set tool height adjustment. However, it is more costly than the tool post previously described, as each tool has to be mounted in a separate tool holder. These separate tool holders are located, when required, on a dove-tail slide on the face of the mounting block which is secured to the lathe and retained by a quick-acting cam locking device.

Work holding on the lathe can be achieved in various ways depending on the geometry of the work piece.

## Work-holding between centres

This is the traditional method of work-holding from which the centre lathe gets its name, and is shown in Fig. 3.28(*a*). It can be seen that the workpiece is located between centres and is driven by a catchplate and carrier. Since the driving mechanism can 'float' it has no influence on the accuracy of location of the workpiece. The centres themselves have Morse-taper shanks and are located in taper sockets in the spindle and in the tailstock barrel. The use of taper locations ensures axial alignment irrespective of variations due to manufacturing tolerance and wear. Figure 3.28(*b*) shows the restraints acting on the workpiece held between centres.

For parallel turning, the axis of the spindle centre and the axis of the

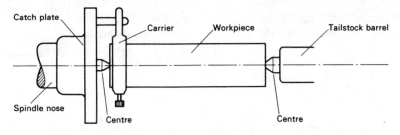

(a) Work-holding between centres

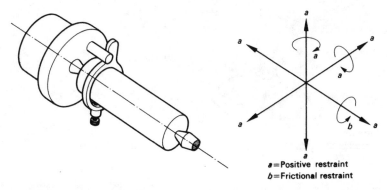

a=Positive restraint
b=Frictional restraint

(b) Restraints

**Fig. 3.28** Work-holding between centres

tailstock centre must be coincident with each other and parallel to the bed slideways. The tailstock is provided with lateral (sideways) adjustment to achieve this alignment. If the axes of the centres are not coincident, the turned component will be conical (tapered). This is considered further in section 4.7.

## Work-holding in a self-centring chuck

Figure 3.29(a) shows the construction of a typical three-jaw self-centring chuck. It can be seen that the scroll not only restrains the workpiece, but locates it as well. This is fundamentally bad practice, since any wear in the scroll and/or the jaws impairs the accuracy of location. Further, there is no means of adjustment possible to compensate for this wear. However, because of its convenience in use, the self-centring chuck is widely used and, providing it is treated with care, it retains its initial accuracy for a considerable time. To maintain the initial accuracy, *never*

(a)  try to hammer the work true;
(b)  hold on an irregular surface;
(c)  hold on the tips of the jaws.

The jaws of this type of chuck are not reversible and separate internal and external jaws have to be used as shown in Fig. 3.29(*b*). It is essential that the sets of jaws carry the same serial number as the chuck body, otherwise they will not close concentrically upon the workpiece. The restraints acting on the workpiece held in a three-jaw self-centring chuck are shown in Fig. 3.29(*c*).

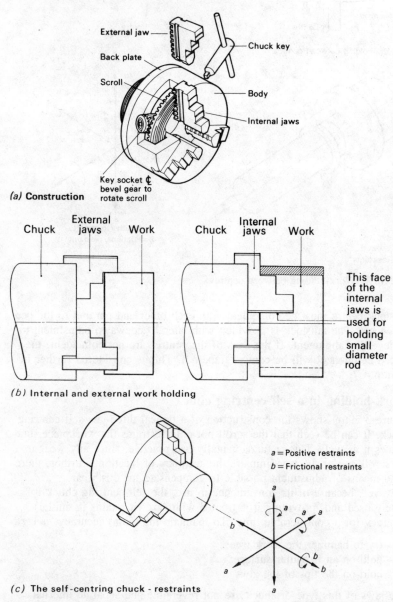

*(a)* **Construction**

*(b)* **Internal and external work holding**

*a* = Positive restraints
*b* = Frictional restraints

*(c)* **The self-centring chuck - restraints**

**Fig. 3.29** The three-jaw self-centring chuck

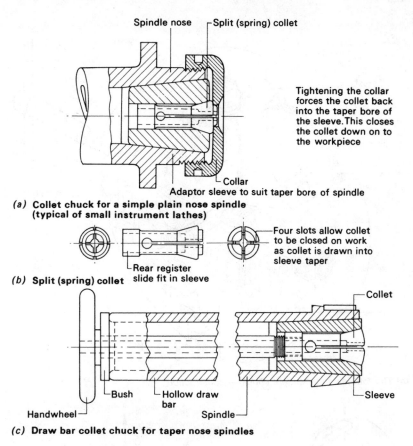

Tightening the collar
forces the collet back
into the taper bore of
the sleeve. This closes
the collet down on to
the workpiece

Collar
Adaptor sleeve to suit taper bore of spindle

*(a)* **Collet chuck for a simple plain nose spindle
(typical of small instrument lathes)**

Four slots allow collet
to be closed on work
as collet is drawn into
sleeve taper

*(b)* **Split (spring) collet** Rear register
slide fit in sleeve

*(c)* **Draw bar collet chuck for taper nose spindles**

**Fig. 3.30** The split collet chuck

## Work-holding in a collet chuck

This type of chuck is shown in Fig. 3.30. It has the advantage over the
self-centring chuck that it provides a higher level of concentricity but,
compared with a three-jaw, self-centring chuck it has a limited range of
sizes and can only hold on bar stock or blanks cut from bar stock. The
restraints acting on the workpiece are similar for those of a three-jaw
self-centring chuck.

## Work-holding in an independent-jaw chuck

Figure 3.31(*a*) shows the construction of a four-jaw independent chuck. It
is much more heavily built than the self-centring chuck and has much
greater holding ability. It gets its name from the fact that each jaw can be
moved independently. Each jaw is moved independently by a square
thread screw, and each jaw is reversible. The restraints acting on a

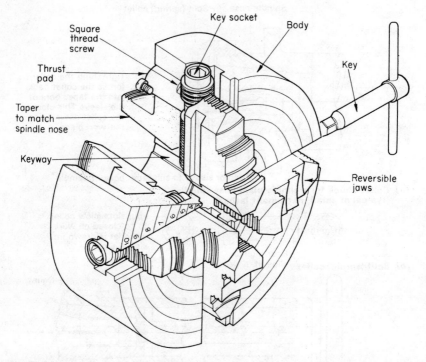

(a) The four-jaw independent chuck — construction

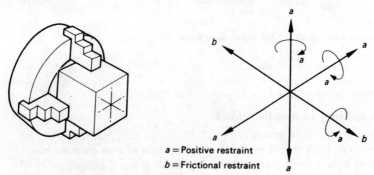

a = **Positive restraint**
b = **Frictional restraint**

(b) The four-jaw chuck — restraints

**Fig. 3.31** The four-jaw chuck

rectangular workpiece are shown in Fig. 3.31(b). This type of chuck is used for holding

(a) work with four or a multiple of four sides;
(b) irregularly shaped work;
(c) work which must be trued up to run concentrically;
(d) work which must be deliberately offset to run eccentrically.

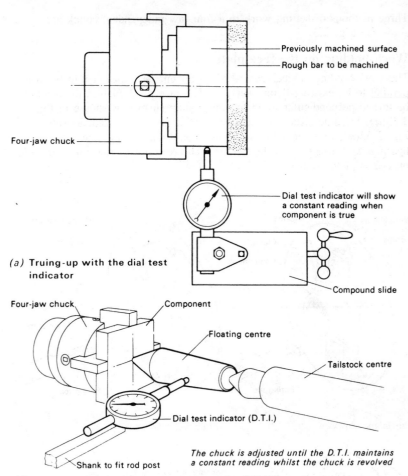

(a) Truing-up with the dial test indicator

(b) Setting work in the four-jaw chuck - using D.T.I. and centre

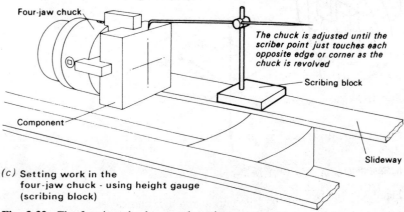

(c) Setting work in the four-jaw chuck - using height gauge (scribing block)

**Fig. 3.32** The four-jaw chuck — work setting

126

Three methods of setting work in a four-jaw independent chuck are shown in Fig. 3.32.

## Work-holding on the face plate

The work-holding devices described so far enable a diameter to be turned parallel to an existing datum surface. The face plate enables diameters to be turned perpendicular to an existing datum surface as shown in Fig. 3.33(a). In some circumstances the work must be balanced, as shown in Fig. 3.33(b), to avoid vibration which could damage the machine bearings and affect the surface finish. The restraints acting on work held on a face plate are shown in Fig. 3.33(c).

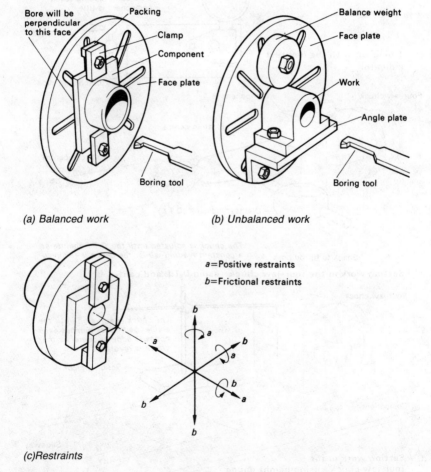

(a) Balanced work        (b) Unbalanced work

a = Positive restraints
b = Frictional restraints

(c) Restraints

**Fig. 3.33** The face plate

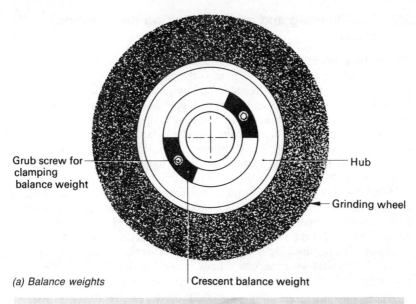

Grub screw for clamping balance weight

Hub

Grinding wheel

Crescent balance weight

*(a) Balance weights*

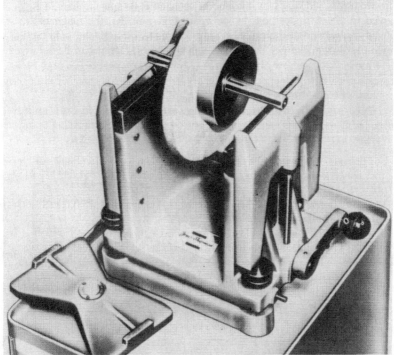

*(b) Balancing fixture*

**Fig. 3.34** Grinding wheel balancing

## 3.7 Tool-holding and work-holding on the grinding machine

The abrasive wheels for precision grinding machines are not mounted directly onto the machine spindle, as is the case with simple off-hand grinding machines, but are mounted on hubs which have built-in adjustable balance weights as shown in Fig. 3.34. These balance weights enable the wheel and hub assembly to be statically balanced before the assembly is mounted on the machine spindle. The hub has a taper bore which locates on the taper on the machine spindle and ensures axial alignment and true running. Large abrasive wheels are built up on the hub in segments as shown in Fig. 3.35.

Work-holding on surface grinding machines is usually on a magnetic chuck. Modern magnetic materials enable permanent magnetic chucks to have very great holding ability. The magnetic flux field attracts the component against the face of the chuck with sufficient force that the workpiece is restrained by friction between the work and chuck faces. Figure 3.36(*a*) shows a magnetic chuck in the 'on' position with the magnetic flux passing through the component which must be of a ferro-magnetic material such as steel. The magnets are located in a grid which can be moved sideways by the operating handle. When the handle is moved to the 'off' position, as shown in Fig. 3.36(*b*), the magnets are moved sideways and their flux is short circuited through the pole pieces. Since the flux no longer passes through the workpiece it can be removed.

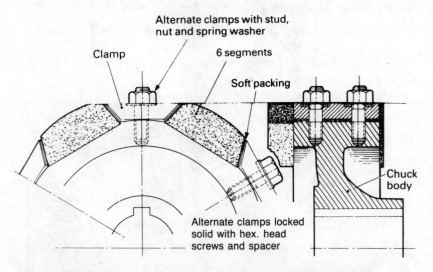

**Fig. 3.35** Segmental wheel and chuck for a large vertical spindle grinding machine

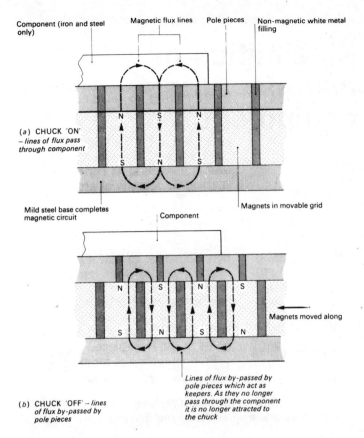

Component (iron and steel only)

Magnetic flux lines

Pole pieces

Non-magnetic white metal filling

(a) CHUCK 'ON' – lines of flux pass through component

Mild steel base completes magnetic circuit

Magnets in movable grid

Component

Magnets moved along

Lines of flux by-passed by pole pieces which act as keepers. As they no longer pass through the component it is no longer attracted to the chuck

(b) CHUCK 'OFF' – lines of flux by-passed by pole pieces

**Fig. 3.36** Permanent magnetic chuck

Cylindrical grinding machines use the same work-holding devices as the centre lathe. The work is held between centres, or in chucks. In addition, flat work can be held on a rotary magnetic chuck.

# 4 Kinematics of manufacturing equipment

## 4.1 Generation and forming of surfaces

Figure 4.1 shows a component which consists of a number of surfaces that are basic geometrical shapes. These surfaces can be produced by selecting the appropriate manufacturing process. For example:

(a) the circular plain surface on the end of the stem could be produced on a lathe at the same setting as the conical and cylindrical surfaces (b) and (c);

(b) the cylindrical surface could be produced on a lathe;

(c) the conical surface could be produced on a lathe using a taper turning technique;

(d) the rectangular plain surface adjacent to the cylindrical surface could also be produced on a lathe at the same setting as (b) and (c);

(c) the plain surfaces which are mutually parallel or perpendicular could be produced on a milling machine;

(f) the inclined plain surfaces could also be produced on a milling machine;

(g) the hole could be produced on a drilling machine.

Should a high level of surface finish be required, then the turned surfaces could be finished on a cylindrical grinding machine and the plain surfaces could be finished on a surface grinding machine. Most engineering components are designed as combinations of geometrical surfaces with specific manufacturing processes in mind. Where more complex surfaces

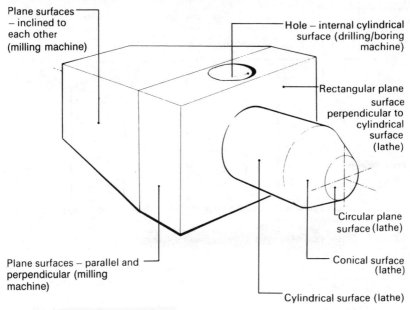

Plane surfaces – inclined to each other (milling machine)

Hole – internal cylindrical surface (drilling/boring machine)

Rectangular plane surface perpendicular to cylindrical surface (lathe)

Circular plane surface (lathe)

Conical surface (lathe)

Plane surfaces – parallel and perpendicular (milling machine)

Cylindrical surface (lathe)

**Fig. 4.1** Basic geometric shapes

are required, as for instance, in the press tools for stamping out motor car body panels, copy-machining techniques or computer controlled (CNC) machine techniques can be employed as these processes have greater flexibility (see Chapter 5).

Conventional machine tools were chosen in the above example because they generate the geometrical surfaces and solids required. A surface is said to be *generated* when its geometry is wholly dependent upon the relative movements of the cutting tool and the workpiece and wholly independent of the shape of the cutting tool. Figure 4.2 shows a piece of metal being turned in a lathe. Irrespective of the profile of the turning tool used, a cylindrical component will be produced, that is, a cylindrical surface will be *generated*.

Figure 4.3 shows surfaces being produced by a slab milling cutter and a side and face milling cutter, such as would be used on a horizontal spindle milling machine. It also shows surfaces being cut by a face milling cutter and a long reach shell end milling cutter, such as would be used on a vertical spindle milling machine. Irrespective of which cutter is used, and despite the fact that the cutters are circular and rotating about an axis, plain surfaces are produced by all the cutters, that is, plain surfaces are being *generated*.

Figure 4.4 shows a selection of surfaces being produced by a variety of cutters. In each case the profile of the surface produced is dependent on the shape of the tool. These surfaces are said to be *formed*. It can also

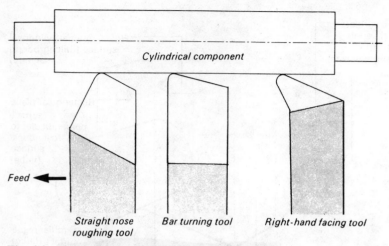

**Fig. 4.2** Generation of a cylindrical surface by turning

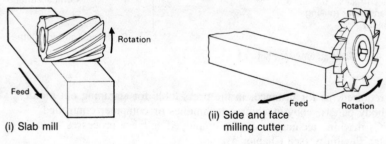

(i) Slab mill

(ii) Side and face milling cutter

*(b) Cutters suitable for a vertical milling machine*

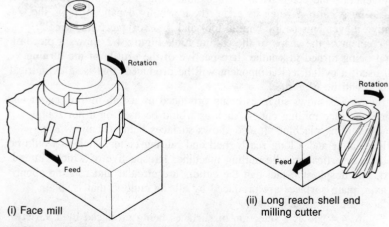

(i) Face mill

(ii) Long reach shell end milling cutter

*(a) Cutters suitable for a horizontal milling machine*

**Fig. 4.3** Generation of plain surfaces using milling cutters

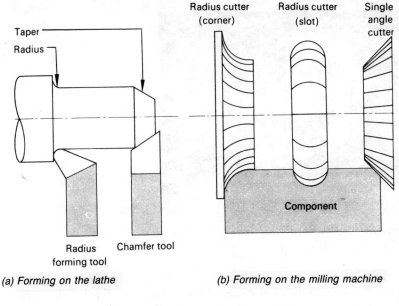

(a) Forming on the lathe

(b) Forming on the milling machine

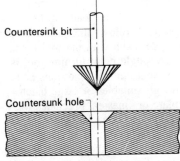

(c) Countersinking on the drilling machine

**Fig. 4.4** Forming surfaces

be seen that the formed surface is superimposed upon the surface normally generated by the machine, that is, you can generate without forming but, when forming, generation also occurs at the same time.

Forming operations are strictly limited by the rigidity of the workpiece, the cutting tool, and the machine tool used. A forming operation increases the length of the cutting edge in contact with the workpiece and can cause chatter. Where an extensive forming operation is required, copy machining is preferred to a form tool. An example is shown in Fig. 4.5. A template or 'master' is produced to the shape of the finished component. In this example the 'master' is mounted between

**Fig. 4.5** Copy turning

centres on the back of the lathe. As the saddle traverses along the bed of the lathe, a stylus mounted on the copying attachment fixed to the cross-slide traces the profile of the 'master'. The stylus, through a system of valves and hydraulic cylinders and pistons, controls the path of the cutting tool so that the cutting point of the tool follows the outline of the required component. A succession of cuts are taken with the tool being fed further into the workpiece each time. A single point turning tool is used, no form tool being required, thus normal cutting conditions and metal removal rates can be applied. Although suitable for large batch production, the cost of producing a template or 'master' precludes the use of this process for one-off and small batch production. The use of a computer controlled (CNC) turning centre gives the same advantages of cutting with a conventional single-point tool, but has the added advantage that no template or 'master' is required (see Chapter 5).

## 4.2 Requirements of a machine tool

The basic requirements of a machine tool may be summarised as follows.

(*a*) It must provide the geometrically inter-related movements of tool and workpiece necessary to generate the surfaces and shapes for which it has been designed.

(*b*) The machine must have a suitable level of accuracy and repeatability for the class of work for which it is intended, that is, once set, all the components within a given batch of work must lie within the dimensional and geometrical tolerances specified.

(*c*) The machine must provide a surface finish appropriate for the class of work for which it is intended, provided that the tooling, tool-maintenance and tool-setting are of an adequate standard.

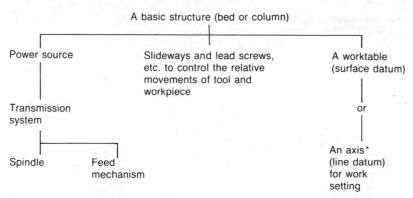

*Since an axis is not a physical body, it is represented in practice by centres, a chuck, or the taper nose of a spindle.

**Fig. 4.6** Fundamental requirements of machine tools

(*d*)  The machine must be capable of an economic rate of material removal.

(*e*)  The machine must be safe and convenient to use and set up.

(*f*)  Maintenance must be minimal and easy to carry out.

To achieve these aims the machine should follow the principles of good kinematic design, that is, each moving element of the machine involved in the generation of the required surface should be designed to carry out a specific function and not duplicate functions or interfere with the function of an associated machine element. For example, the conventional use of the lead-screw and nut of a milling machine table is an example of bad kinematic design. Not only must the lead-screw and nut provide linear motion to the work table as it is driven against the thrust of the cutter, but it is usual to fit a micrometer dial to the screw so that it can be used as a measuring and positioning device as well. Any wear and strain resulting from its driving function will affect the accuracy of its measuring function. Good kinematic design is found on many modern machines where these functions are separated. The lead-screw and nut merely providing table movement, whilst a separate scale and transducer provide a digital readout of the table position. Here, the measuring and positioning system is unaffected by any wear in the lead screw and nut.

The basic contructional features of a number of machine tools will now be considered. It will be seen that they have a number of features in common as shown in Fig. 4.6.

## 4.3  The basic structure

Figure 4.7 shows examples of the basic structures upon which all machine tools are built. Those which lie in the horizontal plane are called *beds*, whilst those which stand in the vertical plane are called *columns*.

136

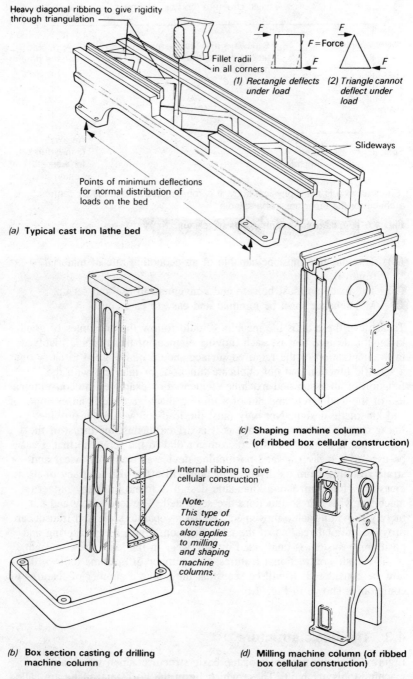

Heavy diagonal ribbing to give rigidity through triangulation

Fillet radii in all corners

$F$ = Force

(1) Rectangle deflects under load

(2) Triangle cannot deflect under load

Slideways

Points of minimum deflections for normal distribution of loads on the bed

(a) Typical cast iron lathe bed

(c) Shaping machine column (of ribbed box cellular construction)

Internal ribbing to give cellular construction

Note:
This type of construction also applies to milling and shaping machine columns.

(b) Box section casting of drilling machine column

(d) Milling machine column (of ribbed box cellular construction)

**Fig. 4.7** Machine beds and columns

These beds and columns should have the following properties.

(a)  *Strength* to resist the cutting forces, and to support the weight of the workpiece and any work-holding devices (e.g. jigs and fixtures), and the weight of any sub-assemblies such as the headstock and gearbox in the case of a lathe.

(b)  *Rigidity* to resist deflection resulting in misalignment when subject to the weight of the component and to the thrust of the cutting forces.

(c)  *Stability* so that the basic structure will not distort due to the slow release of internal stresses resulting from its manufacture. Castings should be made from high-stability alloys and stabilised after rough-machining by heat-treatment or by 'weathering' out of doors.

(d)  *Damping* properties should be inherent in the material used so that vibrations produced by the cutting process are absorbed before they can affect the accuracy and finish of the workpiece. That is the material used for machine beds and columns should be non-resonant.

Reference to Fig. 4.7 shows that most of these requirements are met with by the use of high-quality iron castings which are heavily ribbed or are of cellular construction. The high rates of material removal associated with CNC machine tools have necessitated improvements in bed and column design as shown in Fig. 4.8.

Steel has also been tried for machine tool beds and columns, but it has the following disadvantages.

(a)  As steel is stronger and more expensive than cast iron, the designer is tempted to use thinner sections which are less rigid.

(b)  It is more difficult to cast since it has a much higher melting point than cast iron. It is also more viscous (like treacle) than cast iron when molten and will not flow into intricate moulds.

(c)  When fabricated from plate, it can only be formed into square box shapes which limits the design possibilities.

(d)  Steel is not a good bearing material, so anti-friction pads have to be fastened to the basic fabrication to form slideways.

(e)  Steel is a resonant material and does not damp vibrations.

It is widely used for welded cabinet bases, supporting the beds and columns of small machines at a convenient working height. One application where steel is superior to cast iron is in the frames of large power presses used in the sheet-metal stamping industry.

## 4.4  Power systems

Power has to be transmitted from the drive motor to the spindle and feed mechanisms of the machine tool. Provision has to be made for connecting and disconnecting the drive from the various machine elements easily and safely. Provision has also to be made for varying the speed of the drive to suit various cutting conditions.

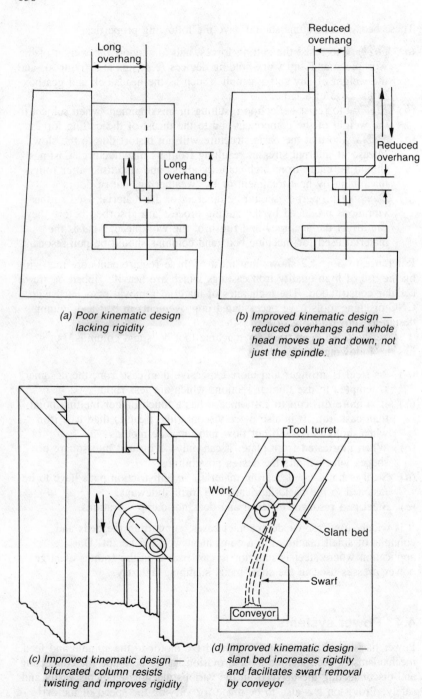

(a) Poor kinematic design
lacking rigidity

(b) Improved kinematic design —
reduced overhangs and whole
head moves up and down, not
just the spindle.

(c) Improved kinematic design —
bifurcated column resists
twisting and improves rigidity

(d) Improved kinematic design —
slant bed increases rigidity
and facilitates swarf removal
by conveyor

**Fig. 4.8** Improved bed and column design for CNC machines

## Starting and stopping

There are two basic methods of starting and stopping machine tools.

(a) *Electrical*, that is switching the drive motor on and off either directly or through a relay or contactor. The motor is permanently coupled to the machine transmission system. This is only suitable for small machines with a low inertia transmission system which only lightly loads the motor at switch-on.

(b) *Mechanical*. The motor is left permanently switched on whilst the machine is in use and the drive is connected to or disconnected from the machine input by a clutch. Since the drive should be taken up gradually under the control of the operator, this is usually a multiplate clutch.

## Speed control

There are various methods of speed control. The following examples are the more commonly used.

(a) *Pole-changing motors*. These are somewhat limited in that they can only be switched to give a limited number of set speeds (usually four). Unfortunately the torque decreases with the speed.

(b) *Electronic motor control*. This provides an infinite variation in speed within the range of the motor. Again, the torque decreases as the speed decreases. Electronic speed control is widely used on computer controlled machine tools.

(c) *Belt drive*. The use of a V-belt with stepped pulleys, as shown in Fig. 4.9(a), is used on small machines and, in particular, bench type sensitive drilling machines.

(d) *Gear box*. This is the most widely used method of speed control on conventional machine tools. A schematic diagram for a typical milling machine gearbox is shown in Fig. 4.9(b).

## Power transmission

Energy is transmitted from one part of a machine tool to another in a variety of ways.

(a) *Electrical*. To avoid complex mechanical drives, separate electrical motors are employed for each separate drive, for example the table traverse mechanism of a milling machine. The power to the motor can be supplied through flexible conductors and this is less complex than the use of telescopic drive shafts fitted with universal joints.

(b) *Hydraulic*. Rotary hydraulic motors tend to be smaller than electric motors for the same power output, and they have greater starting torque. Energy can also be transmitted by flexible hose, thus giving flexibility of movement to the system. However hydraulic transmission systems are more costly than electrical systems and are less easily linked to electronic control systems. Hydraulic drives are used for such applications as the work table traverse drives of large machine tools.

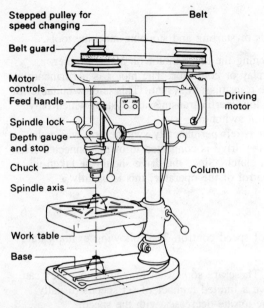

Stepped pulley for speed changing

Belt

Belt guard

Motor controls

Feed handle

Spindle lock

Depth gauge and stop

Chuck

Driving motor

Spindle axis

Column

Work table

Base

*(a) Belt drive with stepped pulleys (sensitive drilling machine)*

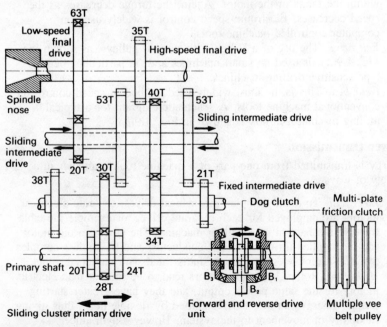

63T

Low-speed final drive

35T

High-speed final drive

Spindle nose

53T

40T

53T

Sliding intermediate drive

Sliding intermediate drive

20T

30T

21T

38T

Fixed intermediate drive

Dog clutch

Multi-plate friction clutch

34T

Primary shaft  20T   24T

B₃   B₁

B₂

28T

Sliding cluster primary drive

Forward and reverse drive unit

Multiple vee belt pulley

*(b) Typical machine tool gearbox (milling machine)*

**Fig. 4.9**  Speed control

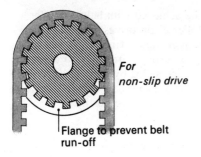

For
non-slip drive

Flange to prevent belt
run-off

*(a) Toothed belt and pulley*

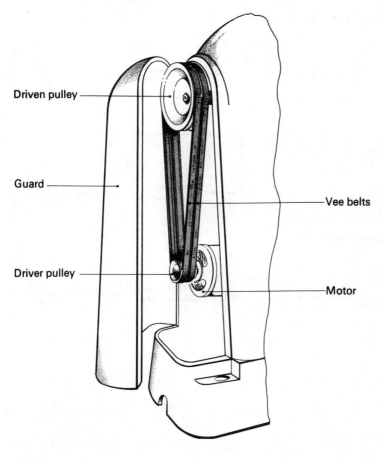

Driven pulley

Guard

Driver pulley

Vee belts

Motor

*(b) Vee belt drive*

**Fig. 4.10**   Belt drives

(*c*)  *Belt drives.* Long centre drives can be achieved with belts or roller chains (similar to bicycle chains). Roller chain drives have the advantage that they are synchronous (non-slip) but require regular maintenance, regular lubrication, and a clean environment to operate successfully. They have been largely superseded by toothed belt drives, as shown in Fig. 4.10(*a*). These are lower in cost, quieter, do not require lubrication, and can work in a more hostile

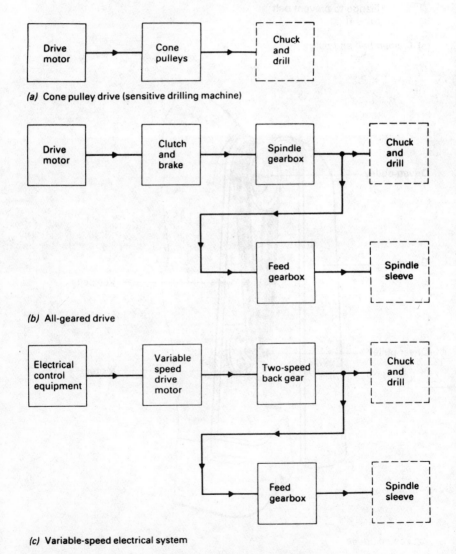

*(a)*  Cone pulley drive (sensitive drilling machine)

*(b)*  All-geared drive

*(c)*  Variable-speed electrical system

**Fig. 4.11**  Drilling machine power transmission systems

environment than chain drives. They are now widely used in machine tools where a synchronous drive is required, for example transmitting the drive from a stepper motor to a lead screw in a computer controlled machine tool. V-belts are widely used for transmitting mechanical energy from the drive motor of a machine to the main drive pully of the gear box as shown in Fig. 4.10(*b*).

(*d*) *Gear drives*. These are used for short centre drives. They are

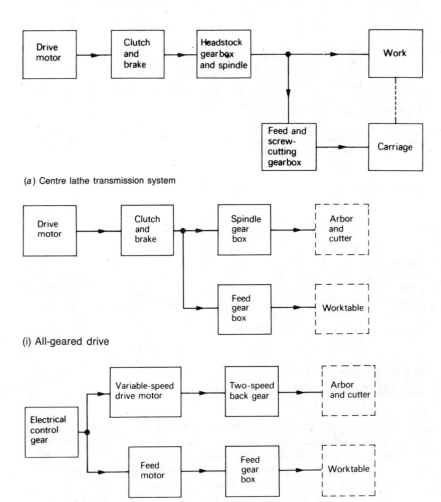

(*a*) Centre lathe transmission system

(i) All-geared drive

(ii) Variable-speed electrical system

(*b*) Milling machine transmission systems

**Fig. 4.12** Lathe and milling machine power transmission systems

144

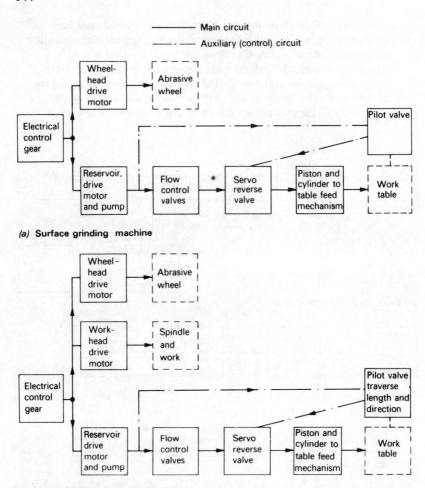

*(a)* Surface grinding machine

*(b)* Cylindrical grinding machine

**Fig. 4.13** Grinding machine power transmission system

compact, reliable and synchronous (non-slip) but relatively expensive and require continuous lubrication. They are used in machine tool gear boxes and for such applications as the transmission of energy from the spindle gear box of lathes to the feed gear box, where slip can not be tolerated and the velocity ratio needs, at times, to be changed. Block diagrams of some typical machine tool power transmission systems are given in Figs 4.11 to 4.13 inclusive.

## Bearings

Plain and rolling bearings are used in machine tools. Plain bearings are the simplest and the cheapest to manufacture. However they are dependent upon adequate lubrication if they are not to fail prematurely.

Bearing bushes cannot be adjusted for wear or preloaded to increase radial stiffness. They also exhibit relatively high frictional losses. Figure 4.14(*a*) shows a typical plain bearing. At rest there is little lubricant between the shaft and the bearing shell and, on start-up, wear is very heavy. Once the shaft is rotating it drags a wedge of oil between itself and the bearing and it depends upon this wedge of oil to provide lubrication and prevent wear. This wedge of oil is called a *hydrodynamic*

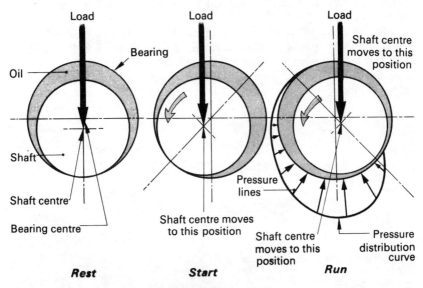

(a) Simple bearing — movement of centre line

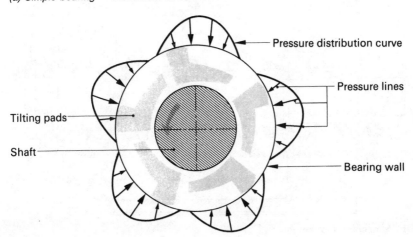

(b) Constant centre line bearing

**Fig. 4.14** Plain journal bearings

146

wedge as its presence depends on the movement (rotation) of the shaft. It can also be seen from Fig. 4.14 that the axis of the shaft moves about the centre point of the bearing and this causes inaccuracies if such a bearing is used for the spindle of a machine tool. Figure 4.14(b) shows a constant centreline plain bearing. Instead of a single pressure lobe, the tilting pads 'float' until a system of pressure lobes are built up symmetrically around the shaft and it is centred in the bearing. Any disturbing force upsets the balance of the system, causing a local pressure increase to oppose the disturbance and return the shaft to the centre of the bearing.

Modern practice favours the use of anti-friction, rolling bearings. A typical machine spindle of good kinematic design is shown in Fig. 4.15. The minimum number of bearings are used and they do not act against each other. The spindle nose is at A and is supported in a pair of opposed taper rolling bearings B. These bearings provide axial and radial

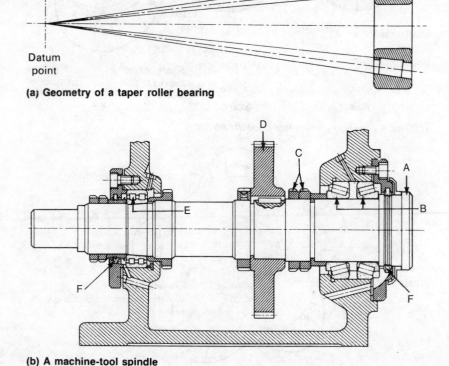

**(a) Geometry of a taper roller bearing**

**(b) A machine-tool spindle**

**Fig. 4.15** Roller bearings

location of the nose end of the spindle and are self-centring. They are pre-loaded against any disturbing forces by the screwed rings C which can also be used to take up wear. The drive to the spindle is through the gear D, and the 'tail' of the spindle is supported in a roller bearing at E. The shaft is free to slide axially in the bearings at E, so that as it warms up and expands there is no tendency for the shaft to bend and any expansion does not disturb the plane of the spindle nose. Oil seals are provided at F to prevent lubricating oil getting out and dirt getting in.

## 4.5 Guidance systems

Slideways are linear bearings which support and guide the sliding members of machine tools. They should provide the easiest possible movement in the required direction and the maximum possible resistance to movement or deflection (stiffness) in all other directions. Many different types of slideways are used on machine tools and some of these will now be considered.

### Flat slides

The flat slide was the earliest form of slideway to be used extensively. It is simple to produce, robust and accurate when new. However, when subject to uneven wear it is virtually impossible to keep in adjustment. For example, most of the wear on a lathe occurs in the vicinity of the chuck and if the gib strip of the carriage is adjusted to take up the wear in this area, it would be over-tight when the saddle is moved to less worn areas of the bed slides as shown in Fig. 4.16. Flat slideways are still used where the wear is uniform or limited by only occasional use.

### Inverted V-slides

This type of slide is self adjusting for wear and is found on most modern lathe beds. Provided that contact between the carriage and the bed is only on the flanks of the V-slide, any wear only results in the carriage settling lower onto the V, and there is no lateral displacement. This design of slideway is largely kinematic and resists the disturbing forces without redundant restraint. Details of this type of slideway are shown in Fig. 4.17, where it can be seen that there is only one V-slide. This provides support for the front of the carriage as well as lateral restraint. Only one V-slide is provided as only one slide is required to provide lateral restraint and also because it is impossible to manufacture two perfectly parallel V-slides. Any deviance from perfect parallelism would result in the slides pulling against each other. Instead, the rear of the carriage is supported on a flat slide but which provides no additional lateral control. In practice a second inverted V-slide and flat-slide are provided for the support and guidance of the tail-stock of the lathe. Figure 4.17 also shows the various forces acting on the carriage and how the V-slide resists them.

148

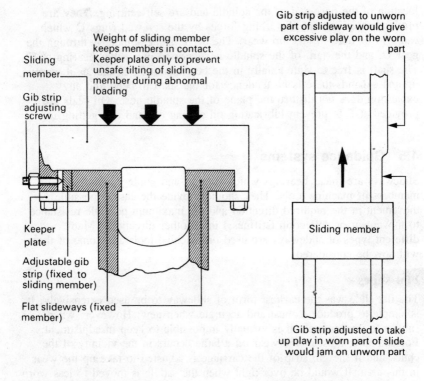

**Sliding member**

**Gib strip adjusting screw**

Weight of sliding member keeps members in contact. Keeper plate only to prevent unsafe tilting of sliding member during abnormal loading

Gib strip adjusted to unworn part of slideway would give excessive play on the worn part

**Keeper plate**

**Adjustable gib strip (fixed to sliding member)**

**Flat slideways (fixed member)**

Sliding member

Gib strip adjusted to take up play in worn part of slide would jam on unworn part

*(a)* **Section through a flat slideway**      *(b)* **Adjustment of gib strip**

**Fig. 4.16**  Flat slideway

## Dovetail slide

This type of slideway is used where the applied forces form a *couple* which tries to rotate the sliding member. Figure 4.18 shows a dovetail slide and the forces acting upon it. Because of its ability to provide a restoring couple, the dovetail slide is used where the applied force is outside the sliding member. It can be seen that the cutting force $F_c$ and the reaction force $R_1$ form a *disturbing couple*, and that the reaction forces $R_1$ and $R_2$ form a *restoring couple*. Another advantage of this type of slideway is that adjustment of the gib-strip to compensate for wear restores the vertical and horizontal restraints simultaneously.

## Anti-friction slides

Ball and roller bearings are used for shafts rotating in journal bearings because the rolling friction of such a bearing is very much less than the sliding friction of a plain bearing. Similarly, ball and roller bearing slideways exhibit less friction than the plain slideways described so far.

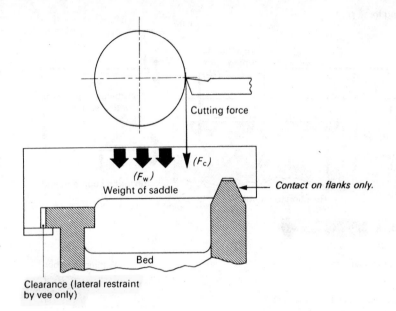

Cutting force

$(F_c)$

$(F_w)$

Weight of saddle

Contact on flanks only.

Bed

Clearance (lateral restraint by vee only)

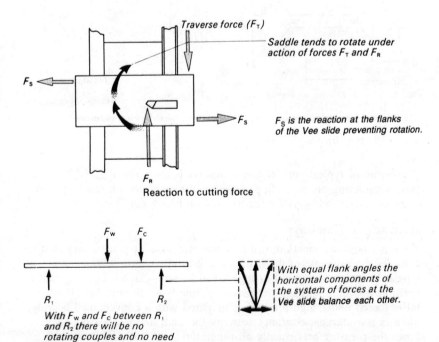

Traverse force $(F_T)$

Saddle tends to rotate under action of forces $F_T$ and $F_R$

$F_S$

$F_S$

$F_S$ is the reaction at the flanks of the Vee slide preventing rotation.

$F_R$

Reaction to cutting force

$F_W$    $F_C$

$R_1$    $R_2$

With $F_w$ and $F_c$ between $R_1$ and $R_2$ there will be no rotating couples and no need for upward restraint.

With equal flank angles the horizontal components of the system of forces at the Vee slide balance each other.

**Fig. 4.17** Inverted-V slideway

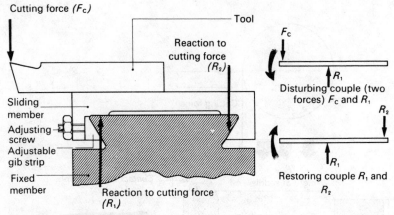

**Fig. 4.18** Dovetail slideway

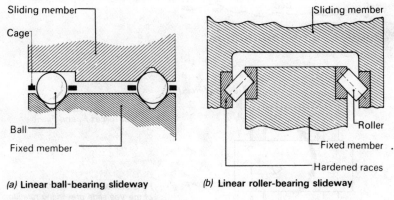

*(a)* **Linear ball-bearing slideway**      *(b)* **Linear roller-bearing slideway**

**Fig. 4.19** Anti-friction slideways

The layout of typical anti-friction slideways is shown in Fig. 4.19. Since the forces acting on the sliding members are supported on much smaller surfaces, these slideways cannot be used on heavy duty machine tools.

## Hydrostatic slideways

To understand the function of the hydrostatic slide, it is necessary first to consider the principle of the hydrostatic bearing. Figure 4.20(a) shows a typical hydrostatic journal bearing. It can be seen that the bearing shell is perforated with a symmetrical pattern of fine holes through which air or oil is forced under high pressure. Compared with a conventional bearing, there is considerable clearance between the shaft and the bearing shell. Since the pressure acts equally all round the shaft it is forced into the centre of the bearing. It can also be seen that any deflection of the shaft causes an imbalance in the fluid forces acting on the shaft in such a

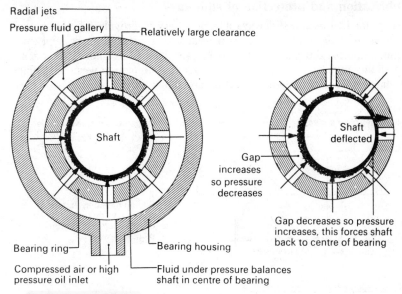

Radial jets

Pressure fluid gallery

Relatively large clearance

Shaft

Shaft deflected

Gap increases so pressure decreases

Gap decreases so pressure increases, this forces shaft back to centre of bearing

Bearing ring

Bearing housing

Compressed air or high pressure oil inlet

Fluid under pressure balances shaft in centre of bearing

*(a)* **The hydrostatic bearing**

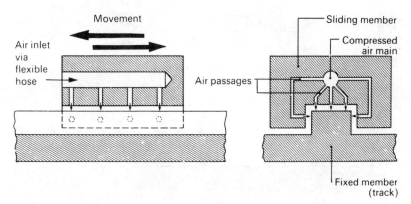

Movement

Air inlet via flexible hose

Sliding member

Compressed air main

Air passages

Fixed member (track)

*(b)* **Application of the hydrostatic bearing principle to the linear slideway**

**Fig. 4.20** Hydrostatic slideways

direction that the shaft is restored to the centre of the bearing. This type of bearing has a very low friction whilst its stiffness to deflection is very much greater than a conventional bearing. Figure 4.20(*b*) shows the application of this principle to a hydrostatic slide. The sliding member floats over the slideway like a hovercraft. Because the slide is self-centring it exhibits a much higher degree of lateral stiffness than a conventional slideway. At the same time, because there is no metal-to-metal contact, both friction and wear are much reduced.

# Lubrication and protection of slideways

Except for hydrostatic slideways it is necessary to provide efficient
lubrication of the contact surfaces if wear and friction are to be kept to a
minimum. Also dirt and swarf must be prevented from entering between
the sliding members and causing excessive and premature wear. Examples
of slideway lubrication and protection are shown in Fig. 4.21.

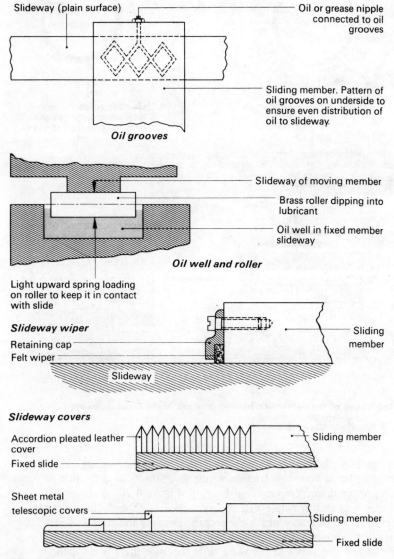

**Fig. 4.21** Lubrication and protection of slideways

## 4.6 Positioning systems

In all machine tools, means must be provided for moving the sliding members, such as the carriage of a lathe or the work table of a milling machine, along the slideways in a controlled manner. This movement acts not only for setting purposes but also against the thrust of the cutting forces during machining operations. The two most common means of doing this are to use a screw and nut, or a rack and pinion. Both these mechanisms convert rotary motion into linear motion.

### Screw and nut

A typical screw and nut assembly for traversing a milling machine table is shown in Fig. 4.22(*a*). Since the screw is being used to transmit power with minimum friction, the locking action of a V-thread form is undesirable and a square thread form or an acme thread form is used. The lead screw is made of alloy steel and toughened and thread-ground to reduce wear and ensure a high degree of accuracy. The nut is made from a hard-wearing, anti-friction material such as phosphor bronze. Preferably, the nut should wear out first as it is easier and cheaper to replace than the screw. The lead screw of a lathe is always given an acme thread form. This thread form has slightly tapered flanks which ease the engagement and disengagement of the half-nut when screw-cutting as shown in Fig. 4.22(*b*).

Recirculating ball screws and nuts are used on computer controlled machines to reduce the friction and, therefore, reduce the torque required by the driving motor. Such screw and nut systems have a higher accuracy and less backlash than conventional screws and nuts. Because there is less wear, they maintain their accuracy longer. Figure 4.23 shows the principle of such a mechanism.

### Rack and pinion

This mechanism is simple and relatively cheap. It also has the advantage that rapid rates of traverse are easily obtained with little effort. However the accuracy of control is lower than with a screw and nut. The rack and pinion mechanism is conventionally used for the movement of a lathe carriage when performing normal cylindrical turning operations as shown in Fig. 4.24(*a*). Figure 4.24(*b*) shows how a rack and pinion is used for the feed mechanism of sensitive drilling machines. The lead screw and nut is used when screw-cutting on a lathe to give more accurate control.

### Hydraulics

Hydraulic systems are used to provide the table traverse for grinding machines. Such systems provide a smoother drive than can be obtained mechanically, and are less likely to leave a vibration pattern on the ground surface. A simple example is shown in Fig. 4.25.

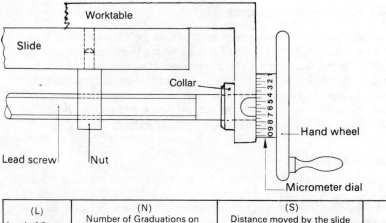

| (L)<br>Lead of Screw | (N)<br>Number of Graduations on<br>Micrometer Dial | (S)<br>Distance moved by the slide<br>for each dial graduation | $\dfrac{L}{N} = S$ |
|---|---|---|---|
| 5 mm | 100 | 0·05 mm | |
| 6 mm | 120 | 0·05 mm | $L = N \times S$ |
| 8 mm | 400 | 0·02 mm | |

*(a) Screw and nut — milling machine table*

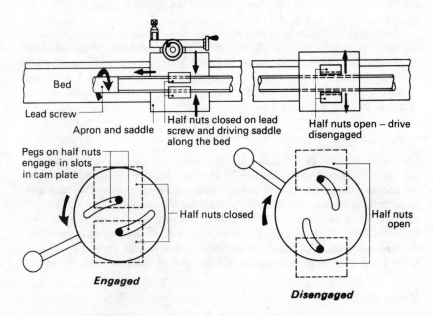

*(b) Half nut and lead screw*

**Fig. 4.22** Screw and nut

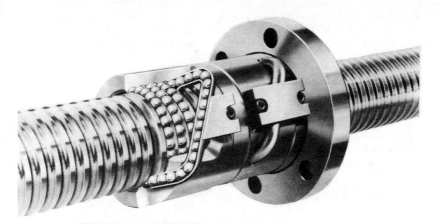

**Fig. 4.23** Recirculating ball screw

## Measurement

To produce accurate work from a machine tool it is necessary to be able to position the various sliding elements which control the work and tool movements accurately, and suitable measuring systems have to be built into the machine. The use of a lead screw and nut to impart linear motion to the sliding members of a machine has already been introduced above. By the addition of a calibrated dial to the screw, the same screw and nut can also be used to position the sliding member, for example the table of a milling machine (as previously shown in Fig. 4.22(a)) or the cross-slide of a lathe. Each revolution of the dial moves the nut along the screw a distance equal to the lead of the nut. The movement is relative and it does not matter whether the nut is fixed and the screw moves or the screw is fixed and the nut moves.

For example, consider a nut of lead 5 millimetres and a dial with 50 divisions.

(a) Rotation of the dial through 2 complete rotations would move the nut along the screw through $2 \times 5$ mm $= 10$ mm.

(b) Rotation of the dial through 8 divisions would move the nut along the screw through 5 mm $\times$ 8/50 $=0.8$ mm.

(c) Rotation of the dial through 4 complete rotations and 18 divisions would move the nut along the screw through:
$(4 \times 5$ mm$) + (5$ mm $\times 18/50) = 20$ mm $+ 1.8$ mm $= 21.8$ mm.

It has already been stated that use of the same mechanism for traversing sliding members of the machine and for measurement is bad kinematic design since wear in the traverse mechanism can lead to inaccuracy when it is used as a measuring device. It is better practice to use a separate measuring system to control positioning of the work and cutting tool. Various optical and mechanical measuring systems have been used, but

156

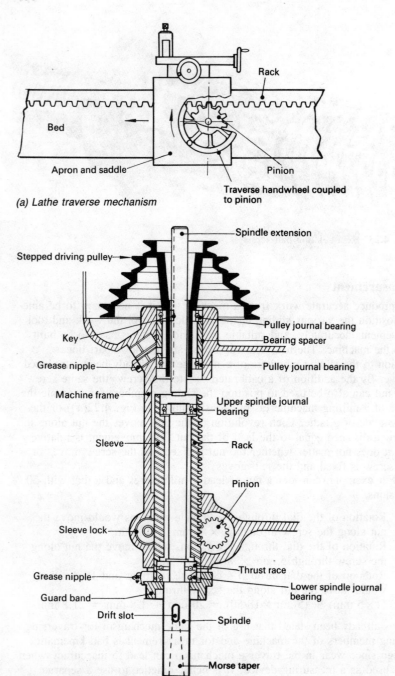

Rack

Bed

Apron and saddle

Pinion

Traverse handwheel coupled
to pinion

*(a) Lathe traverse mechanism*

Spindle extension

Stepped driving pulley

Pulley journal bearing
Bearing spacer

Key

Pulley journal bearing

Grease nipple

Machine frame

Upper spindle journal
bearing

Sleeve

Rack

Pinion

Sleeve lock

Thrust race

Grease nipple

Lower spindle journal
bearing

Guard band

Drift slot

Spindle

Morse taper

*(b) Spindle feed mechanism (drilling machine)*

**Fig. 4.24** Rack and pinion

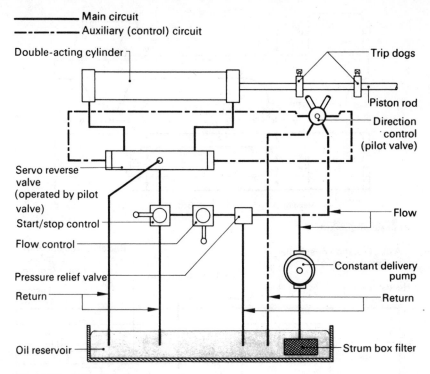

**Fig. 4.25** Hydraulic circuit

modern practice favours electronic systems because of the ease of providing digital read-out and of linking the positioning system to a computer numerical control unit.

## 4.7 Machine tool alignments

### The lathe

Figure 4.26(*a*) shows the basic alignment of the headstock spindle and the tailstock barrel on a common axis which, itself, is parallel to the bed slideways in both the vertical and the horizontal plane. This common axis is the datum of the machine to which all other alignments are referred. The bed slideways are also called the 'shears' in some parts of the UK. The rotation of the workpiece and the movement of the carriage alone is shown in Fig. 4.26(*b*). Since this moves the tool in a path parallel to the datum axis, these movements and alignments will generate a true cylinder.

The *cross-slide* on top of the carriage is aligned at 90° to the spindle axis as shown in Fig. 4.27(*a*). This slide has two purposes:

(*a*) to control the depth of cut (in-feed of the tool) when cylindrical

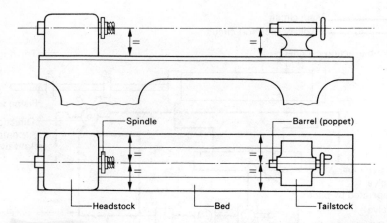

*(a)* **Basic alignment**

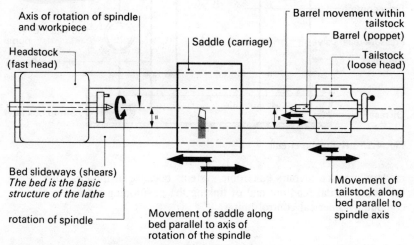

*(b)* **The carriage or saddle provides the basic movement of the cutting tool parallel to the work axis**

**Fig. 4.26** Centre lathe — basic alignments

turning, and for this purpose the cross-traverse screw is fitted with a micrometer dial.

*(b)* to move the tool in a path at right-angles to the datum axis when generating a plain surface. This operation is called facing and is used for machining the ends of components and shoulders.

The *compound-slide* (top-slide) is mounted on the cross-slide and can be set at an angle to the datum axis as shown in Fig. 4.27(*b*). It has two purposes:

*(a)* to control the depth of cut (in-feed of the tool) when a facing

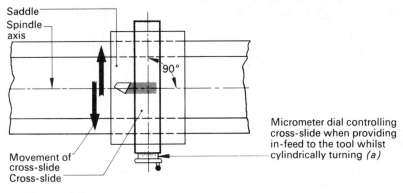

Saddle

Spindle axis

90°

Micrometer dial controlling cross-slide when providing in-feed to the tool whilst cylindrically turning *(a)*

Movement of cross-slide

Cross-slide

(a) The cross-slide

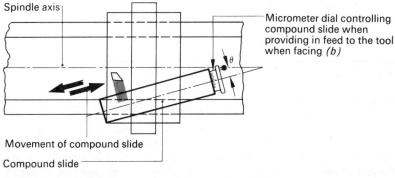

Spindle axis

Micrometer dial controlling compound slide when providing in feed to the tool when facing *(b)*

θ

Movement of compound slide

Compound slide

(b) The compound slide

**Fig. 4.27** Centre lathe — cross-slide and compound-slide

operation is being performed. For this purpose the compound slide is set parallel to the datum axis and the traverse screw is fitted with a micrometer dial.

(b) to move the tool in a path at an angle to the datum axis in order to generate a conical surface (taper) as shown in Fig. 4.27(b). Taper turning is considered more fully in section 4.9.

## The drilling machine

Figure 4.28 shows the basic alignments of the drilling machine. Here the working surface of the work table is the machine datum. The spindle locates and rotates the drill or other devices such as reamers or countersinking cutters and counterboring cutters. The spindle itself is located in bearings in a sleeve and can move in the head of the drilling machine. The complete assembly of spindle, bearings and sleeve is known as the 'quill'. A section through such an assembly has already

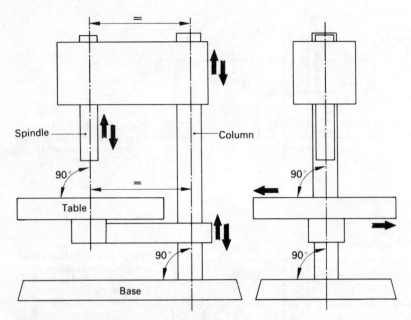

**Fig. 4.28** Drilling machine — basic alignments

been shown in Fig. 4.24. To produce accurate work, the fundamental alignment of the machine requires the spindle axis to be perpendicular to the work table and to remain perpendicular throughout its travel as it is fed into or out of the workpiece. The head itself is mounted on a column which is, in turn, perpendicular to the base of the machine. To compensate for drills of differing lengths and work of differing thicknesses, the head and work table can be raised or lowered on the column without upsetting the fundamental alignment of spindle axis and work table. Provision is made to tilt the table when holes need to be drilled at an angle to the datum surface.

## Horizontal milling machines

These machines generate plain surfaces using rotating multi-tooth cutters. The basic movements and alignments required are:

(a) a spindle with a *horizontal axis* to rotate and locate the cutter(s) in a given plane;

(b) a work table which will locate and move the workpiece in a given plane beneath, and relative to, the cutter.

The work table has to be able to traverse longitudinally to feed the work into the cutter as cutting proceeds. It is also necessary to be able to move the work table in a direction at right angles to the direction of table traverse for setting purposes, and it is also necessary to be able to raise and lower the work table in order to control the depth of cut and to

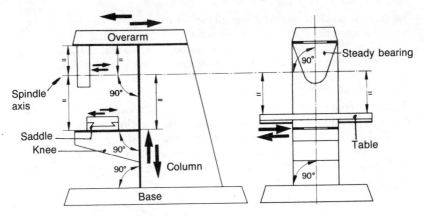

**Fig. 4.29** Horizontal milling machine — movements and alignments

compensate for differing thicknesses of work. All these movements and alignments are brought together to build up the outline of a horizontal spindle milling machine as shown in Fig. 4.29.

## Vertical milling machine

This machine only differs from the horizontal machine in that the spindle rotating and locating the cutter has its axis in the vertical plane. The movements and alignments of the work table and work are the same as for the horizontal spindle milling machine. All these movements and alignments are brought together to build up the outline of a vertical spindle milling machine as shown in Fig. 4.30. In both the horizontal and

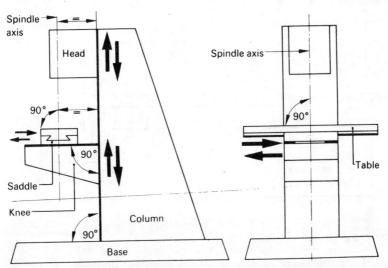

**Fig. 4.30** Vertical milling machine — movements and alignments

the vertical machine the working surface of the work table provides the basic datum surface from which all other alignments are taken. The vertical machine may also have an inclinable head so that the spindle axis may be inclined to the work table when angular surfaces are required.

## Precision grinding machines

Figure 4.31(a) shows the relative alignments and movements of a surface grinding machine. It can be seen that these have a close similarity to those of the horizontal spindle milling machine considered above. This is because both machines are designed to generate plain surfaces using a cylindrical, rotating cutter whose axis is horizontal. The precision surface

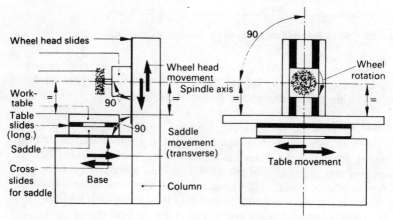

(a) Surface grinding machine

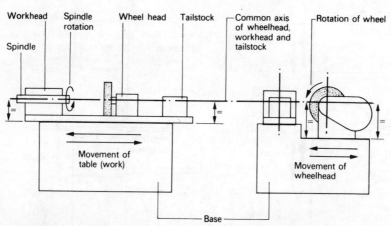

(b) Cylindrical grinding machine

**Fig. 4.31** Precision grinding machines — movements and alignments

grinding machine produces work of greater accuracy and superior surface finish than the milling machine, but at a lower rate of material removal. It is used for finish machining precision components previously roughed out on machines with higher rates of material removal.

Figure 4.31(*b*) shows the relative alignments and movements of the cylindrical grinding machine. It can be seen that there is a similarity with those of the centre lathe. This is not surprising since both machines are designed to generate surfaces of revolution. The cylindrical grinding machine produces work of greater accuracy and superior surface finish to the centre lathe but at a lower rate of material removal. It is used for finishing precision components which have been previously roughed out on the lathe.

## 4.8 Machine tool accuracy

So far, this chapter has been concerned with the constructional features common to a number of machine types and to the alignments and movements necessary for the production of accurate work. However, no matter how carefully the principles of good kinematic design are observed, no matter how carefully the various sub-assemblies making up the machine are manufactured, the machine will not function effectively unless all sub-assemblies are correctly aligned during the final assembly of the machine. After assembly all machine tools must be tested for alignment to the standards which are laid down and accepted internationally. Machines should be re-tested from time to time throughout their lives to ensure that they are correctly adjusted and maintained. Misalignment can occur through incorrect handling during transportation and through incorrect installation.

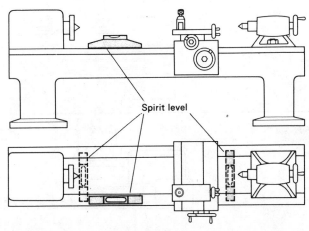

**Fig. 4.32** Levelling a machine tool

164

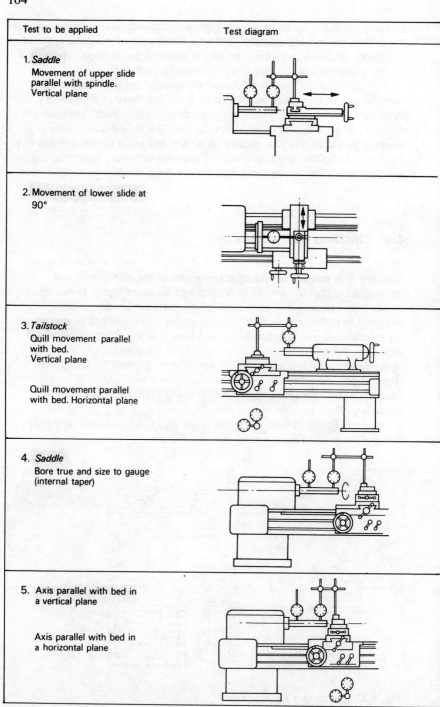

| Test to be applied | Test diagram |
|---|---|
| 1. *Saddle* <br> Movement of upper slide parallel with spindle. Vertical plane | |
| 2. Movement of lower slide at 90° | |
| 3. *Tailstock* <br> Quill movement parallel with bed. Vertical plane <br><br> Quill movement parallel with bed. Horizontal plane | |
| 4. *Saddle* <br> Bore true and size to gauge (internal taper) | |
| 5. Axis parallel with bed in a vertical plane <br><br> Axis parallel with bed in a horizontal plane | |

**Fig. 4.33** Alignment testing (centre lathe)

| Gauge and methods | Tolerances | Test results |
|---|---|---|
| Stationary mandrel. DTI in tool post. Test over mandrel. Set at zero and traverse top slide by hand | 0·02 mm in its movement | |
| DTI in tool post. Test across straight edge on face plate. | 0 to 0·02 mm per ⌀ 250 mm concave only. DTI reading to be minus at centre | |
| DTI and stand. Test over quill which is clamped. Centre must rise | 0 to 0·02 mm in its movement | |
| As above. Test side of quill. Inclination towards tool pressure | 0 to 0·01mm in its movement | |
| Mandrel 250 mm long, one end a gauge for spindle Dial test indicator (DTI). and stand | 0·02 mm maximum eccentric error | |
| Stationary mandrel (as above). Dial test indicator and stand | 0 to +0·02 mm per 250 mm from end of mandrel | |
| Free end of mandrel inclined towards tool pressure | 0 to 0·02 mm per 250 mm from end of mandrel | |

Before any new machine can be tested for accuracy and alignment it must be levelled up to ensure that the basic structure is not distorted. Figure 4.32 shows how a lathe should be levelled. Wedges under the base of the machine, or jacking screws, built into the base of the machine are adjusted until the machine is shown to be level and free from distortion. After levelling, the appropriate standard alignment test should be carried out for the particular machine type and a test report produced. Figure 4.33 shows an abstract from the standard test chart for a centre lathe. The results of the test are entered in the final column and a copy is supplied with the machine. It can be seen that the tolerance is applied over a specified length or diameter. This compensates for the fact that it is easier to maintain a high degree of accuracy over a short distance than over a long one. Further, the tolerances are biased so that any possible deflection of the member being tested due to its own weight, the weight of the workpiece, and the cutting forces improves rather than detracts from the alignment accuracy.

## 4.9  Setting accuracy

No matter how accurately a machine tool is manufactured, the ultimate factor in controlling the quality of the work produced is the alignment of the work-holding device and workpiece. The alignment of work-holding devices and work will now be considered for a number of typical machines.

### Centre lathe

It has already been stated that for parallel turning, the axis of the headstock spindle and the axis of the talistock barrel must be coincident and parallel with the bed slideways. The tailstock is provided with lateral adjustment to achieve this alignment. When turning between centres a trial cut should be taken along the workpiece. Its diameter is then measured at each end with a micrometer caliper. If the readings are the same then a true cylinder is being generated, and turning may proceed. If the readings are different, then the tailstock has to be adjusted as shown in Fig. 4.34(a). Adjustment proceeds, largely by trial and error, taking further trial cuts, until parallel work is produced.

A more convenient method of bringing the tailstock axis into alignment is shown in Fig. 4.34(b). It is essential that the test bar is accurately centred and ground parallel.

When a conical (tapered) surface is required, it is necessary to disturb the alignments deliberately to produce the required amount of taper. Figure 4.35 shows three methods of taper turning. The advantages and limitations of each method are summarised in Table 4.1. It can be seen that methods (a) and (c) require the basic alignments of the machine to be disturbed. After taper turning is finished, the alignments should be restored for normal parallel turning and checked against a parallel test bar using a dial test indicator (DTI) as previously shown in Fig. 4.34.

To ensure all the diameters turned are concentric, as many diameters as possible should be turned at one setting as shown in Fig. 4.36(*a*). Where the work has to be turned round or reset for finishing, it should either be held in a self-centring chuck using *soft jaws* which have been bored out true to hold the workpiece, or it should be held in a four-jaw independent chuck. If the latter method is used the component is checked on a previously turned diameter using a dial test indicator (DTI) as previously shown in Fig. 3.32. Alternatively the work may need to be deliberately offset in the independent jaw chuck to turn an eccentric diameter as shown in Fig. 4.36(*b*). When turning eccentric diameters, it must be remembered that the 'throw' of an eccentric diameter is twice the offset.

The height of the tool point can also affect the accuracy of the surface being produced when taper turning, screw-cutting, copy turning, and facing to the centre of the work. The height has little effect on the accuracy of parallel work but, in all instances, it affects the cutting efficiency of the tool. The tool point should always be aligned with the axis of the workpiece. Failure to do this can cause the effective rake and clearance angles to be very different from those to which the tool has been manufactured or reground. Figure 4.37(*a*) shows the effect of tool height on the cutting angles for external work, whilst Fig. 4.37(*b*) shows the effect of tool height when boring.

### Drilling machine

Normally, holes are drilled so that their axes are perpendicular to the surface of the workpiece. Thus the spindle axis must be perpendicular to the surface of the work table of the machine. It is possible for this alignment to be disturbed on some machines fitted with an inclinable table. Therefore the table should be checked as shown in Fig. 4.38 before commencing work. Where work is held in a machine vice, care should be taken to clean the table and the underside of the vice, as any dirt or swarf under the vice will tilt it and disturb the alignment of the drill and the work. The same applies when the work is clamped directly to the machine table. If 'through' holes are to be drilled, the work should be supported on parallel strips so that neither the table nor the vice is damaged as the drill breaks through the workpiece, since this would damage and eventually destroy the basic datum surfaces required for setting.

### Milling machine

To set the fixed jaw of a milling machine vice parallel to the spindle axis of a horizontal milling machine, a DTI is used as shown in Fig. 4.39(*a*). Alternatively a ground parallel strip can be held in the vice and 'clocked up' with a DTI. This latter method is more accurate because the length of the parallel strip is greater than the length of the vice jaw. When the vice

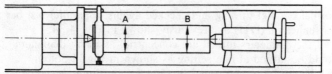

For parallel cylindrical turning the axis of the headstock spindle must be in alignment with the tailstock barrel. If this is so, then the diameter of the component at 'A' will be the same as the diameter at 'B'

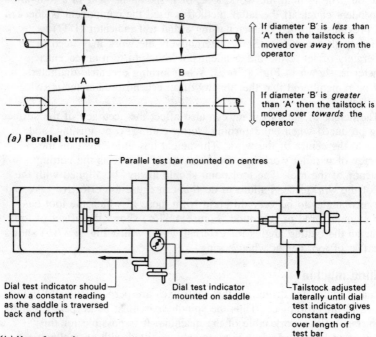

If diameter 'B' is *less* than 'A' then the tailstock is moved over *away* from the operator

If diameter 'B' is *greater* than 'A' then the tailstock is moved over *towards* the operator

*(a)* **Parallel turning**

Parallel test bar mounted on centres

Dial test indicator should show a constant reading as the saddle is traversed back and forth

Dial test indicator mounted on saddle

Tailstock adjusted laterally until dial test indicator gives constant reading over length of test bar

*(b)* **Use of test bar**

**Fig. 4.34** Parallel turning — setting the tailstock

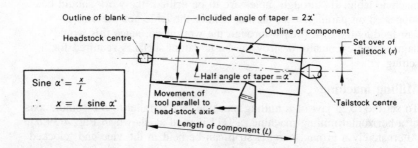

Outline of blank

Headstock centre

Included angle of taper = $2x°$

Outline of component

Set over of tailstock (x)

Half angle of taper = $x°$

$$\text{Sine } \alpha° = \frac{x}{L}$$
$$\therefore \quad x = L \text{ sine } \alpha°$$

Movement of tool parallel to head-stock axis

Tailstock centre

Length of component (L)

*(a)* **set over of centres**

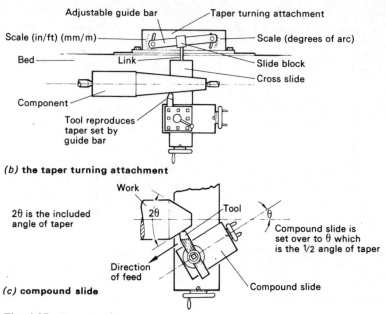

*(b)* **the taper turning attachment**

*(c)* **compound slide**

**Fig. 4.35**  Taper turning

**Table 4.1**  Comparison of taper turning techniques

| Method | Advantages | Limitations |
|---|---|---|
| Set over of tailstock | 1. Power traverse can be used<br>2. The full length of the bed used | 1. Only small angles can be accommodated<br>2. Damage to the centre holes can occur<br>3. Difficulty in setting up<br>4. Only applies to work held between centres |
| Taper turning attachments | 1. Power traverse can be used<br>2. Ease of setting<br>3. Can be applied to chucking and centre work | 1. Only small angles can be accommodated<br>2. Only short lengths can be cut (304–457 mm (12–18 in) depending on make) |
| Compound slide | 1. Very easy settting over a wide range of angles. (Usually used for short steep tapers and chamfers)<br>2. Can be applied to chucking and centre work | 1. Only hand traverse available<br>2. Only very short lengths can be cut. Varies with m/c but is usually limited to about 76–101 mm (3–4 in) |

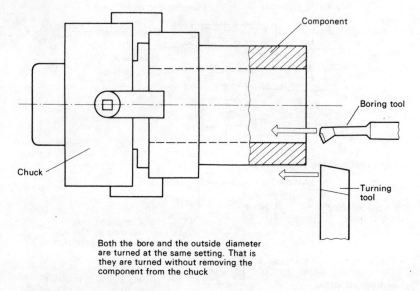

Both the bore and the outside diameter are turned at the same setting. That is they are turned without removing the component from the chuck

*(a) Maintaining concentricity*

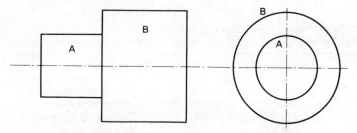

(i) Concentric diameters (both diameters have the same centres)

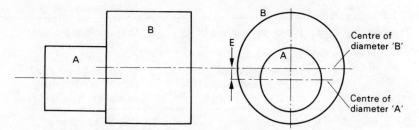

(ii) Eccentric diameters (each diameter has a different centre)

*(b) Concentricity and eccentricity*

**Fig. 4.36** Concentric and eccentric turning

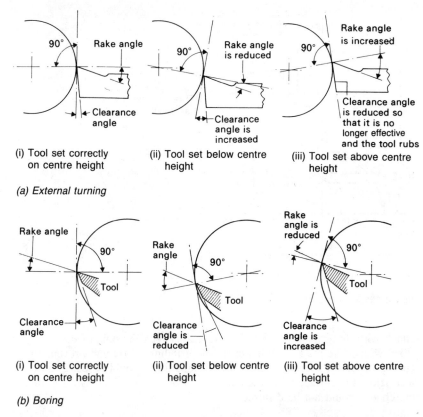

(i) Tool set correctly on centre height

(ii) Tool set below centre height

(iii) Tool set above centre height

*(a) External turning*

(i) Tool set correctly on centre height

(ii) Tool set below centre height

(iii) Tool set above centre height

*(b) Boring*

**Fig. 4.37** Effect of tool height on cutting angles

is correctly set, the DTI reading should be constant as the cross slide is wound back and forth. Figure 4.39(*b*) shows a component being set parallel with a milling machine table.

In the case of a vertical spindle milling machine with an inclinable head, it is essential that the spindle axis is perpendicular to the machine table or a hollow surface will be machined when a face cutter is used. The method of checking the alignment of the machine head with the table is the same as for checking a drilling machine as previously shown in Fig. 4.38.

## Surface grinding machine

The basic datum surface of a surface grinding machine is the work table. However, most work is held on the magnetic chuck and this provides a secondary datum which must have a plain surface parallel to the work table. Therefore when a new chuck is fitted to a precision surface grinding machine it is usual to take a cut over the working surface of the

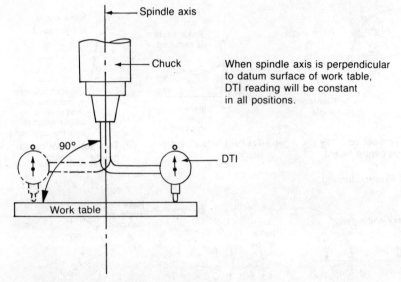

When spindle axis is perpendicular to datum surface of work table, DTI reading will be constant in all positions.

**Fig. 4.38** Setting a drilling machine table

chuck with the grinding wheel. The space between the pole pieces is filled with white-metal and this clogs the grinding wheel and prevents it cutting properly. Therefore the white-metal filling should be cut away to just below the surface with a narrow chisel before grinding. Once ground the chuck should not be disturbed.

## Cylindrical grinding machine

The alignments for this machine are similar to the centre lathe and its standard work-holding devices. There is, however, one essential difference. Instead of setting over the tailstock to set the machine for parallel or tapered components, the whole work table, carrying the

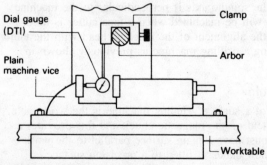

*(a) Setting a milling machine vice*

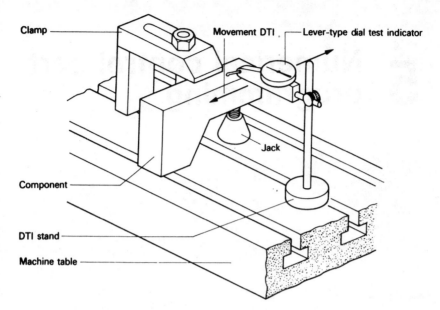

*(b) Checking surface for parallelism (constant reading of DTI indicates upper surface of component is parallel with machine table)*

**Fig. 4.39** Setting work on a milling machine table

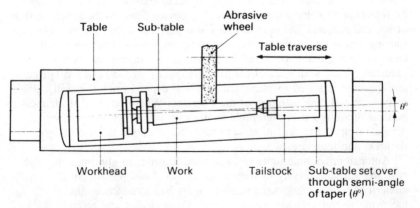

**Fig. 4.40** Grinding tapered components

workhead and the tailstock, is pivoted about its centre, as shown in Fig. 4.40, and has a fine screw adjustment. If parallel grinding is required, the table is adjusted until the work measures the same diameter at each end.

# 5 Numerical control part programming

## 5.1 Background to numerical control

When a machine tool is manually operated as shown in Fig. 5.1(a), the operator directly controls the relative movements of the tool and workpiece. The amount and accuracy of these movements are controlled by reference to some form of measuring device fitted to the machine slide or its lead screws. The operator will also perform such functions as starting and stopping the machine, turning the cutting fluid on or off, changing the spindle speed and feed rate, and changing the tools if required. Thus, with manual control, the quality of the final workpiece and the time required to manufacture it will depend upon the skill, judgement and concentration of the operator. Where batches of identical parts are required it is preferable to use methods which are not so dependent upon the skill of the operator, for example the use of jigs, fixtures, and templates.

Automatic machine tools are also used in order to eliminate the high cost and variable quality of manual operation. Until the advent of *numerical control*, automatic machine tools had to be controlled mechanically by such devices as cams. Although fast and reliable, such machines were time consuming and expensive to reset when a new and different workpiece was required. For each new component, a single-spindle automatic lathe not only required a new set of cams but, if the component had a complex profile, form tools were also required. Such cams and form tools were not only expensive, but took a considerable

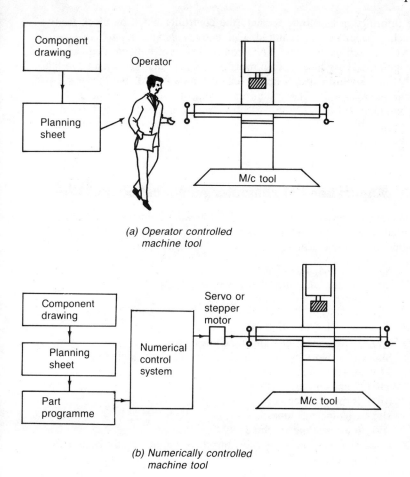

(a) Operator controlled
machine tool

(b) Numerically controlled
machine tool

**Fig. 5.1** Control of machine tools

time to produce. This increased the lead time for bringing a new component into production, that is, the time taken to produce the tooling and gauges before production can even start.

On a *numerically controlled* machine tool, the decisions which govern the operation of the machine are not made directly by the operator or by a set of cams, but by a series of numbers in binary code which are interpreted by an electronic system. The electronic system converts these numerical commands into the physical movement of the machine elements as shown in Fig. 5.1(*b*). Thus each component is an exact replica of this stored data and high levels of repeatability and consistent quality are achieved.

Early numerically controlled machines had very limited memories, and the information had to be fed into the controller block by block from a punched paper tape as required. Currently, *computer numerical control (CNC)* is used exclusively. CNC controllers have built-in, dedicated computers. These have very powerful memory facilities which can not only store sophisticated system management software, but the whole part-programme as well. The system management software interprets the alpha-numerical data of the part programme and feeds the information for each operation into the electronic system which operates the machine movements.

## 5.2  Applications of computer numerical control

Computer numerical control is used throughout industry. For example it is used in wood-machining, weaving, carpet-making, as well as engineering. Some typical engineering applications are as follows:

(*a*)  Machine tools, including:
    (i)  milling machines and machining centres;
    (ii)  centre lathes and turning centres;
    (iii)  drilling machines;
    (iv)  precision grinding machines;
    (v)  EDM (spark-erosion) machines.
(*b*)  Sheetmetal working and fabrication equipment, including:
    (i)  turret punching machines;
    (ii)  flame-cutting machines;
    (iii)  forming machines;
    (iv)  welding machines;
    (v)  tube bending machines.
(*c*)  Inspection machines for checking three-dimensionally contoured components.

This chapter is only concerned with simple part-programming for CNC milling machines and lathes.

## 5.3  Advantages and limitations of computer numerical control

Although, at first sight, numerically controlled machines appear to be costly and complicated to use, the fact that they are increasingly employed by industry is evidence that their advantages far outweigh their limitations.

### Advantages
*High productivity*. Although there is no difference in cutting speeds and feed rates between CNC machines and manually operated machines of similar power and rigidity, production time is saved by rapid traversing

and positioning between operations. CNC machines also have greater flexibility. For example, milling, drilling and boring can all be achieved on a CNC machine at the same setting of the workpiece. This avoids the need for separate and expensive jigs and fixtures for each operation. The amount of work in progress stored between operations and the time spent in setting work as it is passed from one machine to the next, is largely eliminated. CNC machines do not become tired but maintain a constant, high rate of productivity. Their electronic computerised control systems allow them to be easily linked to a robot for work loading and unloading so that 'lights out' production can be maintained round the clock.

*Tool life*. Since the tool approach and cutting conditions are controlled by the programme and are constant from one component to the next, tool wear is more even and tool life is extended. Further, since profiles and contours are generated by the programme controlled workpiece and tool movements, complex and delicate form tools which are susceptible to damage are not required.

*Work-holding*. Since each workpiece merely has to be positioned relative to the same datum point on the machine table, as dictated by the programme, and securely clamped, complex jigs and fixtures are no longer required (see section 5.13).

*Component modification*. When using jigs and fixtures on manually operated machines, even small changes to the workpiece design can result in costly modifications or even replacement of those jigs and fixtures. However when using CNC machines it is usually only necessary to make small modifications to the part-programme, taking but a few minutes, before production of the modified component can commence.

*Design flexibility*. Components with complex profiles and components requiring three-dimensional contouring can be produced more easily and accurately on CNC machine tools than on manually controlled machines. In fact, it is possible to produce components on CNC machines which cannot be produced on manually operated machines.

*Reduced lead time*. The fact that writing a part-programme is very much quicker than, for example, producing the cams required for an automatic lathe; the fact that complex form tools are not required since CNC machines generate the required profile; and the fact that workholding is simplified, results in a reduced lead time before new components can be brought into production.

*Management control*. Since machine performance is controlled by the programme rather than by the operator, there is greater management control over the cost and quality of production when using CNC machines.

*Quality*. Since there is less operator involvement, CNC machines produce components of more consistent quality than manually operated machines. If the machine is fitted with *adaptive control* the machine will always run the tooling at the optimum production rate. It will also sense tool failures or other variations in performance and either stop the machine or, if fitted with automatic tool changing, select back-up tooling from the tool magazine. Automatic gauging can also be fitted.

178

## Limitations

*Capital cost*. The initial cost of CNC machine tools is substantially higher than for similar manually operated machines. However, in recent years, the cost differential has narrowed somewhat.

*Depreciation*. As with all computer based devices, CNC controllers rapidly become out of date. Therefore CNC machine tools should be 'written-off' over a relatively short period of time, and should be replaced more frequently than has been the practice with manually controlled machines.

*Tooling costs*. To exploit the production potential of CNC machine tools, specialised tooling has been developed for use with them. Although the initial cost is high, much of this cost is for the tool shanks and tool-holding devices which do not have to be replaced frequently. The cost of replacement tool tips is no higher than for manually operated machines.

*Maintenance*. CNC machine tools and their controllers are extremely complex and it is unlikely that small- and medium-sized companies will have the expertise to maintain and repair them, except for routine lubrication and adjustments. Therefore an approved maintenance contract for each machine or group of machines is required. Such contracts are expensive — usually about 10 per cent of the original purchase price per annum.

*Training*. Comprehensive programmer and operator training is required to convert the workforce from being expert in the use of conventional, manually operated machines to being expert in the programming and operation of CNC machines. Further, since there is little standardisation between different makes of controller or even between different types and generations of the same make, extensive type specific familiarisation training is required for each new machine. Familiarisation training is normally provided by the equipment supplier within the purchase cost of the equipment. Nevertheless training is time consuming and therefore costly in terms of lost production.

## 5.4 Axis nomenclature

An important feature of the information which is supplied to the control system is slide displacement. Most machines have two or more slides (usually perpendicular to each other) and, in addition, these slides can be moved in one of two directions. It is essential that the control system knows:

(*a*)  which slide is to be actuated;
(*b*)  in which direction the slide is to move;
(*c*)  how far the slide is to move.

BS3635 provides axis and motion nomenclature which is intended to simplify programming and to standardise machine movements. The basic principle of this notation is shown in Fig. 5.2(*a*), from which it can be seen that there are three basic axes of movement.

(*a*) *The Z-axis* which is always the main spindle axis and is positive in a direction towards the toolholder (away from the work). This is a safety feature, so that should the programmer omit the directional sign (in this case negative) from in front of the numerical positional data, the tool will always move away from the work.

(*b*) *The X-axis* which is always horizontal and parallel to the working surface.

(*c*) *The Y-axis* which is perpendicular to both the X and Z axes.

Once the positive Z direction has been found, the positive X and Y directions can be found from the 'right-hand rule', as shown in Fig. 5.2(*b*). Examples of axis and motion nomenclature for typical machine tools, in accordance with BS3635, are shown in Fig. 5.3.

The programmed movements of a CNC machine tool can be described in three ways:

(*a*) *Point-to-point systems.* These are designed to position the tool at a series of different points. The path of the tool between the points

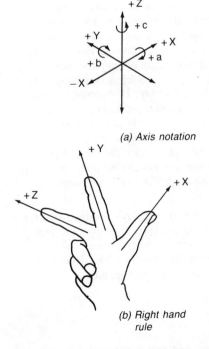

*(a) Axis notation*

*(b) Right hand rule*

**Fig. 5.2** Axis notation

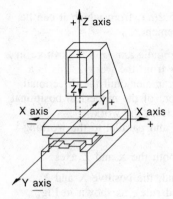

Axes for vertical milling
machines and drilling machines

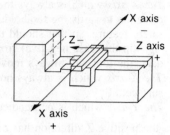

Axes for lathes, horizontal
boring machines and cylindrical
spindles

**Fig. 5.3** Examples of axis notation

and the traverse rate between the points are neither under the control
of the programmer nor the operator. The machine usually takes the
shortest path between any two points. Such a system is suitable for
simple drilling operations or for a sheet metal turret punching
machine. It is not suitable for profile machining or contouring.

(*b*) *Parallel path systems*. These systems are designed to move the tool
from one position to the next so that the tool path is always in a
straight line parallel to the X or Y axis. The traverse rate is under
the control of the programmer and machining operations such as
milling can take place between these points. Such a system is
unsuitable for profile machining or contouring. Both point-to-point
systems and parallel path systems are known as *linear path* systems.

(*c*) *Continuous path system*. This is the most widely used system. The
path taken by the tool in moving from one point to the next and the
traverse rate at which this occurs are fully under the control of the
programmer. Angular and curved movements can be made in two or
three axes simultaneously and complex profiles and contoured
components can be generated.

*Note.* For convenience when programming, it is always assumed that the
cutter moves and follows the profile of the workpiece, despite the fact
that, in practice, it is the work table and work which moves. The
computer in the controller automatically makes the transition from the
programmed cutter movement to the actual work movement.

## 5.5 Control systems

The importance of anti-friction slideways and anti-friction leadscrews for
CNC machine tools has already been discussed in Chapter 4. The method

of rotating the lead screws so as to move and position the tool and/or work accurately and under the control of the programme will now be considered.

## Open loop system

In an open loop control system the machine slides are displaced, according to information loaded from the part programme into the control system, without their positions being monitored. Hence there is no measurement of slide position and no feed-back signal for comparison with the input signal. The correct movement of the slide is entirely dependent upon the ability of the drive system to move the slide through the exact distance required. Such a system is shown in Fig. 5.4(*a*).

The most common method of driving the lead screw is by a *stepper motor* either directly or via a toothed belt drive. A stepper motor is an electric motor energised by a train of electrical pulses rather than by a continuous electrical signal. Each pulse causes the motor to rotate through a small discrete angle. Thus the motor rotates in a series of steps according to the number of pulses supplied to it. The direction of rotation depends upon the polarity of the pulses and the feed rate depends upon the number of pulses per second. Unfortunately stepper motors have only limited torque compared with servo-motors and are only suitable for small- and medium-sized machines. Further, if overloaded, they may stall and miss one or more pulses. Since there is no feed-back in open loop systems any slip results in dimensional inaccuracy.

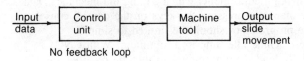

*(a) Open loop control*

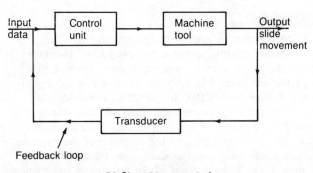

*(b) Closed loop control*

**Fig. 5.4** Control systems

## Closed loop system

In this system a signal is sent back to the control unit, from a measuring device (called a transducer) attached to the slideways, indicating the actual movement and position of the slides. Until the slide arrives at the required position, the control unit continues to adjust its position until correct. Such a system is said to have *feed-back* and is shown in Fig. 5.4(*b*). Although more complex and costly than open loop systems, closed loop systems give more accurate positioning especially on medium and large machines where the forces involved in moving the machine elements can be high.

For this type of system *servo-motors* are used to drive the lead screws. Unlike stepper motors, these are continuously running d.c. motors with a high starting torque to overcome the inertia of the machine slides and workpiece. They can be used on all sizes of machine up to the largest.

Various types of transducer are used with closed loop systems to determine the movement and position of the slides and these will be considered in *Manufacturing Technology: volume 2*.

## 5.6 Data input

### Manual data input

This is used for entering complete programmes, for editing the programme, or for making adjustments whilst setting the machine. Data input is achieved by manually pressing the keys on the control console. Loading of complete programmes should be limited to simple programmes to keep machine idle time to a minimum. With CNC machines, the manually loaded programme can then be recorded on a suitable storage medium such as magnetic tape, magnetic disc, or punched tape for subsequent re-use if a further batch of components are required at a later date.

### Conversational data input

This again involves the operator in loading the programme into the control console by manually depressing the appropriate keys. However instead of writing out the programme in machine code in advance of loading it, the programme is entered in response to questions (prompts) appearing on a visual display unit (VDU) in everyday, conversational English. The computer is pre-programmed with standard data stored in 'files' within the computer memory. Each item of data is numerically identified and called into the programme by the response of the operator to a question. To reduce idle time, most modern conversational control units allow a new programme to be entered whilst an existing programme is still operating the machine.

## Punched tape

Punched tape was the original method of loading data into numerically controlled machines. In fact, at the start, numerically controlled machining was often called 'tape-controlled' machining. Punched tape is still the most common method of data input. It has a number of advantages: it can be read visually; any damage is easily identified by visual inspection; and it is not corrupted under normal work conditions. Unfortunately, the paper tape is easily torn and current practice favours the use of stronger plastic (mylar) and metallised plastic tapes. The tapes have to be prepared on a electro-mechanical tape punch and read by an electro-mechanical or optical-electrical tape reader.

There are two tape standards in current use and examples of these are shown in Fig. 5.5. It can be seen that the numbers, letters and symbols are represented by rows of holes punched across the width of the tape. The tape for both standards is 25 mm wide. The EIA (Electrical Industries Association) system shown in Fig. 5.5(a) requires that each row has an *odd* number of holes. If the required character is expressed by an even number of holes, an extra hole has to be punched in track eight which is known as the *parity track*. If the required character is expressed by an odd number of holes, there is no hole in the parity track. Thus the EIA standard is referred to as an 'odd parity' system. The ISO (International Standards Organisation) system shown in Fig. 5.5(b) requires that each row has an *even* number of holes, and the eighth (parity) track is used to make up an even number of holes in the row if a required character is expressed by an odd number of holes. This is the converse of the EIA system. The ISO standard is referred to as an 'even parity' system. Only those characters of immediate use when part programming have been shown. *Tape format* is shown in Fig. 5.6. Each row of holes across the tape is termed a 'character', each set of characters is termed a 'word', and each set of words making a complete statement is termed a 'block'.

## Magnetic tape

The data is recorded on magnetic tape and read from magnetic tape in much the same way as recording music onto a cassette tape. Although the tape cassettes are compact and easily stored, and recording and reading is quicker than for punched tape, magnetic tape has two major disadvantages.

(a)  The recorded data cannot be read visually.
(b)  The recorded data is easily corrupted under workshop conditions.

## Direct numerical control

The programme is prepared on a remote computer and stored in the memory of that computer. It can be checked on the computer using simulation software. The programme can then be loaded 'down-line' directly into the CNC machine, with a copy of the programme retained

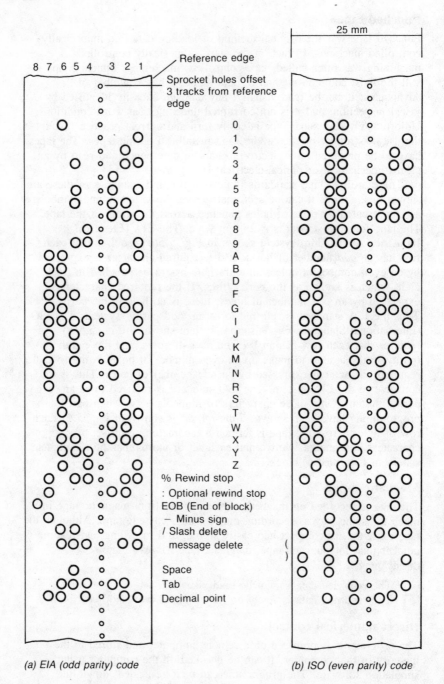

(a) EIA (odd parity) code    (b) ISO (even parity) code

**Fig. 5.5** Punched tape codes

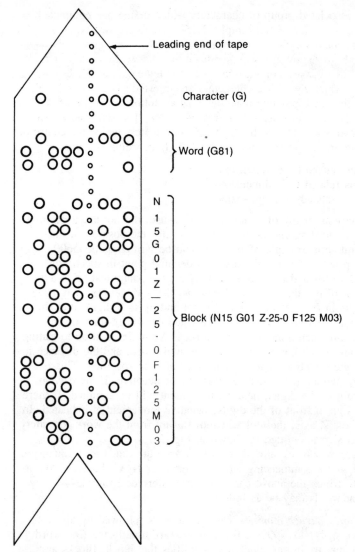

**Fig. 5.6** Punched tape format ISO

on magnetic disc. The computer software has to be compatible with the machine controller's management software. DNC is rapidly becoming the most widely used method of programming CNC machines.

## 5.7 Programme terminology

**Character.** A number, letter or symbol which is recognised by the controller.

**Word**. An associated group of characters which define one complete element of information. For example: N150. There are two types of word: *dimensional words* and *management words*.

**Dimensional words** are any words related to a linear dimension. They are shown by any word commencing with the letters X, Y, Z, I, J, K, or any word in which the above characters are inferred. The letters X, Y, Z, refer to the corresponding machine axes as defined in section 5.4. The letters I, J, K, refer to circles and arcs of circles. The start and finish positions of arcs are defined by X, Y, Z coordinates, whilst the centre of radius of the arc or circle is defined by I, J, K coordinates with:

I dimensions related to X dimensions;
J dimensions related to Y dimensions;
K dimensions related to Z dimensions.

Older systems, many of which are still in use, did not use a decimal point but used leading and trailing zones to infer the position of the decimal point. For example 35.6 mm would be written as 0035600.

Current practice favours the use of a decimal point in specifying dimensional words and a machine manual may stipulate that an X-axis dimension word has the form X4,3, that is, the X-dimension may have up to 4 digits in front of the decimal point and up to 3 digits after the decimal point. This is standard practice when the dimensions are in millimetres. For inch dimensions the form is X3,4. In addition to stating the axis along which the machine element will move, and the distance it will move, the direction of movement must also be specified. This is indicated by making the dimension positive or negative. If there is no 'sign' in front of the digits, positive movement will be assumed. If there is a minus sign in front of the digits, negative movement is indicated. In the case of the Z axis, the tool will move away from the work for safety if the minus sign is omitted as shown in Fig. 5.7.

**Management words** are any words which are not related to a dimension but are the words commencing with the character N, G, F, S, T, M, or any word in which the above characters are inferred. Examples of management words may be as follows.

N4 *Block or sequence number*. The character N followed by up to 4 digits (i.e. N1 to N9999). Block words are usually the first word which appears in any block and identifies that block. Blocks are usually numbered in steps of 5 or 10 so that additional blocks can be inserted in the event of an omission.

G2 *Preparatory code or function*. The character G followed by up to 2 digits (i.e. G0 to G99). These are used to inform the machine controller of the functions required for the next operation. The preparatory codes as specified in BS 3635 are listed in Table 5.1. Unfortunately these codes vary slightly between different makes and types of controller, so the maker's programming manual should always be consulted. Many preparatory codes are *modal*, that is, once selected, they remain in operation until changed or cancelled.

187

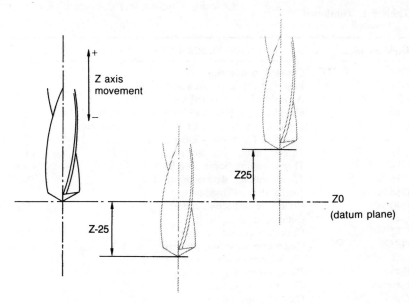

**Fig. 5.7** Z axis movement

**Table 5.1** Preparatory functions

| Code number | Function | |
|---|---|---|
| G00 | Rapid positioning, point to point | (M) |
| G01 | Positioning at controlled feed rate ⎱ Normal | (M) |
| G02 | Circular interpolation ⎰ dimensions | (M) |
| G03 | Circular interpolation CCW | (M) |
| G04 | Dwell for programmed duration | |
| G05 | Hold. Cancelled by operator | |
| G06 ⎱ G07 ⎰ | Reserved for future standardisation | |
| G08 | Programmed slide acceleration | |
| G09 | Programmed slide deceleration | |
| G10 | Linear interpolation (long dimensions) | (M) |
| G11 | Linear interpolation (short dimensions) | (M) |
| G12 | 3D interpolation | (M) |
| G13–G16 | Axis selection | (M) |
| G17 | XY plane selection | (M) |
| G18 | ZX plane selection | (M) |
| G19 | YZ plane selection | (M) |
| G20 | Circular interpolation CW (long dimensions) | (M) |
| G21 | Circular interpolation CW (short dimensions) | (M) |
| G22 | Coupled motion positive | |

**Table 5.1  continued**

| Code number | Function | |
|---|---|---|
| G23 | Coupled motion negative | |
| G24 | Reserved for future standardisation | |
| G25−G29 | Available for individual use | |
| G30 | Circular interpolation CCW (long dimensions) | (M) |
| G31 | Circular interpolation CCW (short dimensions) | (M) |
| G32 | Reserved for future standardisation | |
| G33 | Thread cutting, constant lead | (M) |
| G34 | Thread cutting, increasing lead | (M) |
| G35 | Thread cutting, decreasing lead | (M) |
| G36−G39 | Available for individual use | |
| G40 | Cutter compensation, cancel | (M) |
| G41 | Cutter compensation, left | (M) |
| G42 | Cutter compensation, right | (M) |
| G43 | Cutter compensation, positive | |
| G44 | Cutter compensation, negative | |
| G45 | Cutter compensation +/+ | |
| G46 | Cutter compensation +/− | |
| G47 | Cutter compensation −/− | |
| G48 | Cutter compensation −/+ | |
| G49 | Cutter compensation 0/+ | |
| G50 | Cutter compensation 0/− | |
| G51 | Cutter compensation +/0 | |
| G52 | Cutter compensation −/0 | |
| G53 | Linear shift cancel | (M) |
| G54 | Linear shift X | (M) |
| G55 | Linear shift Y | (M) |
| G56 | Linear shift Z | (M) |
| G57 | Linear shift XY | (M) |
| G58 | Linear shift XZ | (M) |
| G59 | Linear shift YZ | (M) |
| G60 | Positioning exact 1 | (M) |
| G61 | Positioning exact 2 | (M) |
| G62 | Positioning fast | (M) |
| G63 | Tapping | |
| G64 | Change of rate | |
| G65−G79 | Reserved for future standardisation | |
| G80 | Fixed cycle cancel | (M) |
| G81−G89 | Fixed cycles | (M) |
| G90−G99 | Reserved for future standardisation | |

Note: (1) Functions marked (M) are modal.

(2) The above codes are based on BS3635. However codes vary between makes and types of controller and the manufacturer's programming manual should always be consulted.

(3) Most controllers use: G90 to establish the programme in *absolute* dimensional units, G91 to establish the programme in *incremental* dimensional units

(4) FANUK controllers use G20 in place of G90 and G21 in place of G91.

F4 *Feed rate command*. The character F followed by up to 4 digits (i.e. F1 to F9999). This indicates to the controller the desired feed rate for machining and may be defined in terms of: millimetres/minute; inches/minute; millimetres/revolution; inches/revolution; or a feed rate number. Feed rate numbers are an older system in which typical feed rates in, say, millimetres/minute or millimetres/revolution are pre-determined by the manufacturer and selected by an appropriate F-code, together with a G-code to tell the controller which system is being used.

S4 *Spindle speed command*. The character S followed by up to four digits (i.e. S1 to S9999). Again there are various ways of defining the spindle speed, such as: revolutions/minute (direct spindle speed); surface cutting speed in metres/minute; and constant surface cutting speed in metres/minute. The latter method is used when facing across the end of a component so that, as the effective diameter gets smaller, the spindle speed is increased to a pre-determined safe maximum so that the surface cutting speed is maintained at a constant value.

T2 *Tool number*. The character T followed by up to 2 digits (usually, 1 to 20) identifies which tool is to be used. Each tool used will have its own tool number and, as well as memorising the tool number, the computer also memorises such additional data as the tool length offset, and/or the tool diameter/nose radius compensation for each tool. In a machine with automatic tool changing, the position of the tool in the tool-magazine is also memorised by the computer under the tool number file.

M2 *Miscellaneous commands*. The character M followed by up to two digits (i.e. M0 to M99). Apart from the preparatory functions (G-codes), there are a number of other commands which are required throughout the programme, for example starting and stopping the spindle, turning the coolant on or off, changing speed, and changing tools. The miscellaneous codes are listed in Table 5.2.

**Table 5.2**  Miscellaneous functions

| Code number | Function |
| --- | --- |
| M00 | Program stop |
| M01 | Optional stop |
| M02 | End of program |
| M03 | Spindle on CW |
| M04 | Spindle on CCW |
| M05 | Spindle off |
| M06 | Tool change |
| M07 | Coolant 2 on |
| M08 | Coolant 1 on |
| M09 | Coolant off |

**Table 5.2** continued

| Code number | Function |
|---|---|
| M10 | Clamp slide |
| M11 | Unclamp slide |
| M12 | Reserved for future standardisation |
| M13 | Spindle on CW, coolant on |
| M14 | Spindle on CCW, coolant on |
| M15 | Motion in the positive direction |
| M16 | Motion in the negative direction |
| M17⎱<br>M18⎰ | Reserved for future standardisation |
| M19 | Oriented spindle stop |
| M20−M29 | Available for individual use |
| M30 | End of tape |
| M31 | Interlock bypass |
| M32−M35 | Constant cutting speed |
| M36 | Feed range 1 |
| M37 | Feed range 2 |
| M38 | Spindle speed range 1 |
| M39 | Spindle speed range 2 |
| M40−M45 | Gear changes |
| M46−M49 | Reserved for future standardisation |
| M50 | Coolant 3 on |
| M51 | Coolant 4 on |
| M52−M54 | Reserved for future standardisation |
| M55 | Linear tool shift, position 1 |
| M56 | Linear tool shift, position 2 |
| M57−M59 | Reserved for futture standardisation |
| M60 | Workpiece change |
| M61 | Linear workpiece shift, position 1 |
| M62 | Linear workpiece shift, position 2 |
| M63−M67 | Reserved for future standardisation |
| M68 | Clamp workpiece |
| M69 | Unclamp workpiece |
| M70 | Reserved for future standardisation |
| M71 | Angular workpiece shift, position 1 |
| M72 | Angular workpiece shift, position 2 |
| M73−M77 | Reserved for future standardisation |
| M78 | Clamp slide |
| M79 | Unclamp slide |
| M80−M99 | Reserved for future standardisation |

*Note:* N, G, T, M, commands *may* require a leading zero to be programmed on some older but still widely used systems. For example: G0 becomes G00; G1 becomes G01; M2 becomes M02.

An example of CNC programme using the above codes and commands could look like:

N5   G90 G71 G00 X35.4 Y25.5 T01 M06
N10  X15.0 Y15.0 S1250
N15  G01 Z-25.0 F120 M03

Using the lists of typical G and M codes provided, try to decode the above blocks of information.

## 5.8   Programme formats

Different control systems use different formats for the assembly of each block of data. Thus the programming manual for the machine being programmed should always be consulted.

### Word (or letter) address system

Currently, this is the most widely used system. Each 'word' commences with a letter character called an *address*. Hence a word is identified by its letter and not by its position in the block (see, fixed block (sequential) format system, below). The word or letter address system has the advantage that instructions which remain unchanged from a previous block may be omitted from the subsequent blocks until a change becomes necessary.

A typical letter address structure (format), as given in a maker's handbook, could be:

*Metric:*   N4 G2 X4,3 Y4,3 Z4,3 I4,3 J4,3 K4,3 F3 S4 T2 M2.
*Inch:*      N4 G2 X3,4 Y3,4 Z3,4 I3,4 J3,4 K3,4 F3 S4 T2 M2.

The letter signifies the function of the 'word'. The number determines the maximum number of digits which may follow the letter. The comma determines the position of the decimal point if required.

### Fixed block (sequential) format system

This is an outdated system which is still widely used on older machines. The instructions in the blocks are always written and recorded in the same fixed sequence. No letter commences each word, but the letter is implicit from the position of the word in the block or sequence. For example a block could read:

20 1 25.0 37.550 80 1500 2 6

Since the first word in the sequence is 20, the controller reads this as N20 because of its position. Again, since the third word in the sequence is 25.0 the controller reads this as X25.0 because of its position, and so on. Thus *all* instructions have to be given in *every* block including those instructions which have not changed from the preceding block to ensure each word is in its identifying position in the sequence.

## cycles

~~~d fixed cycles, or *canned cycles* as they are more commonly ~~~, are used to save the repetitive programming of frequently used ~~~ations. The sequence of events for such a cycle of operations is embedded in the memory of the controller's computer at the time of manufacture and is called up, when required, by an appropriate G-code. One of the most commonly used 'canned' cycles is the drilling cycle which is shown in Fig. 5.8. This is called up by using a G81 code, and the cycle of events which the machine performs automatically are as follows:

(1) Rapid traverse to centre of first hole.
(2) Rapid traverse to clearance plane height.
(3) Feed to depth of hole.
(4) Rapid out.
(5) Rapid traverse to centre of next hole — repeat for as many holes as required.

The only data the programmer has to provide is:

(*a*) The positions of the hole centres.
(*b*) The spindle speed.

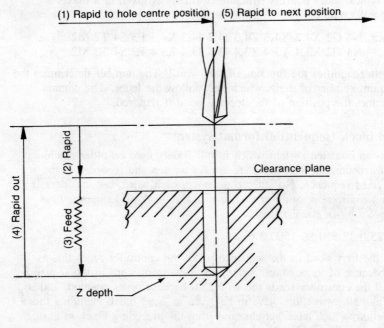

**Fig. 5.8** Canned drill cycle (G81)

(c)  The feed rate.

(d)  The tool number. (The machine setter will provide the tool length offset for the drill and any other information which needs to be recorded under the tool number file in the computer memory.)

Another important 'canned cycle' used on milling machines is the rectangular pocket milling cycle as shown in Fig. 5.9. This cycle is called up by using the G78 preparatory code. The movements involved in this cycle are as follows:

(a)  Rapid traverse to position (1) inside the pocket boundary.

(b)  Rapid down to the clearance plane height.

(c)  Feed down in the Z axis to the roughing depth. (Since the cutter is plunging into solid metal, a slot drill must be used and *not* an end mill.)

(d)  Machine out the pocket as the cutter path moves sequentially through positions (2) to (15) inclusive, as shown in Fig. 5.9 (less a finishing allowance on the profile).

(e)  Rapid up to the clearance plane height in the Z axis, and return to position (1).

(f)  Feed down to finish pass depth.

(g)  Repeat movements (2) to (15) inclusive to finish machine bottom and sides of pocket. Note the number of movements when roughing and finishing will depend upon the diameter of the cutter and the size of the pocket. In actual practice the paths overlap by as much as 60 per cent of the cutter diameter.

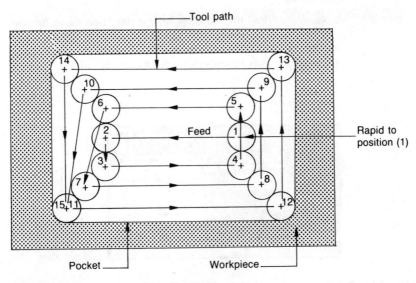

**Fig. 5.9**  Canned pocket mill cycle (G78)

194

(*h*) At point (15) in this example, rapid up to the clearance plane height
and return to position (1).

The programmer has to provide the positional data, the dimensions for
the pocket, and the cutter and cutting data.

Circular pockets can be generated using the G77 preparatory code.
The ability to produce circular pockets and bores immediately shows a
major advantage in using CNC milling machines. With conventional,
manually operated machines any circular pocket in a milled surface would
have to be produced on a lathe or a boring machine, thus requiring the
work to be removed from the milling machine and reset in another
machine. With a CNC milling machine all the operations of milling,
drilling, tapping, and the production of circular and rectangular pockets,
circular and rectangular islands, or pockets and islands of complex
profiles can all be machined at one setting.

Some other examples of 'canned cycles' used on CNC milling
machines are:

G80  cancels all 'canned cycles';   G82  drilling cycle with dwell;
G83  deep hole drilling cycle;      G84  tapping cycle;
G85  boring cycle;                  G87/88  deep hole boring cycle.

'Canned cycles' can also be used with CNC lathes and some typical
examples are:

G66/67  contouring cycles;          G68/69  rough turning cycles;
G81  turning cycle;                 G82  facing cycle;
G83  deep hole drilling cycle;      G84/85  straight threading cycles;
G88  auto-grooving cycle.

Note how the 'canned cycles' for use on a lathe differ from those for use
on a milling machine despite having the same code number. Figure 5.10
shows the sequence of events activated by the G68 preparatory code on a
lathe. After the roughing cuts have been made, the profile of the

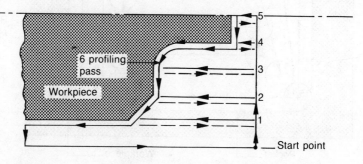

**Fig. 5.10**  Rough turning cycle (G68)

component would be finish turned to size. The sequence of events for the G68 rough turning cycle are:

(*a*)   rapid to the start point;
(*b*)   rough out using a sequence of parallel roughing passes. The number of passes will depend upon the depth of cut and the profile;
(*c*)   a profiling pass leaving a finishing allowance on the component;
(*d*)   return in rapid to start point.


## 5.10   Tool length offset

Tool length offset (TLO) allows tools of various lengths to be used with a common datum, without having to alter the programme. As shown in Fig. 5.11. setting commences with tool T01 which is 'touched' onto the work surface or a setting block (depending upon the Z axis datum height) and the Z axis readout is set to zero. T01 is now the master tool. Each subsequent tool is then 'touched' onto the Z axis datum and its Z axis readout is noted. Using this information, Z axis offset is then applied to each tool in turn to compensate for differences in length compared with T01. The tool length offsets are recorded in the memory of the machine's computer under the tool number file. Each time a tool is called up by its 'T' code, the correct length offset will be automatically applied. If this parameter changes for a particular tool (tool is reground), the offset can be reset and no change has to be made to the programme.

The application of tool length offsets to turning tools is shown in Fig. 5.12. In this case it can be seen that offsets are required in both the X and the Z axes relative to a common datum. Usually a number of different tools are located in the lathe turret and each tool will require its

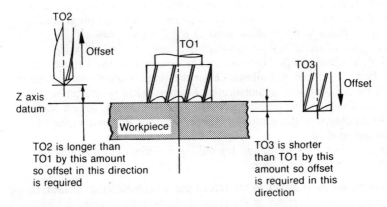

**Fig. 5.11**   Tool length offset — milling

196

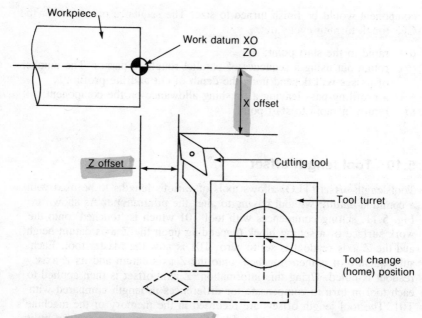

**Fig. 5.12** Tool length offset — turning

own offsets since each tool protrudes by a different distance. The offset for any one tool becomes operative as soon as that tool is called into the programme by its T-number.

## 5.11 Cutter compensation

Like tool length offsets, cutter diameter compensation (milling) and tool-nose radius compensation (turning) are also facilities to aid programming. Not only do these facilities allow tools of differing size to be interchanged without alteration to the programme, they simplify the writing of the programme. The tool can be assumed to travel round the profile being machined and allowance for the actual diameter of the cutter is made by the controller automatically. Further, when programming for turning on the lathe, the programmer can assume the tools have a sharp nose. In this instance the controller compensates for the nose radius of the tool automatically.

Cutter diameter compensation for milling machines is controlled by the following preparatory codes:

G41   compensates — cutter to the left of the workpiece (Fig. 5.13(*a*)).
G42   compensates — cutter to the right of the workpiece (Fig. 5.13(*b*)).
G40   compensation cancelled.

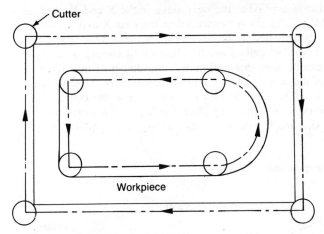

*(a) Compensation to the left (G41)*

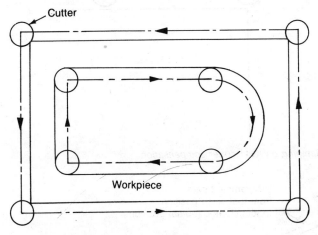

*(b) Compensation to the right (G42)*

**Fig. 5.13** Cutter compensation — milling

At first sight the 'handing' of the compensation is a little difficult to interpret. Consider Fig. 5.13(*a*). Start at any point and face in the direction of the cutter travel by following the arrows. It can be seen that the path of the cutter is always to the left of the surface being machined. Similarly in Fig. 5.13(*b*) the path of the cutter is always to the right of the surface being machined. The path of the cutter traverse is determined by whether up-cut or down-cut (climb) milling techniques are being used.

Whenever the G41 or G42 code is activated, the cutter diameter

198

compensation is always applied at the next move in the X and Y axes, as shown in Fig. 5.14(*a*), and always cancelled at the next X and Y move after the G40 code is activated as shown in Fig. 5.14(*b*). Diameter compensation can never be applied or cancelled whilst cutting is taking place. Further, it can be seen that preliminary movement of the cutter takes place clear of the work so that compensation is fully effective and the cutter has achieved its required feed rate by the time the cutter is in contact with the workpiece. This is to allow the feed servo-motor to accelerate up to speed and is referred to as *ramping on*. Similarly, at the

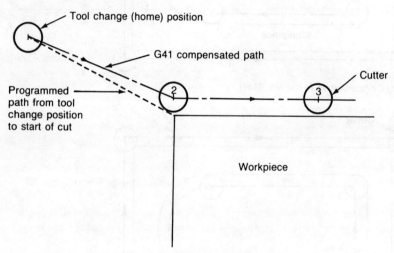

(a) 'Ramping on' G41 cutter compensation

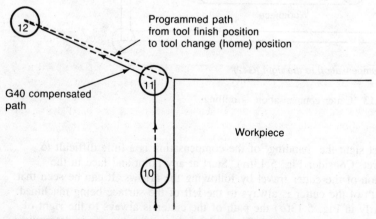

(b) 'Ramping off' G40 compensation cancelled

**Fig. 5.14** Application of cutter compensation

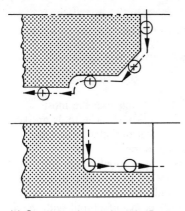 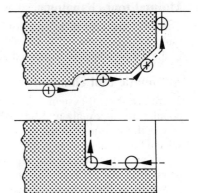

(a) Compensation to the left (G41)
(Facing direction of movement,
tool is always to the left of
surface being turned)

(b) Compensation to the right (G42)
(Facing direction of movement,
tool is always to the right of
surface being turned)

**Fig. 5.15** Tool nose radius compensation

end of the cut, when the compensation is cancelled, the cutter feeds clear
of the work as the feed servo-motor decelerates. This is referred to as
*ramping off.*

Tool nose radius compensation is used in a similar manner to diameter
compensation when milling and the same preparatory codes are used.
That is:

G41   tool nose radius compensation to the left (Fig. 5.15(*a*));
G42   tool nose radius compensation to the right (Fig. 5.15(*b*));
G40   tool nose compensation cancelled.

The use of tool nose radius compensation simplifies programming as it
allows the *programmed* tool nose path to follow the profile of the
component and also allows the programmer to assume a sharp nosed tool
is being used. Like tool length offsets, diameter compensation and tool
nose compensation are set at the machine itself when the actual tool
parameters are known. After the first trial component has been made, the
compensation settings may need to be 'tweaked' to allow for cutter
deflection and other variables in order to bring the component within its
design tolerances.

## 5.12 Tool retrieval

CNC machines may have their cutting tools changed manually or
automatically. In either case rapid tool changing is required to match the
performance of the machine.

## Manual tool changing

The tools are kept in a 'tool crib' adjacent to the machine as an aid to rapid identification and retrieval. Each tool is kept in a specified position in the 'crib' which is numbered accordingly. (T01, T02, etc.).

## Automatic tool changing

There are several systems of automatic tool changing, but the most popular are indexable tool turrets and chain magazines. The tools are kept in specific positions in the turret or magazine and the appropriate tool is selected and changed as required by the programme.

As an aid to setting and replacement, tooling is usually kept fully maintained and set ready for use in a *tool library* from which it may be drawn for a specific programme prepared ready for use.

**Qualified tooling** (see ISO standard 1832) is manufactured with the dimensions from its datum faces to the tool tip guaranteed to within ±0.08 millimetres as shown in Fig. 5.16(*a*).

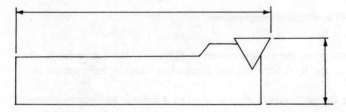

Dimensions shown guaranteed to within ± 0.08 mm

*(a) Qualified tooling (150 — type Q)*

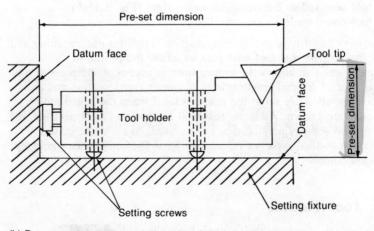

*(b) Pre-set tooling*

**Fig. 5.16** Qualified and pre-set tooling

**Pre-set tooling** is used where qualified tooling is not available, not appropriate or not sufficiently accurate. Pre-setting is carried out away from the machine in a suitable fixture as shown in Fig. 5.16(*b*).

## 5.13 Work-holding

The normal principles of location and restraint apply to CNC machine tools and work-holding devices, for such machines must:

(*a*)  locate the work in the correct position relative to the machine datum;

(*b*)  restrain the work against the cutting forces.

Small work may be held in a machine vice in which the fixed jaw is machined to provide the necessary locations as shown in Fig. 5.17. The fixed jaw has to be aligned with the machine datum.

Alternatively a *grid plate* may be used. Figure 5.18(*a*) shows a typical grid plate. This is usually made from steel or cast iron and has either a matrix of tapped holes and tenon slots or it may consist of alternate tapped holes and reamed location holes. The tapped holes are used for

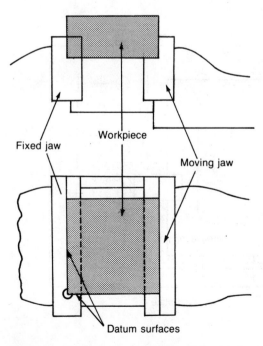

**Fig. 5.17**  Machine vice with formed jaws

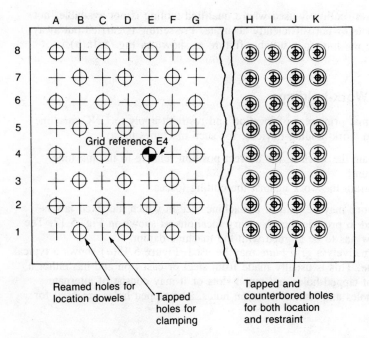

(a) Principle of the grid plate

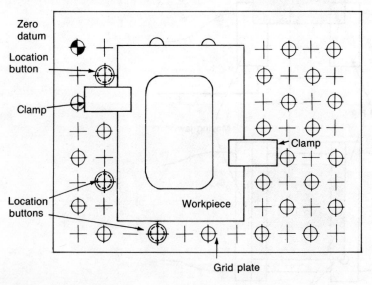

(b) Use of the grid plate

**Fig. 5.18** Work holding — the grid plate

clamping in both instances. The grid plate is often permanently fitted to the machine table so that the part programmer can identify the exact position of the location holes and use this information to establish datums when writing the programme. An example of the use of a grid plate is shown in Fig. 5.18(*b*).

Large components may be mounted directly onto the machine table or, if a large batch is being machined, traditional milling fixtures may be used.

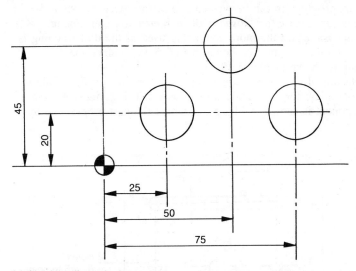

*(a) Absolute dimensioning*

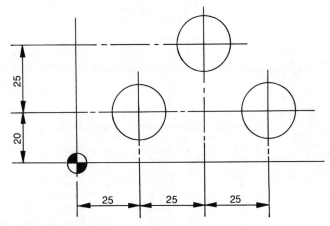

*(b) Incremental dimensioning*

**Fig. 5.19** Dimensioning techniques

Work-holding devices for turning centres (lathes) usually consist of pneumatically or hydraulically actuated plain or stepped collet chucks. For larger work pneumatically or hydraulically actuated self-centring chucks are used. Such chucks are fitted with soft jaws which are bored out to run true and to locate the work axially.

## 5.14 Part programming

Before a part programme can be written one further decision has to be made, that is, to select either *absolute* or *incremental* dimensioning. Absolute dimensions are the more commonly used as the dimensioning is related to a common datum, as shown in Fig. 5.19(*a*). Incremental dimensioning is shown in Fig. 5.19(*b*).

A simple milled and drilled component is shown in Fig. 5.20, whilst the part programme for its manufacture is shown in Fig. 5.21. A simple turned component is shown in Fig. 5.22, whilst the part programme for

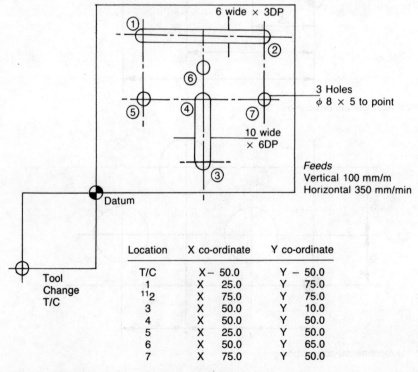

| Location | X co-ordinate | | Y co-ordinate | |
|---|---|---|---|---|
| T/C | X – | 50.0 | Y – | 50.0 |
| 1 | X | 25.0 | Y | 75.0 |
| 11 2 | X | 75.0 | Y | 75.0 |
| 3 | X | 50.0 | Y | 10.0 |
| 4 | X | 50.0 | Y | 50.0 |
| 5 | X | 25.0 | Y | 50.0 |
| 6 | X | 50.0 | Y | 65.0 |
| 7 | X | 75.0 | Y | 50.0 |

**Fig. 5.20**  Component to be milled and drilled

205

| Seq No 90 | Code Programme | Explanation |
|---|---|---|
| N10 | C00 G71 G75 G90 | Default line |
| N20 | X-50.0 Y-50.0 S1000 T1 M06 | TC posn spindle tool/offset (Ø6mm) |
| N30 | X25.0 Y75.0 Z1.0 | Rap posn (1) |
| N40 | G012-3.0 F100 | Feed to depth |
| N50 | G01 X75.0 F350 | Feed to posn (2) |
| N60 | G00 21.0 | Rapid tool up |
| N70 | X-50.0 Y-50.0 S800 T2 NM06 | Tool change Ø1050 offset tool 2 |
| N80 | X-50.0 Y10.0 Z1.0 | Rapid posn (3) |
| N90 | G01 Z-6.0 F100 | Feed to depth |
| N100 | G01 Y50.0 F350 | Feed to posn (4) |
| N110 | G00 Z10 | Rap tool up |
| N120 | X-50.0 Y-50.0 S1100 T3 M06 | T/C tool 3 offsets Ø8 drill |
| N130 | X25.0 Y50.0 21.0 | Rapid posn (5) |
| N140 | G81 X25.0 Y50.0 Z-7.0 F100 | Drill on restate depth (inc) feed |
| N150 | X50.0 Y65.0 | Posn (6) |
| N160 | X75.0 Y50.0 | Posn (7) drill |
| N170 | G80 | Switch off drill cycle |
| N180 | 600 X-50.0 Y-50.0 M02 | TC posn end of prog |
| E | | End of tape |

*CNC programme for milling & drilling Fig. 5.20*
*Machine: Bridgeport series 1: Boss 6.*

**Fig. 5.21** CNC part program for milling and drilling

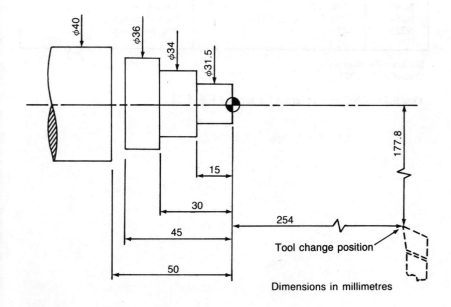

**Fig. 5.22** Component to be turned

its manufacture is shown in Fig. 5.23. The Computer Numerical Control of Machine tools and part programming techniques are developed further in *Manufacturing Technology: volume 2.*

| Seq No | Code Programme | Explanation |
|---|---|---|
| N1Ø | E171 | Metric |
| N2Ø | E195 | Feed in mm/rev |
| N3Ø | E197 S1ØØØ MØ3 | Direct spindle. 1000 rpm Spindle on CW |
| N4Ø | E1ØØ MØ3 | Rapid mode. Coolant on |
| N5Ø | E153 X177.8 2254 TO | To tool change position |
| N6Ø | MØ1 | Optional stop |
| N7Ø | T1ØØ | Rotate turret Pos 1 |
| N8Ø | E154 XØ Z2 T1Ø1 | Move to start with tool 1 |
| N9Ø | E1Ø1 Z-Ø.5 FØ.2 | Move to depth prior to face end |
| N1ØØ | X31.5 | Face end |
| N11Ø | Z-15 | Turn Ø31.5 |
| N12Ø | X34 | Face edge |
| N13Ø | Z-30 | Turn Ø34 |
| N14Ø | X36 | Face edge |
| N15Ø | Z-50 | Turn Ø36 |
| N16Ø | G53 X177.8 2254 TO | To tool change |
| N17Ø | T4ØØ | Rotate turret Pos 4 |
| N18Ø | E154 X40 2-45 T4Ø4 | To part off position. Tool 4 |
| N19Ø | GØ1 X-1.Ø FØ.1 | Part off |
| N2ØØ | E1ØØ X4Ø | Retract |
| N21Ø | E153 X177.8 2254 TO | To tool change |
| N22Ø | M2 | End programme |

Machine: Hardinge lathe
Controller: GE1050

**Fig. 5.23** CNC part program for turning Fig. 5.22

# 6 Assembly

## 6.1 Design of components

Traditionally, ease of assembly has not ranked highly among the design disciplines. However, as labour costs have risen, the need to make assembly quick (and therefore cheaper) and adaptable to automated processes has meant that the assembly of components into a complete unit must now be considered from the earliest stages of design.

Consider the electronic circuit shown in Fig. 6.1(a) for a simple small signal amplifier. There is a transistor, four fixed resistors, one variable resistor and three capacitors; a total of nine components. Compare this with Fig. 6.1(b) which uses an integrated circuit (chip). There is one integrated circuit, three fixed resistors, one variable resistor and one capacitor; a total of six components. The latter circuit not only has fewer components and is easier to assemble; it also has a higher performance. Further, it is easier for a robot to pick and place an integrated circuit chip with its short stiff 'legs' than the fine wire connections of a transistor.

The integrated circuit chip is built into a protective plastic housing with its 'legs' arranged symmetrically. It can therefore be placed into the holes in the printed circuit board in two positions, as shown in Fig. 6.2(a). Thus it is possible for the chips to be inserted the wrong way round. However, to reduce the probability of this happening, the designer of the integrated circuit housing has included a distinctive mark at one end and a dot by pin number one. If the designer of the printed circuit

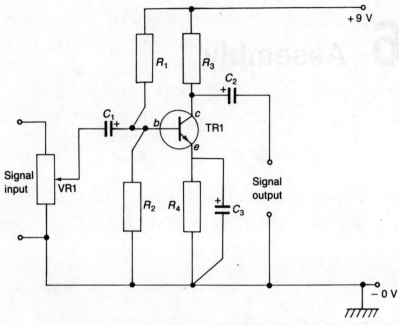

*(a) Small signal amplifier using discrete components*

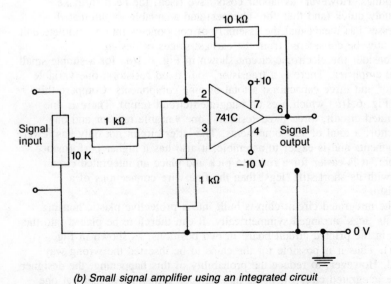

*(b) Small signal amplifier using an integrated circuit*

**Fig. 6.1** Designing for minimum components and ease of assembly

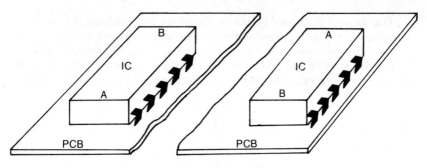

(a) Alternative positioning of integrated
circuit with symmetrical 'legs'

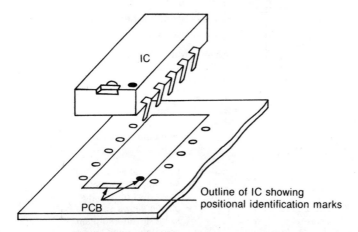

Outline of IC showing
positional identification marks

(b) Positioning an IC using identification marks

**Fig. 6.2** Designing to avoid assembly errors

board arranges for this outline to be reproduced on the board as shown in
Fig. 6.2(b), the assembler can immediately see which way round the
integrated circuit is to be installed.

Consider the plastic box and lid shown in Fig. 6.3(a). From this
'exploded' drawing, it can be seen that the assembler has to fit four
screws, nuts, washers and spring washers to secure the lid to the body.
Since these are small in size in the example shown, this will be a slow
and fiddling job. However there are two redeeming features:

(a)   the lid can be fitted in either of two directions and either way up;
      the assembler has few decisions to make.
(b)   standard screws, nuts, washers and spring washers are used. Any
      nut or washer will fit on any screw which can be used in any hole.
      The use of standardised components speeds up the assembly process.
      It enables *non-selective assembly* to take place.

The box and lid assembly can be simplified by modifying the moulding so that self tapping screws can be used as shown in Fig. 6.3(b). This also reduces the number and cost of the components used.

Finally, the box and lid can be re-designed so as to take advantage of the elastic properties of thermoplastics. Figure 6.3(c) shows how a snap

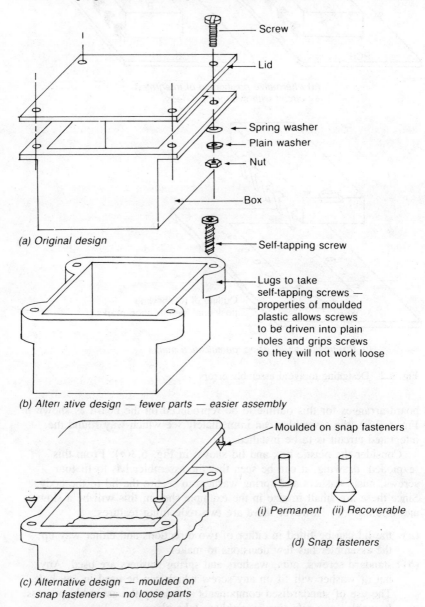

(a) Original design — Screw, Lid, Spring washer, Plain washer, Nut, Box

(b) Alternative design — fewer parts — easier assembly — Self-tapping screw — Lugs to take self-tapping screws — properties of moulded plastic allows screws to be driven into plain holes and grips screws so they will not work loose

(c) Alternative design — moulded on snap fasteners — no loose parts — Moulded on snap fasteners

(d) Snap fasteners — (i) Permanent  (ii) Recoverable

**Fig. 6.3** Exploiting material properties

fastening is used. The snap fastener may provide a permanent joint or it may be designed so that it can be dismantled. These alternatives are shown in Fig. 6.3(*d*).

## 6.2 Batch size

The batch size has a considerable influence on the component design and the method of assembly. In the above example, although the snap fit lid was the cheapest and easiest to assemble, the cost of the complex moulding tools required to make the lid could only be justified if large quantities were required.

Again, in the early days of making motor cars, each car was individually hand built. Therefore the standardisation of components and the ease of assembly was of little consequence. However, in today's volume car assembly lines, every part must be designed and manufactured to fit easily and quickly into place. There is no room for selective assembly and 'fitting': the part must bolt on and work straightaway. Preferably it must be capable of being *picked, placed* and *fixed* automatically by an industrial robot. Only when large batches of a product are being assembled can the cost of the design work and manufacturing accuracy be justified to ensure such a high level of interchangeability and ease of assembly.

## 6.3 Accuracy of fit

It has already been stated that non-selective assembly is only possible if there is complete *interchangeability* between mating components in the assembly. Figure 6.4 shows a shaft which has been dimensioned so that its diameter lies between 74.981 mm and 75.000 mm. The designer has decided, in his wisdom, that any shaft lying between these sizes will

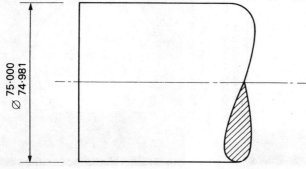

Dimensions in mm

**Fig. 6.4** Application of limits

212

function satisfactorily in a given assembly. These dimensions are called *limits of size* and the algebraic difference between these limits of size is called the *tolerance*. Toleranced dimensions are provided because it is not possible to work to an exact size and, even if it were possible, there is no means of measuring an exact size.

The terms *maximum metal condition* and *minimum metal condition* are often met with in connection with limit systems and the gauging of workpieces. Gauging will be introduced in Chapter 10 of this book. Figure 6.5 explains what is meant by maximum and minimum metal conditions.

The class of fit between two mating components, such as a shaft and a bearing, may be obtained in two ways.

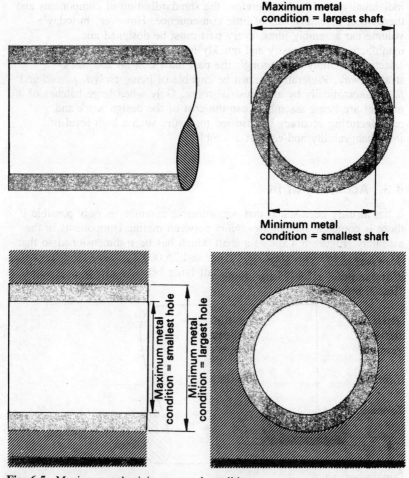

**Fig. 6.5** Maximum and minimum metal conditions

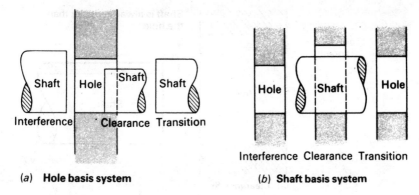

**Fig. 6.6** Hole and shaft basis system

(*a*)  By having a constant size of hole and varying the diameter of the shaft to suit. This is called a *hole basis system*.

(*b*)  By having a constant size of shaft and varying the diameter of the hole to suit. This is called a *shaft basis system*.

The hole basis system is the more usually employed since it is easier to maintain a standard hole size using standard drills and reamers. The shaft diameter is more easily machined to the size required by the fit during a turning or grinding operation. Figure 6.6 shows both these systems.

*Clearance fit* is achieved when the shaft is always smaller than the hole it is mating with, even under maximum metal conditions.

*Interference fit* is achieved when the shaft is always slightly larger than the hole it is mating with, even under minimum metal conditions.

*Transition fits* are achieved when mating shafts and holes which are within limits will give a range of fits from clearance under minimum metal conditions to interference under maximum metal conditions. The above fits are shown diagrammatically in Fig. 6.7.

## 6.4   Toleranced dimensions

Some further terms used in connection with toleranced dimensions will now be considered.

**Nominal size**. This is the size by which a component feature or dimension is known. For example, a 75.015 mm diameter hole would usually be referred to as the 75 mm hole.

**Basic size**. This is the exact functional size from which the limits are derived by the application of the necessary tolerances and clearance. The nominal size and the basic size may sometimes be the same.

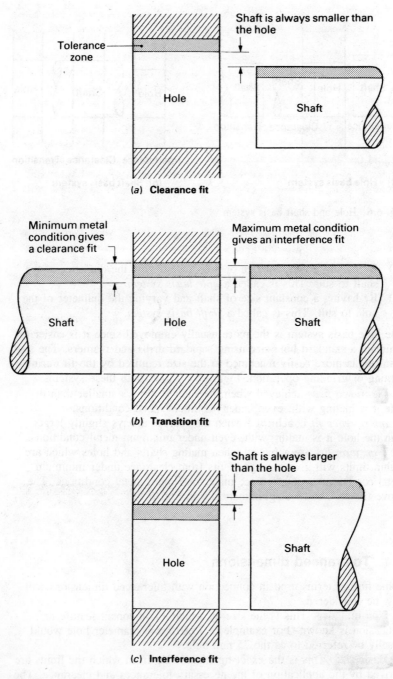

Tolerance zone

Hole

Shaft is always smaller than the hole

Shaft

(a) **Clearance fit**

Minimum metal condition gives a clearance fit

Maximum metal condition gives an interference fit

Shaft

Hole

Shaft

(b) **Transition fit**

Shaft is always larger than the hole

Hole

Shaft

(c) **Interference fit**

**Fig. 6.7** Classes of fit

**Limits of size**. These are the maximum and minimum sizes between which it is permissible to manufacture a given workpiece if it is to function correctly.

**Tolerance**. This is the algebraic difference between the upper and lower limits of size. Its magnitude and disposition is determined by the functional needs of the component and the economics of production. Generally, it can be assumed that the smaller the tolerance, the more costly will be the production process to achieve that tolerance.

**Minimum clearance**. This used to be known as the 'allowance' and is the arithmetical difference between the maximum metal condition of the shaft and the maximum metal condition of the hole, that is, the largest shaft and the smallest hole giving the 'tightest' fit which will function correctly. Figure 6.8 shows how these terms are applied to a shaft and hole assembly.

The *actual size* of a component feature is the measured size corrected to 20°C. Figure 6.9 shows how tolerances are applied to the basic size, together with alternative methods of dimensioning. *Unilateral tolerances* are those where the tolerance zones lie to one side only of the basic size. *Bilateral tolerances* are those where the tolerance zones cross the basic size. In all the examples shown the basic size is 20.00 mm.

As dimensional tolerances get smaller and the precision of components becomes greater to satisfy present day quality requirements and facilitate assembly, geometrical tolerancing also becomes of importance. A slightly oval shaft can be within the dimensional limits if these are relatively coarse. However the same shaft could lie within the dimensional limits

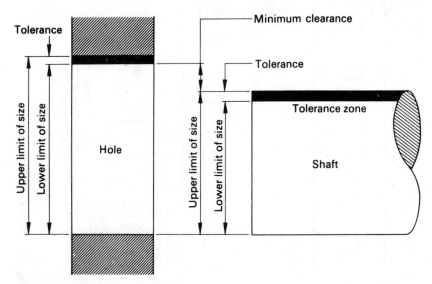

**Fig. 6.8** Limit systems — definitions

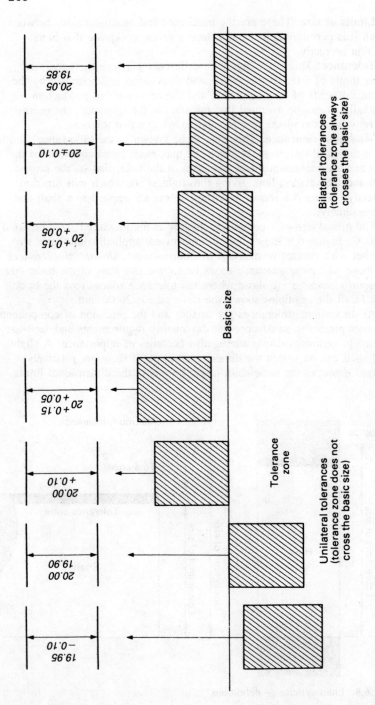

**Fig. 6.9** Methods of tolerancing

when measured across its minor diameter and lie outside those limits when measured across its major diameter. It is no longer adequate to specify a process and rely on the machine to give an acceptable level of geometrical tolerance. Geometrical tolerancing will be considered in *Manufacturing Technology, volume 2.*

## 6.5 Standard systems of limits and fits

This section is based upon BS4500 — Limits and Fits (Metric Units), which is suitable for all classes of work from the finest instruments to heavy engineering. It allows for the size of the work, the type of work, and provides for both hole basis and shaft basis systems as required.

The tables provide for twenty-eight types of shaft designated by lower-case letters, a, b, c, etc., and twenty-eight types of hole designated by upper-case (capital) letters A, B, C, etc. To each type of shaft or hole the grade of tolerance is designated by a number 01, 0, 1, 2, ... 16, thus giving eighteen grades of tolerance in all.

The letter indicates the position of the tolerance relative to the basic

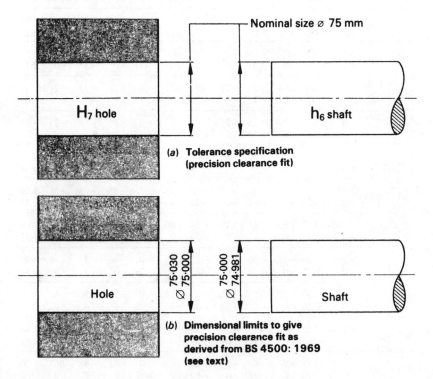

**Fig. 6.10** Tolerance specification (precision clearance fit)

size and is called the *fundamental deviation*. The number indicates the magnitude of the tolerance and is called the *fundamental tolerance*. A shaft is completely defined by its basic size, letter and number, for example: 75 mm h6. Similarly a hole is completely defined by its basic size, letter and number, for example: 75 mm H7. Figure 6.10(*a*) shows how a precision clearance fit is specified by using a 75 mm H7/h6 hole and shaft combination. Table 6.1 shows the primary selection of limits

**Table 6.1**  Primary selection of fits—Abstract from BS4500

| Normal sizes | | Loose clearance | | Average clearance | | Close clearance | | Precision clearance | | Transition | | Inter- ference | |
|---|---|---|---|---|---|---|---|---|---|---|---|---|---|
| Over mm | Up to mm | H9 | e9 | H8 | f7 | H7 | g6 | H7 | h6 | H7 | k6 | H7 | p6 |
| — | 3 | +25 | −14 | +14 | −6 | +10 | −2 | +10 | −0 | +10 | +6 | +10 | +12 |
|  |  | +0 | −39 | +0 | −16 | +0 | −8 | +0 | −6 | +0 | +0 | +0 | +6 |
| 3 | 6 | +30 | −20 | +18 | −10 | +12 | −4 | +12 | −0 | +12 | +9 | +12 | +20 |
|  |  | +0 | −50 | +0 | −22 | +0 | −12 | +0 | −8 | +0 | +1 | +0 | +12 |
| 6 | 10 | +36 | −25 | +22 | −13 | +15 | −5 | +15 | −0 | +15 | +10 | +15 | +24 |
|  |  | +0 | −61 | +0 | −28 | +0 | −14 | +0 | −9 | +0 | +1 | +0 | +15 |
| 10 | 18 | +43 | −32 | +27 | −16 | +18 | −6 | +18 | −0 | +18 | +12 | +18 | +29 |
|  |  | +0 | −75 | +0 | −34 | +0 | −17 | +0 | −11 | +0 | +1 | +0 | +18 |
| 18 | 30 | +52 | −40 | +33 | −20 | +21 | −7 | +21 | −0 | +21 | +15 | +21 | +35 |
|  |  | +0 | −92 | +0 | −41 | +0 | −20 | +0 | −13 | +0 | +2 | + | +22 |
| 30 | 50 | +62 | −50 | +39 | −25 | +25 | −9 | +25 | −0 | +25 | +18 | +25 | +42 |
|  |  | +0 | −112 | +0 | −50 | +0 | −25 | +0 | −16 | +0 | +2 | +0 | +26 |
| 50 | 80 | +74 | −60 | +46 | −30 | +30 | −10 | +30 | −0 | +30 | +21 | +30 | +51 |
|  |  | +0 | −134 | +0 | −60 | +0 | −29 | +0 | −19 | +0 | +2 | +0 | +32 |
| 80 | 120 | +87 | −72 | +54 | −36 | +35 | −12 | +35 | −0 | +35 | +25 | +35 | +59 |
|  |  | +0 | −159 | +0 | −71 | +0 | −34 | +0 | −22 | +0 | +3 | +0 | +37 |
| 120 | 180 | +100 | −85 | +63 | −43 | +40 | −14 | +40 | −0 | +40 | +28 | +40 | +68 |
|  |  | + | −185 | +0 | −83 | +0 | −39 | +0 | −25 | +0 | +3 | +0 | +43 |
| 180 | 250 | +115 | −100 | +72 | −50 | +46 | −15 | +46 | −0 | +46 | +33 | +46 | +79 |
|  |  | +0 | −215 | +0 | −96 | +0 | −44 | +0 | −29 | +0 | +4 | +0 | +50 |
| 250 | 315 | +130 | −110 | +81 | −56 | +52 | −17 | +52 | −0 | +52 | +36 | +52 | +88 |
|  |  | +0 | −240 | +0 | −108 | +0 | −49 | +0 | −32 | +0 | +4 | +0 | +56 |
| 315 | 400 | +140 | −125 | +89 | −62 | +57 | −18 | +57 | −0 | +57 | +40 | +57 | +98 |
|  |  | +0 | −265 | +0 | −119 | +0 | −54 | +0 | −36 | +0 | +4 | +0 | +62 |
| 400 | 500 | +155 | −135 | +97 | −68 | +63 | −20 | +63 | −0 | +63 | +45 | +63 | +108 |
|  |  | +0 | −290 | +0 | −131 | +0 | −60 | +0 | −40 | +0 | +5 | +0 | +68 |

and fits for a wide range of hole and shaft combinations for a variety of applications and is used as follows.

(a) *Hole*. Enter the table along diameter band 50 mm to 80 mm, and where this band crosses the column H7 the limits are given as +30 and +0. These dimensions are in units of 0.001 mm (0.001 mm = 1 micrometre ($\mu$m)). Therefore, when applied to a basic size of 75 mm, they give working limits of 75.030 mm and 75.000 mm as shown in Fig. 6.10(b).

(b) *Shaft*. Enter the table along diameter band 50 mm to 80 mm, and where this band crosses the column h6 the limits are given as −0 and −19. Again these dimensions are in units of 0.001 mm. Therefore, when applied to a basic size of 75 mm, they give working limits of 75.000 mm and 74.981 mm as shown in Fig. 6.10(b).

---

**Example 6.1** *Derive the dimensions for a hole and shaft of nominal diameter 40 mm so that an average clearance fit is obtained.*

Since the nominal size of the shaft/hole is 40 mm, Table 6.1 is entered at the 30−50 mm band. The following conditions then apply:

| Nominal size | H8 | f7 |
|---|---|---|
|  | +39 | −25 |
| 30−50 mm | +0 | −50 |

tolerance unit 0·001 mm.

Hole diameter: (upper limit) 40 + 0·039 = 40·039 mm
                (lower limit) 40 + 0·000 = 40·000 mm

Shaft diameter: (upper limit) 40 − 0·025 = 39·975 mm
                (lower limit) 40 − 0·050 = 39·950 mm

Since only an *average clearance fit* is required, there is no benefit in working to an accuracy of three decimal places. The designer would use his experience and reduce the cost of manufacture by rounding off the limits to:

Hole diameter: (upper limit) = 40·04 mm
                (lower limit) = 40·00 mm

Shaft diameter: (upper limit) = 39·98 mm
                (lower limit) = 39·95 mm

Had a close or precision clearance been required, rounding off would not have been permissible and the increase in accuracy would have increased manufacturing costs and, therefore, unit component cost. There is no advantage in using greater precision than is required. Figure 6.11 shows how these limits are applied.

Other information that can be obtained from the above dimensions:

Hole tolerance $= 40 \cdot 04 - 40 \cdot 00 = \underline{0 \cdot 04}$ mm

Shaft tolerance $= 39 \cdot 98 - 39 \cdot 95 = \underline{0 \cdot 03}$ mm

Maximum clearance $= 40 \cdot 04 - 39 \cdot 95 = \underline{0 \cdot 09}$ mm

(largest hole − smallest shaft)

Minimum clearance $= 40 \cdot 00 - 39 \cdot 98 = \underline{0 \cdot 02}$ mm

(smallest hole − largest shaft)

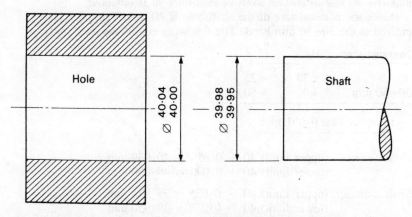

**Fig. 6.11** Average clearance fit — toleranced dimensions

## 6.6 Selection of tolerance grades

From what has already been stated, it is obvious that the closer the limits (smaller the tolerance) the more difficult and expensive it is to manufacture a component. It is no use specifying very small (close) tolerances if the manufacturing process specified by the designer cannot achieve such a high degree of precision. Alternatively there is no point in choosing a process on grounds of low cost if it cannot achieve the accuracy necessary for the component to function correctly.

Table 6.2 (pages 222−3) based upon BS4500 shows the standard tolerances from which the tables of limits and fits are derived. It can be seen that as the International Tolerance (IT) number gets larger the tolerance increases. The recommended relationship between process and standard tolerance is as follows:

IT16 Sand casting, flame cutting;
IT15 Stamping;
IT14 Die-casting, plastic moulding;
IT13 Presswork, extrusion;
IT12 Light presswork, tube drawing;
IT11 Drilling, rough turning, boring;
IT10 Milling, slotting, planing, rolling;
IT9 Low grade capstan and automatic lathe work;
IT8 Centre lathe, capstan and automatic lathe work;
IT7 High quality turning, broaching, honing;
IT6 Grinding, fine honing;
IT5 Machine lapping, fine grinding;
IT4 Gauge making, precision lapping;
IT3 High quality gap gauges;
IT2 High quality plug gauges;
IT1 Slip gauges, reference gauges.

---

**Example 6.2** *Determine a process that is suitable for manufacturing the shaft dimensioned in Example 6.1.*

The diameter of the shaft is 40 mm and the tolerance is 0·03 mm. From Table 6.2 it will be seen that the IT number that corresponds to these conditions lies between IT7 and IT8. Therefore a good turned finish would be sufficiently accurate. However to avoid wear the shaft would probably receive some degree of heat treatment, in which case the tolerance would be easily achieved by commercial quality grinding.

---

## 6.7  Interchangeability

Interchangeability not only leads to reduced assembly costs, it also facilitates maintenance and repairs as standard parts are readily available and can be changed for the original equipment without difficulty or loss of performance. The principles of selective and non-selective assembly are shown in Fig. 6.12. Non-selective assembly can only be achieved by the use of standard specifications and standard dimensioning.

TOLERANCE UNIT = ·001 mm

**Table 6.2**  Standard tolerances

| Nominal sizes | | IT01 | IT0 | IT1 | IT2 | IT3 | IT4 | IT5 | IT6† |
|---|---|---|---|---|---|---|---|---|---|
| Over | Up to and including | | | | | | | | |
| mm — | mm 3 | 0·3 | 0·5 | 0·8 | 1·2 | 2 | 3 | 4 | 6 |
| 3 | 6 | 0·4 | 0·6 | 1 | 1·5 | 2·5 | 4 | 5 | 8 |
| 6 | 10 | 0·4 | 0·6 | 1 | 1·5 | 2·5 | 4 | 6 | 9 |
| 10 | 18 | 0·5 | 0·8 | 1·2 | 2 | 3 | 5 | 8 | 11 |
| 18 | 30 | 0·6 | 1 | 1·5 | 2·5 | 4 | 6 | 9 | 13 |
| 30 | 50 | 0·6 | 1 | 1·5 | 2·5 | 4 | 7 | 11 | 16 |
| 50 | 80 | 0·8 | 1·2 | 2 | 3 | 5 | 8 | 13 | 19 |
| 80 | 120 | 1 | 1·5 | 2·5 | 4 | 6 | 10 | 15 | 22 |
| 120 | 180 | 1·2 | 2 | 3·5 | 5 | 8 | 12 | 18 | 25 |
| 180 | 250 | 2 | 3 | 4·5 | 7 | 10 | 14 | 20 | 29 |
| 250 | 315 | 2·5 | 4 | 6 | 8 | 12 | 16 | 23 | 32 |
| 315 | 400 | 3 | 5 | 7 | 9 | 13 | 18 | 25 | 36 |
| 400 | 500 | 4 | 6 | 8 | 10 | 15 | 20 | 27 | 40 |
| 500 | 630 | — | — | — | — | — | — | — | 44 |
| 630 | 800 | — | — | — | — | — | — | — | 50 |
| 800 | 1000 | — | — | — | — | — | — | — | 56 |
| 1000 | 1250 | — | — | — | — | — | — | — | 66 |
| 1250 | 1600 | — | — | — | — | — | — | — | 78 |
| 1600 | 2000 | — | — | — | — | — | — | — | 92 |
| 2000 | 2500 | — | — | — | — | — | — | — | 110 |
| 2500 | 3150 | — | — | — | — | — | — | — | 135 |

\* Not applicable to sizes below 1 mm
† Not recommended for fits in sizes above 500 mm

## Tolerance grades

| IT7 | IT8 | IT9 | IT10 | IT11 | IT12 | IT13 | IT14* | IT15* | IT16* |
|-----|-----|-----|------|------|------|------|-------|-------|-------|
| 10 | 14 | 25 | 40 | 60 | 100 | 140 | 250 | 400 | 600 |
| 12 | 18 | 30 | 48 | 75 | 120 | 180 | 300 | 480 | 750 |
| 15 | 22 | 36 | 58 | 90 | 150 | 220 | 360 | 580 | 900 |
| 18 | 27 | 43 | 70 | 110 | 180 | 270 | 430 | 700 | 1100 |
| 21 | 33 | 52 | 84 | 130 | 210 | 330 | 520 | 840 | 1300 |
| 25 | 39 | 62 | 100 | 160 | 250 | 390 | 620 | 1000 | 1600 |
| 30 | 46 | 74 | 120 | 190 | 300 | 460 | 740 | 1200 | 1900 |
| 35 | 54 | 87 | 140 | 220 | 350 | 540 | 870 | 1400 | 2200 |
| 40 | 63 | 100 | 160 | 250 | 400 | 630 | 1000 | 1600 | 2500 |
| 46 | 72 | 115 | 185 | 290 | 460 | 720 | 1150 | 1850 | 2900 |
| 52 | 81 | 130 | 210 | 320 | 520 | 810 | 1300 | 2100 | 3200 |
| 57 | 89 | 140 | 230 | 360 | 570 | 890 | 1400 | 2300 | 3600 |
| 63 | 97 | 155 | 250 | 400 | 630 | 970 | 1500 | 2500 | 4000 |
| 70 | 110 | 175 | 280 | 440 | 700 | 1100 | 1750 | 2800 | 4400 |
| 80 | 125 | 200 | 320 | 500 | 800 | 1250 | 2000 | 3200 | 5000 |
| 90 | 140 | 230 | 360 | 560 | 900 | 1400 | 2300 | 3600 | 5600 |
| 105 | 165 | 260 | 420 | 660 | 1050 | 1650 | 2600 | 4200 | 6600 |
| 125 | 195 | 310 | 500 | 780 | 1250 | 1950 | 3100 | 5000 | 7800 |
| 150 | 230 | 370 | 600 | 920 | 1500 | 2300 | 3700 | 6000 | 9200 |
| 175 | 280 | 440 | 700 | 1100 | 1750 | 2800 | 4400 | 7000 | 11000 |
| 210 | 330 | 540 | 860 | 1350 | 2100 | 3300 | 5400 | 8600 | 13500 |

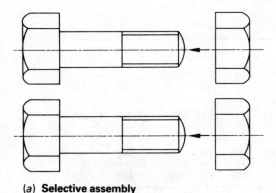

(a) **Selective assembly**

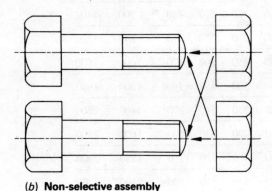

(b) **Non-selective assembly**

**Fig. 6.12**   Interchangeability

The impression may have been given that there is no room for selective assembly in modern engineering production. However, with modern automatic computer controlled gauging systems, semi-selective assembly is still justified where workpieces cannot be made to the required accuracy but can be readily measured and graded. This technique is used, for example, for machining the pistons and cylinder bores of automobile engines.

The bores and pistons are individually and automatically measured and grouped into one of, say, five grades. These components are then automatically given a grade number or a colour code. The cylinder bores are graded similarly. On assembly a grade 3 piston is used in the grade 3 bore and will give the required class of fit, even though the piston and cylinder cannot be made economically to this class of fit. Figure 6.13 shows how this is achieved.

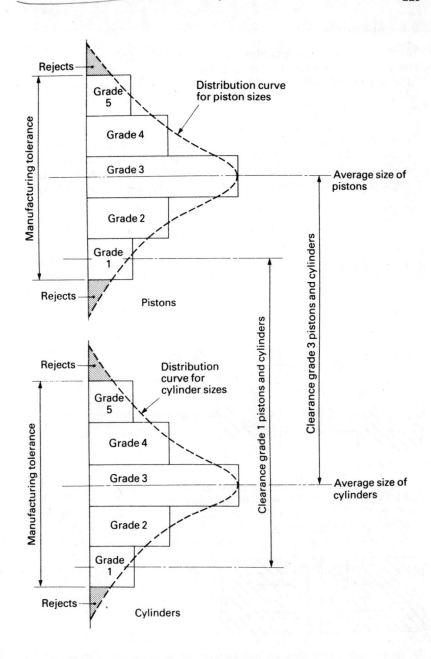

**Fig. 6.13** Semi-selective assembly

## 6.8 Materials

The choice of materials can also affect the assembly process. For example copper conductors can easily be soldered to lugs and terminals. Aluminium conductors, although lighter and cheaper, cannot easily be soldered. Such conductors have to be fitted to terminal lugs by mechanical crimping.

Sections of sheet metal ventilation ducting can be joined by fitting flanges at each end of the section and bolting the flanges of adjacent sections together, or the sections can be oxy-acetylene welded together on site. On the other hand, plastic ducting sections can be welded together using a hot air torch. This is less energy intensive, the fire risk is lower,

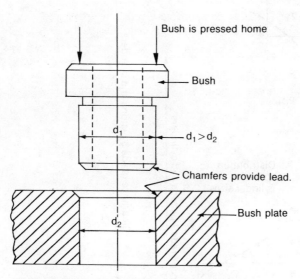

*(a) The bush is compressed and the hole in the bush plate is expanded as the bush is pressed home.*

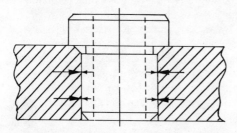

*(b) The elasticity (spring back) of the assembled components results in high friction forces which maintain the joint.*

**Fig. 6.14** Press (compression) joints

and ventilation of the working zone is easier. The plastic ducting is also lighter and easier to handle.

When an assembly is made using compression joints, as shown in Fig. 6.14, the inner component is subjected to compressive stress and the outer component to tensile stress. The materials chosen for these components must be capable of withstanding these stresses. For example cast iron, with its high compressive strength and low tensile strength, would be suitable for the inner component but unsuitable for the outer component of a compression joint.

## 6.9 Joining methods

There are many ways of fastening components together to make an assembly, but all joining processes fall into two main groups.

### Permanent joints

These are joints which cannot be dismantled without the destruction of the joint and, possibly, the components so joined. Such joints include:

(a) riveting;
(b) silver soldering;
(c) welding;
(d) soldering;
(e) brazing;
(f) adhesive bonding.

These joining techniques are dealt with in detail in Chapter 7.

### Semi-permanent joints

A type of joint which can be used for connecting precision components is the compression joint. Compression joints rely upon the elasticity of materials to secure one component to another without the use of any additional fastening devices such as bolts, rivets or adhesives. In a lightly compressed joint, such as a drill bush pressed into a bush plate, friction alone maintains the assembly. Figure 6.14 shows the principles of this type of pressed or 'staked' joint. However in cases of extreme interference, such as when the starter ring gear is shrunk onto the flywheel of a car engine, permanent deformation may take place with one component biting into the other so that positive, as well as frictional restraint takes place. Figure 6.15(a) shows the principles of making a thermal compression joint in which the outer element is expanded by heating before assembly, whilst Fig. 6.15(b) shows the principle of making a thermal compression joint where the inner element is shrunk by cooling before assembly. In either case the outer element is in tension and the inner element is in compression when the assembly is complete. Therefore the materials have to be carefully chosen to resist these forces. For example cast-iron would be suitable for the inner element but totally

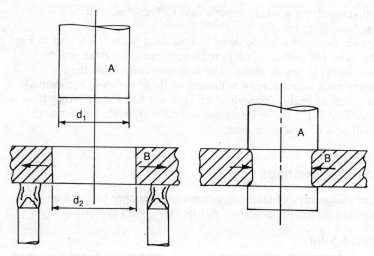

(i) $d_1 > d_2$ when both A and B are cold

(ii) $d_2 > d_1$ when B is heated. This enables A to be inserted into B.

*(a) Hot shrink joint*

(iii) A compression (shrink) joint is made when B cools down to the same temperature as A.

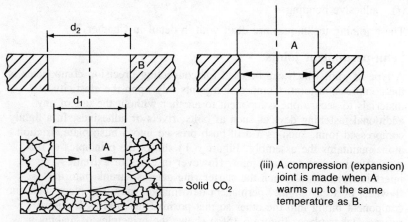

(iii) A compression (expansion) joint is made when A warms up to the same temperature as B.

(i) $d_1 > d_2$ when both A and B are not at room temperature

(ii) $d_1 < d_2$ when A is cooled in solid carbon dioxide.

*(b)*

**Fig. 6.15** Thermal compression joints

unsuitable for the outer element. Although heating of the outer element is the simpler process, care must be taken that this does not affect the structure of the material.

## Temporary joints

These are joints which may be assembled and dismantled as frequently as is required, not only for initial assembly, but also for maintenance and renewal. The more important of these joining techniques will now be considered.

## 6.10  Screwed fastenings

Figure 6.16 shows some typical applications of screwed joints. The bolted joint (Fig. 6.16(a)) shows that the plain shank extends beyond the joint face so that all shear loads are taken on the plain shank and not by the thread.

The stud and nut fixing (Fig. 6.16(b)) is used where a joint is regularly dismantled. The bulk of the wear comes on the stud which can

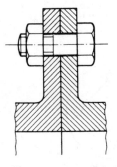

*(a)*  Section through a bolted joint

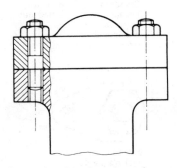

*(b)*  Stud and nut fixing for an inspection cover

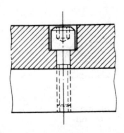

*(c)*  Cap head socket screw

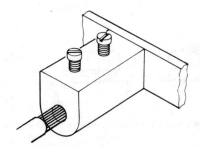

*(d)*  Cheese head brass screws

**Fig. 6.16**  Screwed fastenings

230

eventually be replaced cheaply and easily. This prevents wear falling on the threads of the more expensive casting or forging. If studs cannot be used the component (female) thread can be lined with a 'wire thread insert'. Studs can have dissimilar threads to suit the material into which they are screwed. For example, one end could have a coarse thread for screwing into a soft aluminium alloy cylinder block, whilst the other end of the stud could have a fine thread to increase the clamping force and also to resist vibration loosening the nut.

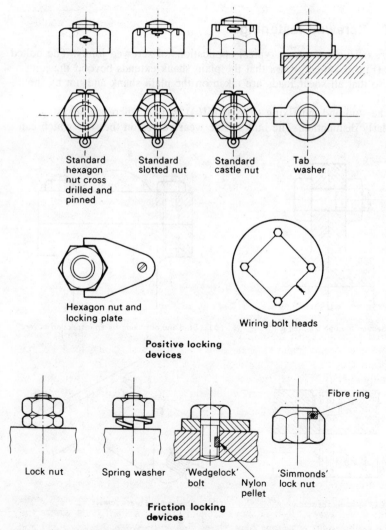

Standard hexagon nut cross drilled and pinned

Standard slotted nut

Standard castle nut

Tab washer

Hexagon nut and locking plate

Wiring bolt heads

**Positive locking devices**

Lock nut

Spring washer

'Wedgelock' bolt

Nylon pellet

Fibre ring

'Simmonds' lock nut

**Friction locking devices**

**Fig. 6.17**  Locking devices

A cap head socket screw (Fig. 6.16(c)) is much more expensive than the ordinary hexagon head bolt. However the cap head socket screw is made from heat-treated, high-tensile steel, upset-forged and thread rolled. This makes them very much stronger, tougher and wear resistant than the ordinary low-carbon steel hexagon head bolt. They are widely used in the manufacture of machine tools. The ability of being able to sink the head flush with the surface of the component they are securing leads to a better appearance, easy cleaning and greater safety.

Cheese head screws can also be used where flush fitting is required, but they are of inferior strength to cap screws and are only used for lightly stressed joints where low cost is important. Figure 6.16(d) shows small brass cheese head screws being used for clamping electric cable into a terminal.

## 6.11 Locking devices

In order to prevent screwed fastenings working loose due to vibration, various locking devices are employed. A selection are shown in Fig. 6.17. It can be seen that these devices can be divided into two main categories: those where the locking action is positive, and those where the locking action is frictional. Positive locking devices are more time consuming to fit, but they are essential for critical joints where failure could cause a serious accident, as in the controls of a machine tool, motor vehicle or aircraft.

## 6.12 Spanners

Spanners are used to tighten screwed fastenings. They are carefully proportioned so that their length enables a man of average strength to fully tighten the fastenings correctly. In order to ensure that critical screwed fastenings are tightened correctly a *torque spanner* should be used. Some torque spanners make use of a pre-set slipping clutch so that when the specified torque has been reached, the clutch slips and the fastening cannot be over tightened. Figure 6.18 shows a cheaper and simpler type of torque spanner which makes use of a pointer to indicate when the correct torque has been applied.

## 6.13 Keys

These are used to connect components such as wheels onto shafts in order to transmit rotary motion without slip. Some typical keys are shown in Fig. 6.19. Taper gib-head keys are only used on shaft ends where they can be withdrawn by means of a 'drift' driven between the key head and the wheel. Woodruff keys are used where axial alignment is required.

232

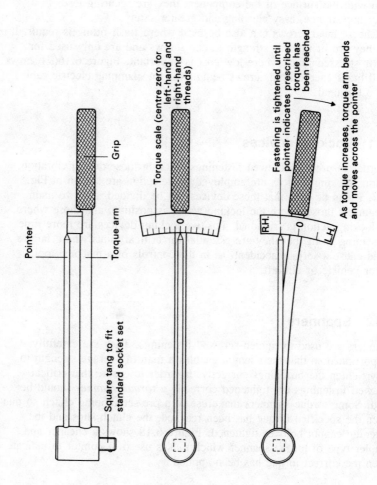

Grip

Torque scale (centre zero for left-hand and right-hand threads)

Pointer

Torque arm

Square tang to fit standard socket set

Fastening is tightened until pointer indicates prescribed torque has been reached

As torque increases, torque arm bends and moves across the pointer

R.H. 0 L.H.

**Fig. 6.18** Torque spanner

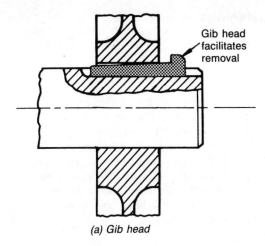

*(a) Gib head*

Gib head
facilitates
removal

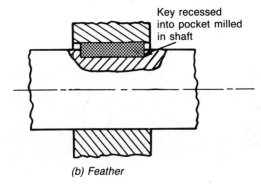

*(b) Feather*

Key recessed
into pocket milled
in shaft

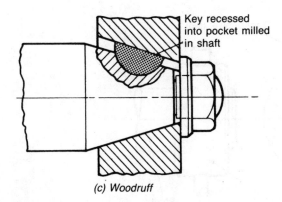

*(c) Woodruff*

Key recessed
into pocket milled
in shaft

**Fig. 6.19**  Keys

234

## 6.14 Miscellaneous fastenings

A selection of dowels, taper pins, cotter pins, and circlips are shown in Fig. 6.20.

### Plain dowels

Screwed fastenings are usually fitted through drilled clearance holes. Therefore, lateral location depends largely upon friction and the fastenings do not come into shear until sufficient movement has occurred to take up all the clearance. More precise location may be achieved by using bolts with ground shanks fitted through reamed holes or by plain dowels as shown in Fig. 6.20(a). Dowels should never be fitted in blind holes since air trapped under a dowel will make it difficult to fit and also because it is impossible to drive a dowel out of a blind hole when the assembly needs to be dismantled. Dowels should be a light drive (interference) fit in a reamed hole.

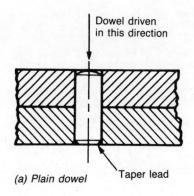

Dowel driven
in this direction

*(a) Plain dowel*    Taper lead

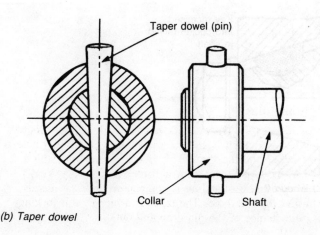

Taper dowel (pin)

Collar    Shaft

*(b) Taper dowel*

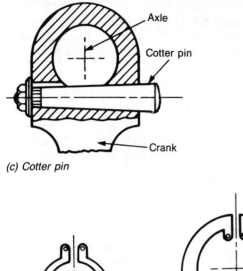

*(c) Cotter pin*

*(d) Circlips*

**Fig. 6.20**  Miscellaneous fastenings

## Taper dowels (taper pins)

These are used for fitting such components as collars to shafts as shown in Fig. 6.20(*b*). When the collar is correctly positioned, a parallel hole is drilled through the collar and the shaft. This is then opened up with a taper pin reamer and the tape dowel (pin) is driven home. Any wear from repeated assembly and dismantling is compensated for by merely driving the pin further into the hole. The taper is a morse, self-locking taper so there is little chance of the pin dropping out.

## Cotter pins

These are parallel pins with a taper flat which engages with a corresponding flat on the shaft as shown in Fig. 6.20(c). The nut secures the pin and prevents it working loose, as well as drawing the tapers tightly together.

## Circlips

These are used to provide a locating shoulder on a shaft or in a hole, as shown in Fig. 6.20(d). They are usually made from spring steel and are fitted or removed with specially shaped pliers which locate in the holes of the circlip. They provide a neat fixing which is easy to assemble or dismantle.

## 6.15  Cost of assembly

The cost of assembly depends upon the time taken, wage rates, and the cost of any special tools and work-holding fixtures required. Consider the plastic box and lid introduced in section 6.1. The cost of assembling the

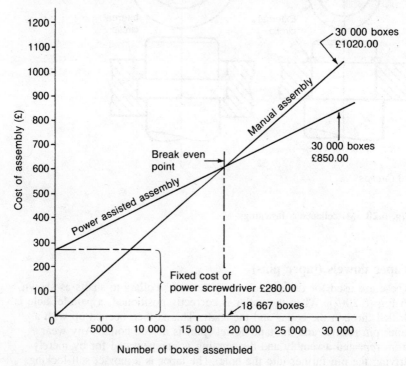

**Fig. 6.21**  Cost of assembly

lid on the box manually using self-tapping screws could be determined as follows.

## Manual assembly

| | |
|---|---:|
| Pick up box and place in convenient position | 2 s |
| Pick up lid and position over box | 2 s |
| Pick up screw fit washer and position in hole | 3 s |
| Run screw home using screwdriver | 5 s |
| Repeat the last two operations for the remaining holes | 24 s |
| Total time | 36 s |

A typical wage rate at the time of publication would be £3.40 per hour. Therefore the cost of assembly would be ...                    *3.4p per box.*

## Power assisted assembly

To speed assembly and reduce costs, the manufacturer decided to provide the assembler with a power driven screwdriver. This reduced the overall time of assembly per box to 20 seconds and the cost to *1.9p per box.*

However, the power assisted screw driver cost £280.000 and this is taken into account by using a 'break-even diagram' (Fig. 6.21). This shows that below 18667 boxes it is cheaper to use a manual screwdriver, but above 18667 boxes it is cheaper to use the power assisted screwdriver. This simple example neglects operator fatigue, the possibility of long term wrist injury, the cost of electricity, maintenance and the eventual replacement of the power assisted screwdriver, all of which would have to be considered in practice.

# 7 Fabrication

## 7.1 Preparation for fabrication

In Chapter 6, *assembly* was described as the joining together of individual components and sub-assemblies to make a single useable device. *Fabrication* is the term used for the forming and joining of assemblies made largely from sheet metal, thin and thick plate, and sections such as standard angles, British standard beams (BSB), and rolled steel joists (RSJ).

### Cutting processes

The cutting out of sheet metal and thin plate blanks, using a guillotine or a blanking tool in a press, has already been discussed in section 1.8. Thick plate is usually *flame-cut* using an oxy-acetylene gas mixture and a special cutting torch. Details of the nozzle of this torch and the method of cutting is shown in Fig. 7.1. This process is only successful with ferrous metals, as the non-ferrous metals tend to conduct the heat away from the cutting zone too rapidly. The metal at the cutting zone is raised to a temperature of about 890°C (bright cherry red) using the oxy-acetylene pre-heating flame. A jet of pure oxygen is then directed onto this spot and instantly reacts with the hot steel. The steel actually burns to iron oxide and as this reaction is *exothermic* (gives out heat), the reaction becomes largely self-sustaining provided that the oxygen supply is not interrupted. The cutting torch may be controlled manually, or the

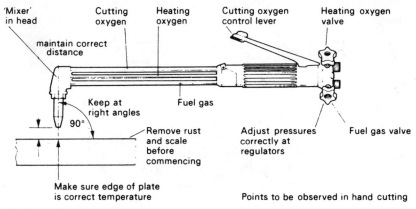

'Mixer' in head

maintain correct distance

Cutting oxygen

Heating oxygen

Cutting oxygen control lever

Heating oxygen valve

Keep at right angles

90°

Fuel gas

Remove rust and scale before commencing

Adjust pressures correctly at regulators

Fuel gas valve

Make sure edge of plate is correct temperature

Points to be observed in hand cutting

*(a) The cutting torch*

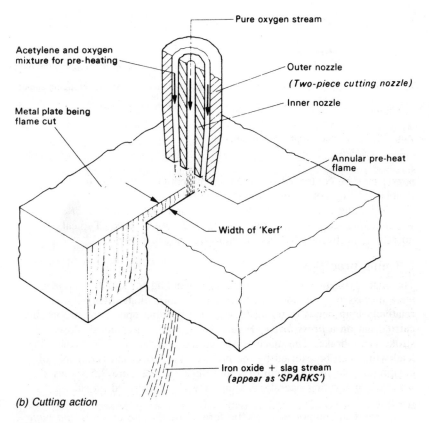

Pure oxygen stream

Acetylene and oxygen mixture for pre-heating

Outer nozzle

*(Two-piece cutting nozzle)*

Inner nozzle

Metal plate being flame cut

Annular pre-heat flame

Width of 'Kerf'

Iron oxide + slag stream *(appear as 'SPARKS')*

*(b) Cutting action*

**Fig. 7.1** Flame cutting

240

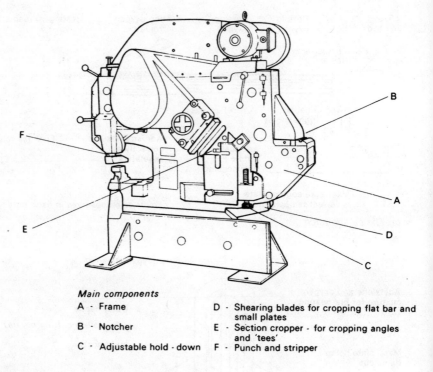

**Main components**

A - Frame
B - Notcher
C - Adjustable hold - down

D - Shearing blades for cropping flat bar and small plates
E - Section cropper - for cropping angles and 'tees'
F - Punch and stripper

**Fig. 7.2** Universal cropping and notching

nozzle may be controlled by a pantograph copying machine using a template, or by computer numerical control.

For cutting angle-sections, tee-sections and plate, a *universal cropping and notching machine* as shown in Fig. 7.2 may be used. Typical operations performed by this machine are shown in Fig. 7.3.

## Forming processes

The basic principles of V-bending and U-bending for small components were discussed in section 1.6. Sheet metal fabrications often require relatively long bends to be made and such bending operations are usually carried out on a *press brake*. Figure 7.4 shows a mechanical, down-stroke press brake. The machine shown has a capacity of 76 tonnes (the load which can be exerted by the press on the tools) and is capable of bending a 2.44 metre length of 4 mm thick steel. Figure 7.5 shows a selection of forming operations which may be performed on such a machine.

Cylindrical components may be formed by the use of *sheet and plate rolling machines*. Figure 7.6 shows a heavy duty, power driven roll bending machine, and Fig. 7.7 shows the sequence of operations for rolling a steel pipe-line section on such a machine. The top roller can be

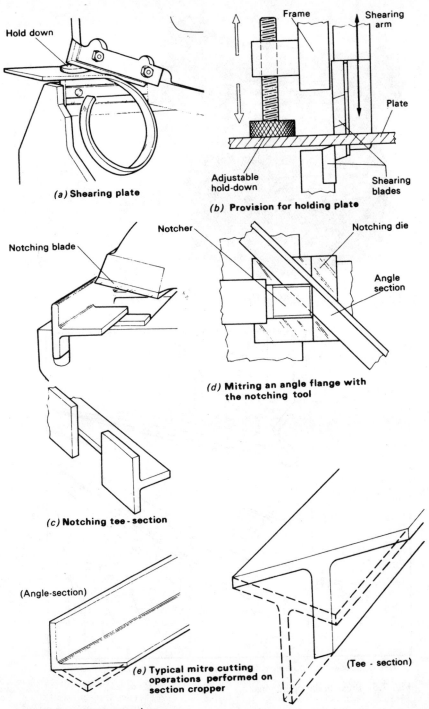

(a) Shearing plate

Hold down

(b) Provision for holding plate

Frame

Shearing arm

Plate

Adjustable hold-down

Shearing blades

(c) Notching tee-section

Notching blade

Notcher

Notching die

Angle section

(d) Mitring an angle flange with the notching tool

(Angle-section)

(e) Typical mitre cutting operations performed on section cropper

(Tee - section)

**Fig. 7.3** Cutting operations

242

**Fig. 7.4** Press brake (mechanical down-stroke type)

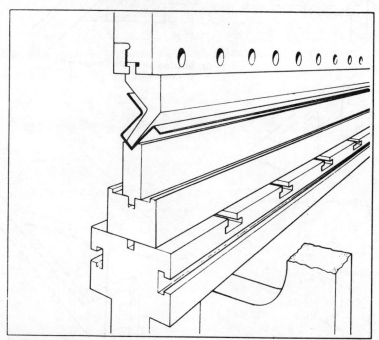

*(a) Use of goose-neck punches*

**Fig. 7.5** Press brake operations

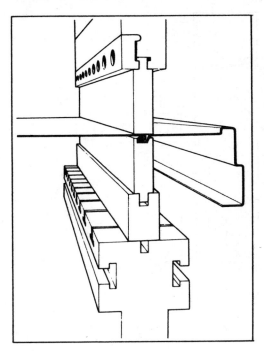

*(b) Flattening*

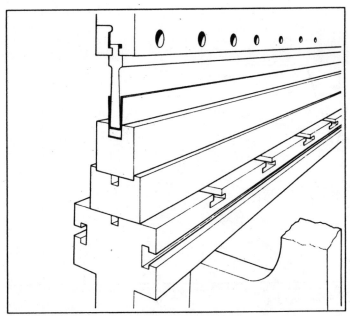

*(c) Channel forming*

244

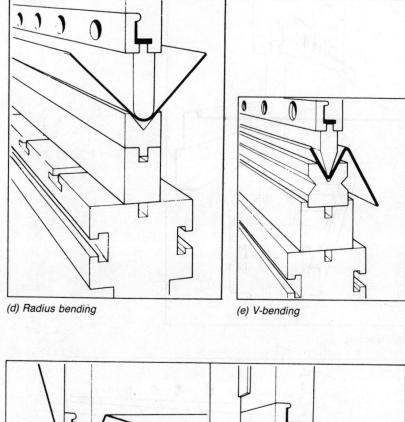

*(d) Radius bending*

*(e) V-bending*

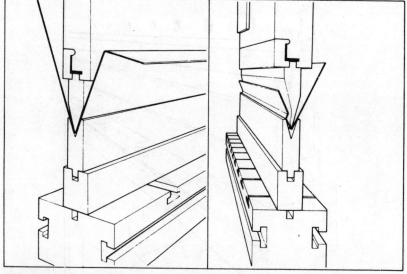

*(f) Acute angle tools*

**Fig. 7.5 (continued)**

duration245

**Fig. 7.6** Plate rolling machine

246

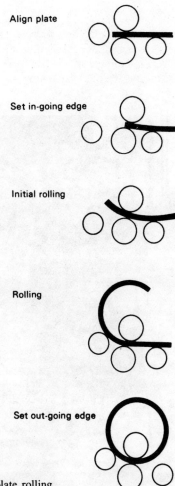

**Align plate**

**Set in-going edge**

**Initial rolling**

**Rolling**

**Set out-going edge**

**Fig. 7.7**  Principle of plate rolling

'slipped' for removal of the finished component. The minimum diameter of a cylinder produced on such a machine is usually considered to be 1.5 to 2 times the diameter of the roller around which it is being rolled.

## 7.2  Location for joining operations

Work which is to be joined using permanent connections such as welding and riveting must be carefully located and restrained since, once joined, errors cannot be corrected. A wide variety of clamping and locating devices are used and some of the specialised types for fabrication processes will now be considered.

## Skin pins

These are frequently used for locating box section, sheet-metal panels prior to riveting, as shown in Fig. 7.8. They are also used in the aircraft industry. The knurled nut is unscrewed and the centre pin is depressed and inserted in the hole in the sheets. Tightening the nut then draws the

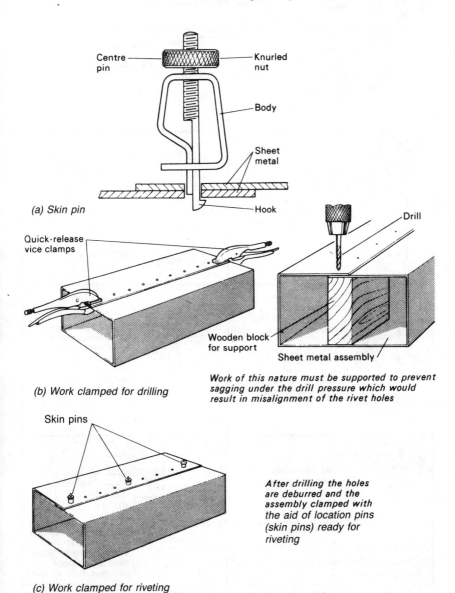

Centre pin

Knurled nut

Body

Sheet metal

*(a) Skin pin*

Hook

Quick-release vice clamps

Drill

Wooden block for support

Sheet metal assembly

*(b) Work clamped for drilling*

*Work of this nature must be supported to prevent sagging under the drill pressure which would result in misalignment of the rivet holes*

Skin pins

*After drilling the holes are deburred and the assembly clamped with the aid of location pins (skin pins) ready for riveting*

*(c) Work clamped for riveting*

**Fig. 7.8** Work-holding for riveting

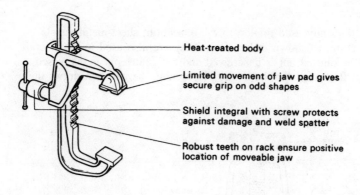

248

Heat-treated body

Limited movement of jaw pad gives
secure grip on odd shapes

Shield integral with screw protects
against damage and weld spatter

Robust teeth on rack ensure positive
location of moveable jaw

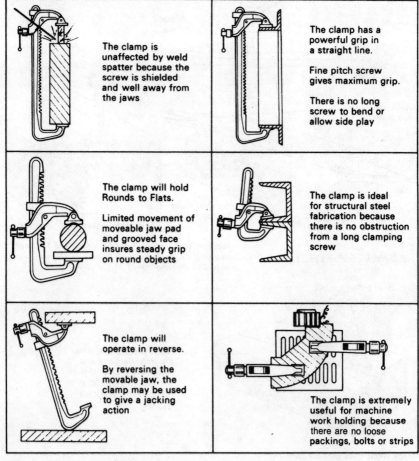

The clamp is
unaffected by weld
spatter because the
screw is shielded
and well away from
the jaws

The clamp has a
powerful grip in
a straight line.

Fine pitch screw
gives maximum grip.

There is no long
screw to bend or
allow side play

The clamp will hold
Rounds to Flats.

Limited movement of
moveable jaw pad
and grooved face
insures steady grip
on round objects

The clamp is ideal
for structural steel
fabrication because
there is no obstruction
from a long clamping
screw

The clamp will
operate in reverse.

By reversing the
movable jaw, the
clamp may be used
to give a jacking
action

The clamp is extremely
useful for machine
work holding because
there are no loose
packings, bolts or strips

**Fig. 7.9** Rack type G-clamps

hooked centre pin upwards, clamping the sheets to be joined between the clamp body and the hook. They are removed by simply releasing the knurled nut and withdrawing the hook. Skin pins, or location pins as they are also called, give quick accurate location, positive grip, no distortion of the hole and single-handed operation.

## Clamping devices for welding

In the assembly of parts before welding, clamps of many types are needed. G-clamps are most commonly used, but care must be taken to prevent welding 'spatter' from damaging the threads, otherwise the life of an ordinary G-clamp will be very short. Protection of the threads can be provided by coating them with an 'anti-spatter compound'. The rack type G-clamp, as shown in Fig. 7.9, is preferable as it is fitted with a shield which protects the screw against damage and spatter.

Many of the clamps used for holding work for welding are quick-acting and can be easily and rapidly adjusted for various thicknesses of workpiece. Quick acting clamps are essential for the batch production of work using welding jigs, where screw type clamps would be too slow and uneconomical. Quick-action clamps are generally of the toggle-action or of the cam-action type, and typical examples of these clamps are shown in Fig. 7.10.

## Magnetic clamps

Figure 7.11(a) shows a magnetic work-holding device suitable for holding sheet metal and thin plate during a welding operation, whilst Fig. 7.11(b) shows a magnetic clamp suitable for holding tube or rod. Care must be taken in positioning magnetic clamps when welding. If they become hot, as the result of radiated or conducted heat energy, they will lose their magnetism.

## 7.3 Screwed fastenings

Screwed fastenings have already been introduced in chapter 6. However, the screw fastenings used in fabrication work tend to differ in detail. For instance, the bolts should be hot forged so as to give them greater strength than bolts machined from hexagon bar. To provide lateral location 'fitted' bolts are sometimes used. These are hot-forged bolts with machined shanks to fit reamed holes. Friction grip bolts are high-tensile forged bolts used in conjunction with hardened washers. These are tightened using a torque spanner and provide lateral location by friction resulting from the very high clamping forces achieved.

## Washers

Washers should be used between the face of a nut and the part being fastened to increase the frictional grip of the nut by providing a smooth

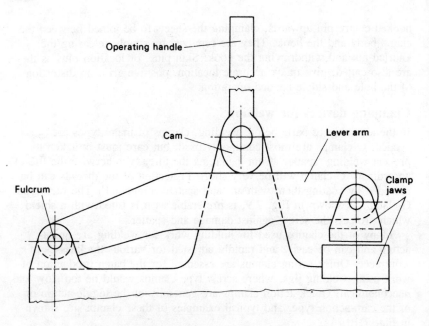

**(a)** Typical hand-cam operated welding clamp

*Quick-acting clamps are essential for holding work in welding jigs*

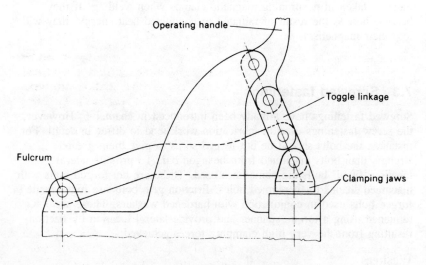

**(b)** Typical hand-toggle operated welding clamp

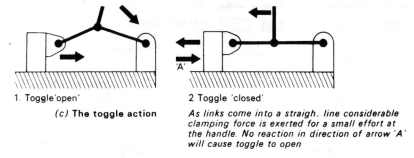

1. Toggle 'open'

*(c)* **The toggle action**

2 Toggle 'closed'

*As links come into a straigh. line considerable clamping force is exerted for a small effort at the handle. No reaction in direction of arrow 'A' will cause toggle to open*

**Fig. 7.10** Quick-acting clamping devices

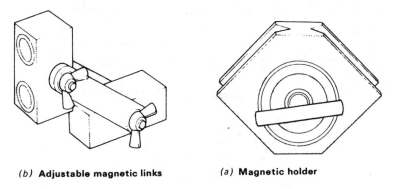

*(b)* **Adjustable magnetic links**

*(a)* **Magnetic holder**

**Fig. 7.11** Magnetic clamps for welding

flat surface for it to bite into and also to prevent damage to the structural member by the scouring action of the corners of the nut as it is tightened. As well as plain washers, tapered washers are also required on structural steel work to ensure that the shank of the bolt is not bent as the fastening is tightened. The use of tapered and flat washers is shown in Fig. 7.12. The taper washers must be chosen to suit the sections being connected. Two standard angles of taper are available, 5° and 8°.

### Fabricated steelwork

Some typical exampes of fabricated steelwork using screwed and riveted connections are shown in Fig. 7.13. Bolted joints should be designed, wherever possible, so that major forces acting on the joint are taken across the shank of the bolt so that it is in shear. For this reason the line of the joint should lie across the shank of the bolt and never across the thread. However, unlike riveted joints, correctly proportioned screwed fasteners should be as strong in tension as they are in shear.

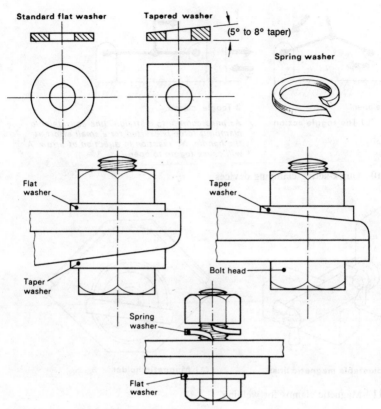

**Fig. 7.12** Flat, taper and spring washers

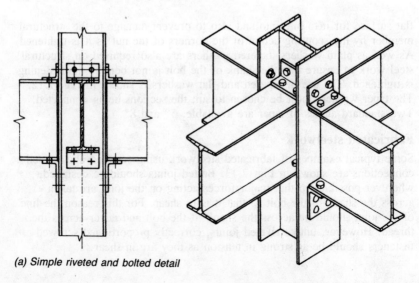

*(a) Simple riveted and bolted detail*

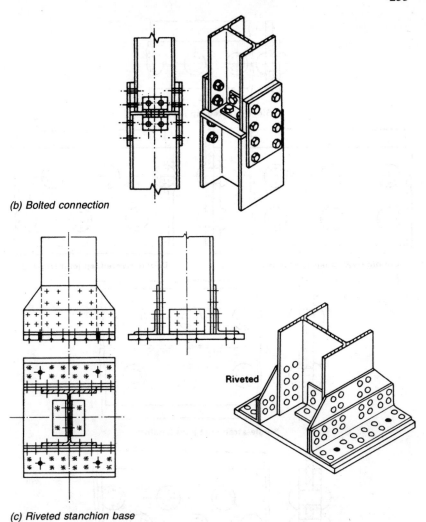

*(b) Bolted connection*

*(c) Riveted stanchion base*

**Fig. 7.13** Bolted and riveted joints in fabricated steelwork

## 7.4 Riveted joints

Riveting is a method of making permanent joints. The members to be
joined are drilled or punched, the rivets are inserted through the holes
and then closed by forming a head on the rivet. Small diameter rivets are
usually closed at room temperature, but large rivets are closed whilst red-
hot. Not only does this reduce the force necessary to close the rivet, but
as the rivet cools and shrinks it pulls the members being joined tightly
together.

254

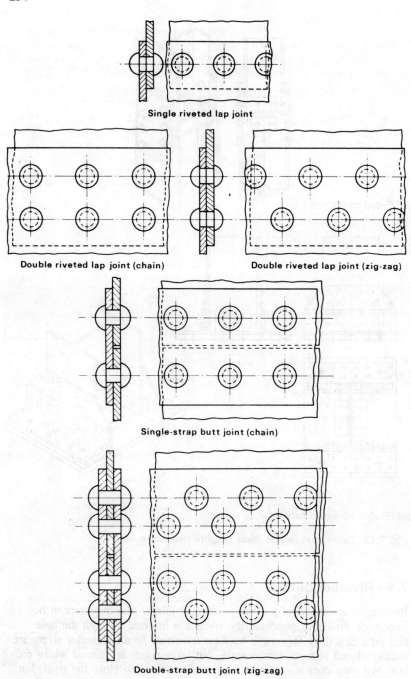

Single riveted lap joint

Double riveted lap joint (chain)

Double riveted lap joint (zig-zag)

Single-strap butt joint (chain)

Double-strap butt joint (zig-zag)

**Fig. 7.14** Types of riveted joint

A variety of riveted joints are used in constructional and fabrication work and some of these are shown in Fig. 7.14. In order to close the rivet correctly, the shank of the rivet must swell to take up the clearance necessary for inserting the rivet in the hole. The length of the rivet must also be correctly chosen so that it will form the required head. The correct proportions for rivet length and hole clearance are shown in Fig. 7.15. The shank diameter of the rivet is dependent upon the forces acting upon the members being joined and the thickness of such members. The

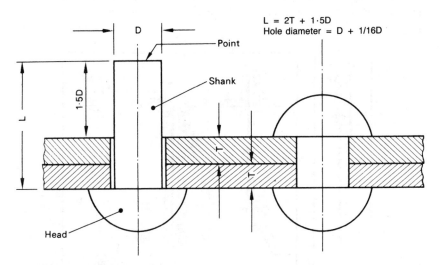

(a) Snaphead or roundhead rivet shape

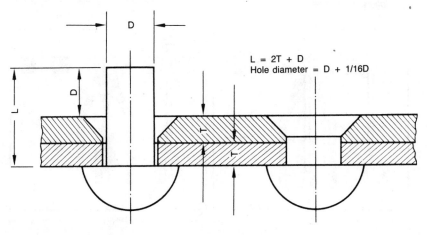

(b) Countersunk rivet shape

**Fig. 7.15** Proportions for riveted joints

joint should be designed so that the major forces act on the rivet so as to place the shank in shear. The heads of the rivets are not intended to be load bearing and should only be lightly loaded. Consider them as merely keeping the rivet in place. Some typical riveted joints used in fabricated steelwork were shown in Fig. 7.13.

Blind riveting (also called 'pop' riveting) systems are used for fabricating closed, hollow, box sections in sheet metal where a hold-up ('dolly') cannot be used to support the rivet head. Figure 7.16(a) shows the principle of blind riveting using the general, open rivet system, and Fig. 7.16(b) shows the principle of the closed rivet system.

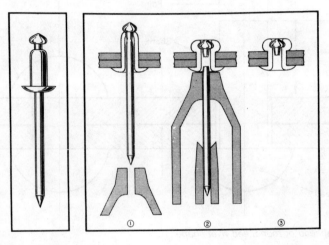

*(a) Hollow 'pop' rivet*

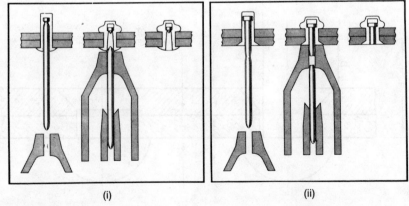

(i)

(ii)

*(b) Solid 'pop' rivet*

**Fig. 7.16**  Blind (pop) riveting

Courtesy: Tucker Easteners

## 7.5 Soldered joints

Soft soldering is a low temperature thermal jointing process in which the metal of the members being joined (parent metal) is not melted. It is an essential feature of soft soldered joints that each of the joint faces is 'tinned' by a film of solder and that these films of solder are made to fuse (melt) with the solder filling the space between them. In a correctly soldered joint, examination under a microscope shows that in the action of tinning such metals as brass, copper and steel, a definite chemical reaction takes place. The surface of the parent metal reacts with the tin content of the solder alloy to form an *intermetallic compound* which acts as a 'key' for the bulk of the solder in the joint.

The intermetallic compound layer will continue to increase in thickness the longer the joint is kept at soldering temperature. Once tinned, this film of solder cannot be mechanically wiped or prised off the parent metal. Soft solders are basically tin-lead alloys. Some solders for special applications have additional alloying elements. The full range of such solders, together with their recommended applications are found in BS 219. Some examples are listed in Table 7.1.

**Table 7.1** Types of solder

| B.S. Solder | Composition % | | | Melting range (°C) | Remarks |
|---|---|---|---|---|---|
| | Tin | Lead | Antimony | | |
| A | 65 | 34·4 | 0·6 | 183—185 | Free running solder ideal for soldering electronic and instrument assemblies. Commonly referred to as **electrician's solder** |
| K | 60 | 39·5 | 0·5 | 183—188 | Used for high-class tin-smith's work, and is known as **tinman's solder** |
| F | 50 | 49·5 | 0·5 | 183—212 | Used for general soldering work in coppersmithing and sheet metal work. |
| G | 40 | 59·6 | 0·4 | 183—234 | **Blow-pipe solder**. This is supplied in strip form with a D cross-section 0·3 mm wide. |
| J | 30 | 69·7 | 0·3 | 183—255 | **Plumber's solder**. Because of its wide melting range this solder becomes 'pasty' and can be moulded and wiped. |

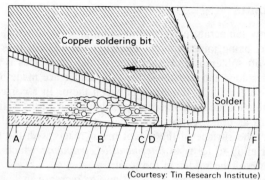

(Courtesy: Tin Research Institute)

Diagrammatic representation of the displacement of flux by molten solder.

A Flux solution lying above oxidised metal surface.
B Boiling flux solution removing the film of oxide (e.g. as chloride).
C Bare metal in contact with fused flux.
D Liquid solder displacing fused flux.
E Tin reacting with the basis metal to form compound.
F Solder solidifying.

**Fig. 7.17** The essential functions of a soldering flux

For successful soldering, the joint surfaces must be physically and mechanically clean, that is, they must be free from dirt, grease and oxide films. The cleaned surfaces must be protected from the action of atmospheric oxygen once they have been cleaned so that the oxide film does not reform.

When a metal is exposed to air at room temperature it acquires a thin film of oxide within a few minutes of being cleaned. Since oxygen combines with metals even more rapidly at elevated temperatures, it is essential that both the joint surfaces and the molten solder are protected from the atmosphere. This protection is provided by a *flux*. The requirements of a soft soldering flux are:

(*a*) it must remain liquid at the soldering temperature;
(*b*) in its liquid state it must cover and protect the joint surfaces from atmospheric oxygen;
(*c*) it must act as a wetting agent so that the molten solder flows freely over the joint faces and does not form into droplets;
(*d*) it must dissolve any oxide film present and any that reforms;
(*e*) it must be readily displaced from the joint surfaces by the molten solder as soldering proceeds.

Figure 7.17 shows the essential functions of a soldering flux. Fluxes may be classified as active or as passive.

### Active fluxes

Active fluxes quickly remove any residual oxide film on a metal as well as protecting the de-oxidised surface from the atmosphere. Unfortunately,

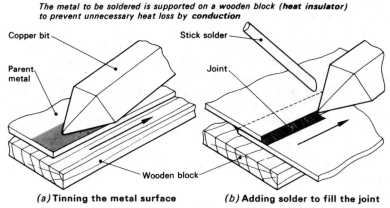

The metal to be soldered is supported on a wooden block *(heat insulator)* to prevent unnecessary heat loss by *conduction*

Copper bit

Parent metal

Stick solder

Joint

Wooden block

*(a)* Tinning the metal surface

*(b)* Adding solder to fill the joint

**Fig. 7.18** Soft-soldered joint

all active fluxes leave a corrosive residue after soldering. Such a residue absorbs moisture from the atmosphere and corrosion sets in. Therefore if an active flux is used the residue must be carefully washed off and the work dried after soldering is complete. Typical active fluxes are: Baker's Fluid which is made from zinc dissolved in an excess of hydrochloric acid together with some ammonium chloride; and Fluxite which is an acidified resin paste.

### Passive fluxes

Passive fluxes are used for soldering joints and connections in electrical and electronic equipment where the acid residue of an active flux could not be tolerated and where washing to remove the residue is not possible. The most widely used passive flux is resin, and solders for electrical purposes are often *resin cored* for convenience. Although the resin protects the joint surface from oxidation, it does not clean the surfaces like an active flux. Therefore greater care in cleaning the joint surfaces is necessary when using passive fluxes. Figure 7.18 shows a simple soft soldered joint. Before making the joint, the soldering iron has to be heated up and tinned. The hot copper 'bit' is cleaned with a file, flux is applied to prevent the oxide film reforming, and the cleaned bit is then loaded with solder. The metal being joined must itself be raised to the soldering temperature by the soldering iron or a sound joint will not be made. For this reason the metal being joined must be supported on a non-conductive surface such as wood.

## 7.6  Hard soldering (brazing)

Hard soldering is a general term used to cover *brazing* and *silver soldering*. In these processes, as in soft soldering, melting or fusion of the parent metals being joined does not take place. The filler material has a lower melting point than the metals being joined.

Hard solders do not possess the low melting points of the soft solders but they produce very much stronger joints. For example, bicycle frames are made from alloy steel tubes hard soldered into malleable iron brackets. The hard solder used in this instance is a brass alloy, so the process is referred to as *brazing*. The melting temperature of the brazing alloy is about 850°C, which is much higher than any soft solder. Brazing can be defined as: *A process of joining metals in which the molten filler is drawn by capillary attraction into the space between closely adjacent surfaces of the parts to be joined.*

The filler materials used for hard soldering can be classified into three main types.

## Silver solders

These are alloys containing a high percentage of the precious metal silver. Therefore they are expensive and are only used for fine work. They produce strong, ductile joints at a temperature lying between the soft solders and the brazing alloys. Common borax type brazing fluxes are not suitable for silver soldering and a proprietary flux matched to the solder alloy should be used.

## Brazing alloys containing phosphorus

These filter materials contain phosphorus and are usually referred to as *self-fluxing* alloys. Typical alloys contain silver, copper and phosphorus or just copper and phosphorus. The alloy containing silver has the lower melting point. The outstanding feature of these alloys is their ability to form high quality joints in air without the use of a flux. The products of oxidation react with the phosphorus to form a fluid compound which acts as an efficient flux. These brazing alloys are used for production brazing in furnaces, and resistance brazing operations. Care must be taken when using these alloys as they have a relatively high melting temperature and in many applications, there is little difference between their melting temperatures and the melting temperatures of the parent metals.

## Brazing brasses

The oldest and most familiar brazing alloys are the copper-zinc (brass) alloys known as *spelters*. A typical alloy is 50 per cent copper and 50 per cent zinc. Although such an alloy is hard and brittle, it has a shorter and lower melting range than other non-ferrous alloys which may need to be brazed. Further, some of the zinc content vapourises off during the brazing operation so that the composition of the finished joint is nearer 60 per cent copper and 40 per cent zinc which is stronger and less brittle. Borax mixed into a paste with water is a suitable flux when brazing with brass alloys. The metals which can be silver soldered and brazed include:

copper and copper based alloys;     plain carbon and alloy steels;

stainless steels and irons;
nickel based alloys;

malleable cast irons;
aluminium alloys (see section 7.7).

## Flame brazing

Flame brazing can be used to fabricate almost any assembly using a gas-air blow pipe with the air being supplied under pressure. For fine work and also the higher melting point alloys, an oxy-propane flame is used as this gives a higher temperature and closer control. No matter what method of heating is used, to successfully braze or silver-solder a joint, the parent metal must be raised to a high enough temperature that the solder or spelter will melt on contact whilst the heat source is temporarily removed.

## Furnace brazing

Furnace brazing is used extensively for quantity production when:

(a)  the parts to be brazed can be pre-assembled or jigged to hold them in position,

(b)  the brazing alloy (spelter) can be pre-formed and pre-placed as shown in Fig. 7.19(a).

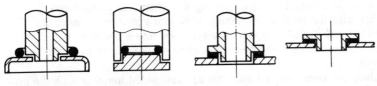

*(a) Pre-placed brazing alloy (spelter)*

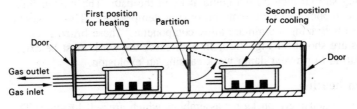

**Schematic layout of batch brazing in a sealed container**

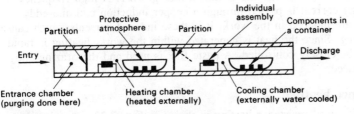

*(b) Schematic layout of continuous brazing furnace*

**Fig. 7.19**  Furnace brazing

The components to be brazed are assembled together with the brazing alloy in the required position and fluxed if necessary. Pre-placed brazing alloy inserts are available in a variety of forms such as wire rings, bent wire shapes, washers and foils.

The method of heating varies according to the application and in general muffle furnaces are used in order that the flame does not impinge directly on the parts being brazed. Furnaces may be heated by gas, oil or electricity, and are classified into two types.

(a) Batch type furnaces with either air or controlled atmosphere.
(b) Conveyor type furnaces with controlled atmosphere.

Schematic layouts of brazing furnaces are shown in Fig. 7.19(b). Individual assemblies or components for batch brazing are loaded into the furnace in sealed containers so that they are not contaminated by the flue gases of the furnace. They are cooled in the sealed containers after removal from the furnace. For continuous brazing the components are mounted on trays and they are passed through the furnace on a conveyor. The furnace is externally heated so that it can have a controlled atmosphere.

## Dip brazing

*Molten spelter bath.* Instead of placing the assembled components together with the preformed brazing alloy into a muffle furnace, the assembled and fluxed components are dipped into a crucible (bath) of molten spelter. Larger components need to be pre-heated to avoid cooling the bath.

*Molten flux bath.* The components are assembled together with the preformed and pre-placed spelter. The components and the spelter must be self-locating so that they do not come apart in the bath. The molten flux raises the components to the required brazing temperature. This process is suitable for brazing aluminium alloy components. These brazing techniques are shown in Fig. 7.20. In both cases the work must be dried by pre-heating to prevent damp work causing an explosion.

## Induction heating

This is used extensively on larger assemblies which are self-locating. The principle of induction heating is shown in Fig. 7.21. A high frequency alternating current is passed through a copper induction coil and eddy currents are induced in the work. It is these induced currents which cause the heating. Since the heat is generated within the work, heating is rapid and can be closely controlled. A paste flux is used and the brazing alloy is pre-placed.

## Resistance heating

The principle of resistance heating is shown in Fig. 7.22. The electric current is passed through the joint and the resistance of the joint to the passage of an electric current raises its temperature to that required by

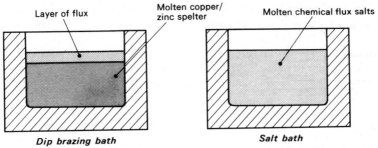

Layer of flux

Molten copper/zinc spelter

Molten chemical flux salts

**Dip brazing bath**

The brazing bath is heated externally

**Salt bath**

Baths are usually fitted with an insulated lid or cover to prevent heat loss.

Parts to be brazed must be dry, since a **VIOLENT EXPLOSION** may occur if they are immersed wet.

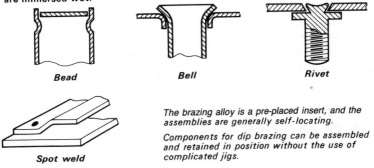

**Bead**

**Bell**

**Rivet**

**Spot weld**

The brazing alloy is a pre-placed insert, and the assemblies are generally self-locating.

Components for dip brazing can be assembled and retained in position without the use of complicated jigs.

**Fig. 7.20** Dip brazing

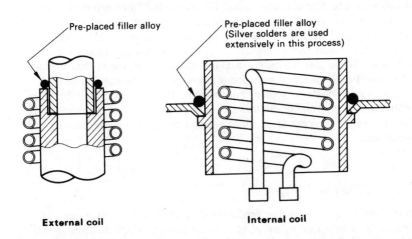

Pre-placed filler alloy

Pre-placed filler alloy
(Silver solders are used extensively in this process)

**External coil**

**Internal coil**

It is usual for induction coils to be designed to surround the joint, but internal coils can be used for certain applications.

**Fig. 7.21** Electric induction brazing

264

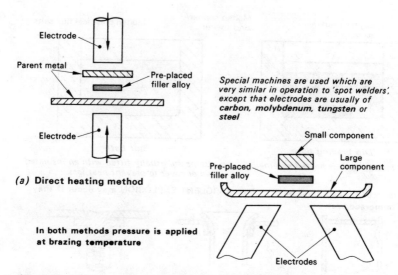

(a) **Direct heating method**

Electrode

Parent metal

Pre-placed
filler alloy

Electrode

*Special machines are used which are
very similar in operation to 'spot welders',
except that electrodes are usually of
carbon, molybdenum, tungsten or
steel*

Small component

Large
component

Pre-placed
filler alloy

**In both methods pressure is applied
at brazing temperature**

Electrodes

**Fig. 7.22** Electric resistance brazing   *(b)* **Indirect heating method**

the brazing process. Heating can be precisely localised and there is no
loss of mechanical properties in the parent metal.

## 7.7   Aluminium brazing

There is a distinction between the brazing of aluminium and the brazing
of other metals. For aluminium and its alloys, the filler material is an
aluminium alloy whose melting temperature is lower than that of the
parent metal. Conventional borax based fluxes are unsuitable when
brazing aluminium and aluminium alloys but proprietary fluxes are
available. These are, basically, mixtures of the alkali-metal chlorides and
fluorides. For example, a standard aluminium brazing flux contains
chlorides of potassium, sodium and lithium. Extreme care must be taken
when aluminium brazing, as there is only a small margin of temperature
which permits the joint to be made without the parent metal melting and
collapsing.

## 7.8   Fusion welding

In the soldering and brazing processes described so far, the joints are
formed by a thin film of metal of a lower melting point than the metals
being joined. In *fusion welding* any additional metal (filler metal) added
to the joint has a similar composition, strength and melting temperature
as the parent metal. Figure 7.23 shows the principle of joining two pieces
of metal by fusion welding where not only the filler metal but also the

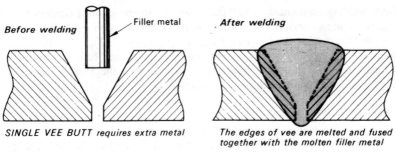

*Before welding*

Filler metal

*After welding*

SINGLE VEE BUTT *requires extra metal*

*The edges of vee are melted and fused together with the molten filler metal*

**Fig. 7.23** Fusion welding

edges of the components being joined are melted. The molten metals fuse together and, when solid, form a homogeneous joint whose strength is equal to the parent metal.

### Oxy-acetylene welding

In this process the heat source is a mixture of oxygen and acetylene gases burning to produce a flame whose temperature can reach 3250°C; this is above the melting point of most metals. Figure 7.24 shows a typical set

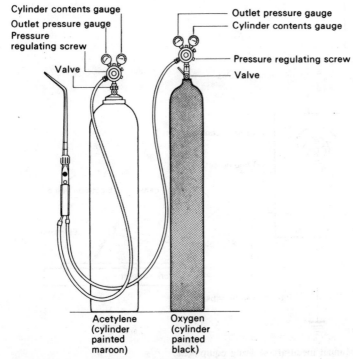

Cylinder contents gauge
Outlet pressure gauge
Pressure regulating screw
Valve

Outlet pressure gauge
Cylinder contents gauge
Pressure regulating screw
Valve

Acetylene (cylinder painted maroon)

Oxygen (cylinder painted black)

**Fig. 7.24** Oxy-acetylene welding equipment

of gas welding equipment. Since the gases are stored in the cylinders under very high pressures and form highly flammable and even explosive mixtures, the equipment must be handled with very great care. This equipment must be used only by persons who have been fully trained in the operating and safety procedures recommended by the Health and Safety Executive and the equipment suppliers.

## Metallic arc welding

This is a fusion welding process where the energy required to melt the edges of the components and the filler material is provided by an electric arc. An *arc* is the name given to the prolonged spark struck between two electrodes. In this process the filler rod forms one electrode and the work forms the other electrode. The filler rod/electrode is coated with a flux which shields the joint from attack by atmospheric oxygen at the very

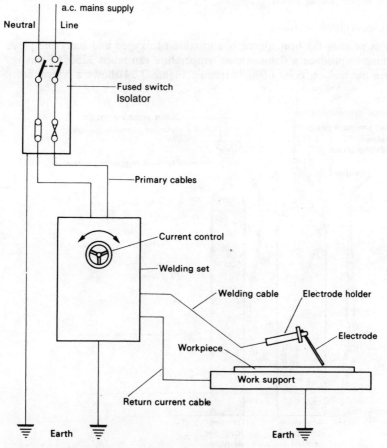

**Fig. 7.25** Manual metal-arc welding equipment

high temperatures involved, and stabilises the arc so that alternating current can be used. (Average arc temperature is about 6000°C.) Figure 7.25 shows the general arrangement of a manual metal-arc welding installation.

A transformer is used to reduce the mains voltage to a safe, low voltage, heavy current supply suitable for welding. As with gas welding equipment, arc welding equipment must not be used by unskilled persons except under the closest supervision during training. Protective clothing, appropriate to the process, must be worn and especially goggles or visors with appropriate filter glasses. A comparison of the gas and arc welding processes is shown in Fig. 7.26.

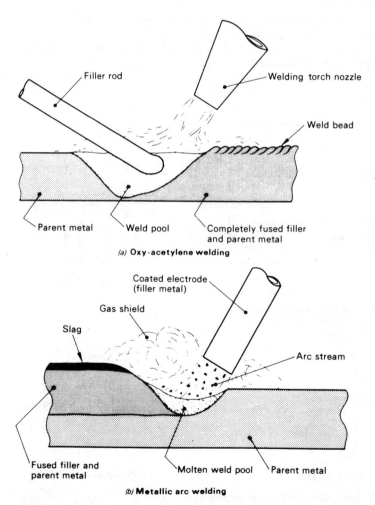

(a) **Oxy-acetylene welding**

(b) **Metallic arc welding**

**Fig. 7.26** Comparison of oxy-acetylene and metal-arc welding

## 7.9 Resistance welding

The resistance welding process depends upon pressure as well as temperature to achieve the joining of the parent metals; fusion does not occur. The parent metal is raised to just below its melting point and the weld is completed by the application of high local pressure as in forge welding. The principle of this process is shown in Fig. 7.27. The temperature of the components to be joined is raised locally by the passage of a heavy electrical current at low voltage through the components and the resistance to its passage causes intense local heating. The cycle of events, which in all resistance welding processes is controlled automatically to ensure uniform quality, is as follows.

(a) *Squeeze time*. The time between the first application of pressure and when the welding current commences to flow.
(b) *Weld time*. The time during which the welding current flows whilst the pressure is maintained.

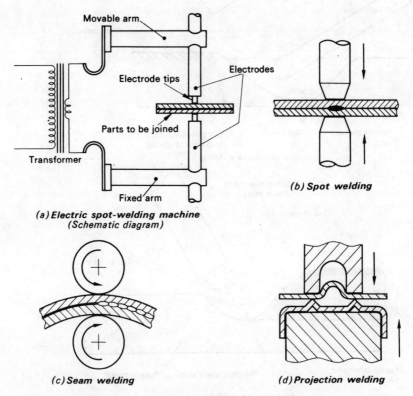

(a) *Electric spot-welding machine* (*Schematic diagram*)

(b) *Spot welding*

(c) *Seam welding*

(d) *Projection welding*

**Fig. 7.27** Principles of resistance welding

(c) *Hold time.* The time during which the joint is maintained under pressure after the current has ceased to flow.

(d) *Off time.* The time during which the electrodes are open for loading and unloading the work.

No additional filler metal is required to make a resistance welded joint. Unlike fusion welding where the joint metal is in the 'as cast' condition, the metal in a resistance weld is in the wrought condition. Therefore resistance welds are surprisingly strong.

## Spot-welding

This process is shown in Fig. 7.27(a) and 7.27(b). It is the most common of the resistance welding processes and is much quicker and neater than riveting but can only be applied to sheet metal. The joint is produced by making a row of individual spot-welds side by side at regular intervals. Such joints are not fluid tight and require sealing to prevent leakage or corrosion. Apart from ensuring that the joint surfaces are clean, no special preparation is required. Spot welding is widely used for joining the body panels of motor vehicles.

## Seam-welding

The components to be joined are clamped between revolving, circular electrodes as shown in Fig. 7.27(c). The current is applied in pulses and this results in a series of overlapping spot welds being made along the seam. This method of welding can be used for the manufacture of fluid tight containers and fuel tanks.

## Projection welding

With this process the electrodes act as locations for holding the parts to be joined. The joint is so designed that projections are preformed on one of the parts as shown in Fig. 7.27(d). Projection welding enables the welding pressure and heated welding zone to be localised at predetermined points.

## Butt-welding

The resistance welds described so far are lap joints connecting sheet metal components. Butt-welding, as shown in Fig. 7.28, is used for connecting more solid sections. For example low-cost plain carbon steel shanks can be butt-welded onto the expensive high-speed steel bodies of the larger twist drills.

To ensure a sound weld, the temperature is raised slightly above that required in theory. Any molten metal which may occur at the joint interface is displaced by the pressure in a shower of sparks until layers of metal at the correct pressure welding temperature are reached and a weld is achieved.

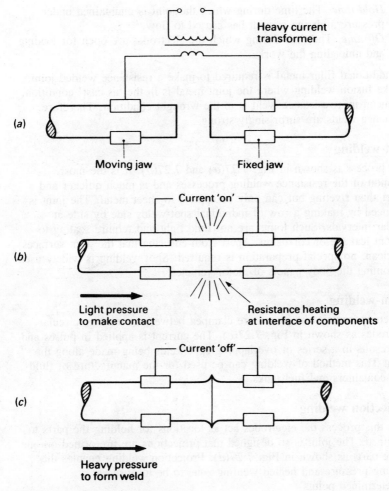

**Fig. 7.28** Resistance butt-welding

## 7.10 Adhesive bonding

Adhesive bonding, using modern synthetic adhesives, is widely used
throughout industry for joining a wide range of materials in a variety of
combinations. The strength of adhesive bonded joints is now so high that
adhesive bonding has replaced welding and riveting for some quite highly
stressed applications. Adhesives can be used for joining metals to metals,
metals to non-metals, and non-metals to non-metals with equal facility.

Figure 7.29(*a*) shows a typical adhesive bonded joint and explains the
terminology used for the various features of the joint. The strength of the
joint depends upon two factors.

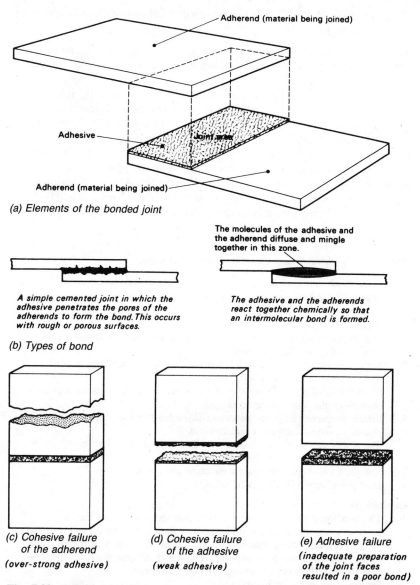

Adherend (material being joined)

Adhesive

Joint area

Adherend (material being joined)

(a) Elements of the bonded joint

The molecules of the adhesive and the adherend diffuse and mingle together in this zone.

**A simple cemented joint in which the adhesive penetrates the pores of the adherends to form the bond. This occurs with rough or porous surfaces.**

*The adhesive and the adherends react together chemically so that an intermolecular bond is formed.*

(b) Types of bond

(c) Cohesive failure of the adherend

(over-strong adhesive)

(d) Cohesive failure of the adhesive

(weak adhesive)

(e) Adhesive failure

(inadequate preparation of the joint faces resulted in a poor bond)

**Fig. 7.29** Adhesive bonding

(a) *Adhesion* which is the ability of the bonding material (adhesive) to stick (adhere) to the materials being joined (adherends). The two ways in which this bond can occur are shown in Fig. 7.29(b).
(b) *Cohesion* which is the ability of the adhesive to resist the applied forces within itself. Two ways in which cohesive failure can occur

are shown in Fig. 7.29(c) and 7.39(d). Adhesive failure is shown in Fig. 7.29(e).

Table 7.2 lists some of the more important advantages and limitations of adhesive bonding as compared with the mechanical and thermal jointing processes discussed earlier.

No matter how effective the adhesive is and how carefully it is applied, the joint will be a failure if it is not correctly designed and executed. It is bad practice to apply adhesive to a joint which was originally proportioned for bolting, riveting or welding. The joint must be proportioned to exploit the properties of adhesives. Most adhesive bonded joints are strong in tension and shear (providing the joint area is adequate) but weak in cleavage and peel; these terms are explained in Fig. 7.30. Further, the success of an adhesive bonded joint depends upon the joint faces being carefully prepared so that they are physically and

**Table 7.2** Advantages and limitations of bonded joints

**Advantages**
1. The ability to join dissimilar materials, and materials of widely different thicknesses
2. The ability to join components of difficult shape that would restrict the application of welding or riveting equipment
3. Smooth finish to the joint which will be free from voids and protrusions such as weld beads, rivet and bolt heads, etc.
4. Uniform distribution of stress over entire area of joint. This reduces the chances of the joint failing in fatigue
5. Elastic properties of many adhesives allow for flexibility in the joint and give it vibration damping characteristics
6. The ability to electrically insulate the adherends and prevent corrosion due to galvanic action between dissimilar metals
7. The joint will be sealed against moisture and gases
8. Heat-sensitive materials can be joined

**Limitations**
1. The bonding process is more complex than mechanical and thermal processes, i.e. the need for surface preparation, temperature and humidity control of the working atmosphere, ventilation and health problems caused by the adhesives and their solvents. The length of time that the assembly must be jigged up whilst setting (curing) takes place
2. Inspection of the joint is difficult
3. Joint design is more critical than for many mechanical and thermal processes
4. Incompatibility with the adherends. The adhesive itself may corrode the materials it is joining
5. Degradation of the joint when subject to high and low temperatures, chemical atmospheres, etc.
6. Creep under sustained loads

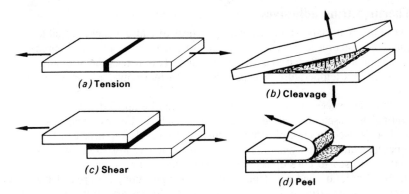

**Fig. 7.30** Stressing of bonded joints

chemically clean, free from grease and, where appropriate, roughened to form a key by wire brushing, vapour or shot blasting or chemical etching.

The adhesive must 'wet' the joint surfaces thoroughly, otherwise voids will occur and the effective joint area will be less than the designed area. This will weaken the joint considerably.

### Thermoplastic adhesives

(a) *Heat activated*. The adhesive is softened when heated and, when sufficiently fluid, is spread over the whole joint area. The materials to be joined are brought into contact, the adhesive adheres to them and, when cooled to room temperature the adhesive sets and a bond is achieved.

(b) *Solvent activated*. The adhesive is softened by a suitable solvent and a bond is achieved by the solvent evaporating. Because evaporation is essential to the setting of the adhesive, a sound bond is almost impossible to achieve at the centre of a large joint area, particularly when joining non-absorbent and non-porous materials.

(c) *Impact adhesives*. These are solvent activated adhesives which are spread separately on the two joint faces and then left to dry by evaporation. When dry, the treated joint faces are brought together whereupon they instantly bond together by intermolecular attraction. This enables non-absorbent and non-porous materials to be joined even when there is a large joint area.

Thermoplastic adhesives are based upon synthetic materials such as polystyrene, polyamides, vinyl and acrylic polymers and cellulose derivatives. They are also based upon naturally occurring materials such as resin, shellac, mineral waxes and rubber. Thermoplastic adhesives are not as strong as thermosetting plastic adhesives but, being more flexible, they are more suitable for joining non-rigid materials.

## Thermosetting adhesives

These are materials which depend upon heat to cause a non-reversible chemical reaction (curing) to take place to make them set. Once cured they cannot be softened again by re-heating. This makes the strength of the joint less temperature sensitive than when thermoplastic adhesives are used.

The heat necessary to cure the adhesive can be applied externally by heating the assembly and adhesive in an autoclave. For example this method is used to cure phenolic resins. Alternatively the heat can be generated internally by adding a chemical hardener. For example, this method is used to cure epoxy resins. Since the setting process is a chemical reaction and not dependent upon evaporation, the area of the joint can be as large as is required to give the necessary strength. Thermosetting adhesives are very strong and can even be used for making structural joints in high strength materials such as metals. The body shells of cars and stressed members of aircraft are increasingly dependent upon these adhesives for their joints in place of spot-welding and riveting. The stresses are more uniformly distributed and the joints are sealed against corrosion. Further, the relatively low temperature rise which occurs during curing does not affect the crystallographic structure of the metal. Thermosetting adhesives tend to be rigid when cured and, therefore, are not suitable for joining flexible (non-rigid) materials.

Care must be taken when working with adhesives as the solvents and the fumes given off by them are both toxic and flammable. The working area must be declared a 'no-smoking' zone.

## 7.11 The manipulation and fabrication of sheet plastic

### Heat bending

Simple, straight bends in thermoplastic materials follow the techniques used for sheet metal working, the only difference being that the plastic material needs to be heated before bending, and bending must take place whilst the plastic sheet is still hot. For this reason the bending jig must be faced with materials having a low thermal conductivity such as wood or Tufnol.

Strip heaters may be used to ensure that heating is localised along the line of the bend. This makes the plastic sheet easier to handle. Rapid cooling is required immediately after bending is complete to avoid loss of shape and degradation of the plastic. Thick sheet should be heated on both sides prior to bending because of the low thermal conductivity of plastic materials.

Other heat bending techniques such as vacuum forming, blow forming and pressing are outlined in Fig. 7.31. In all these examples the thermoplastic sheet is preheated before forming.

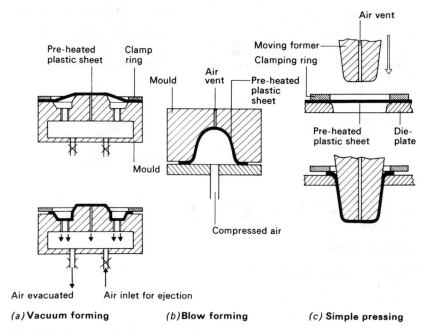

(a) **Vacuum forming**  (b) **Blow forming**  (c) **Simple pressing**

**Fig. 7.31** Forming plastic sheet materials

## Heat welding

Heat welding can only be used to join thermoplastic materials since only these plastic materials soften upon heating. The temperature of a gas welding torch is much too high for plastic welding and would destroy the material being joined. The low thermal conductivity and softening temperatures of thermoplastic materials necessitates the use of a low welding temperature so that the heat can penetrate into the body of the plastic before the surface degrades.

Heat is normally applied to the joint by a welding 'gun'. Air or nitrogen gas is heated in the 'gun' and directed as a jet of hot gas into the weld zone. The easiest plastics to weld are polyvinyl chloride (PVC) and polyethylene (PE) as they have a wide softening range. The basic technique is to apply a jet of heated air or nitrogen into the joint so that the edges of the parent plastic sheet are softened. Filler material, in the form of a rod of the same material as that being welded, is added into the joint in much the same way as when welding metals, except that the joint edges and filler rod are softened but not melted. Some degradation inevitably occurs, so the strength of the joint is slightly below that of the surrounding material.

Figure 7.32 shows examples of edge preparation for a range of joints

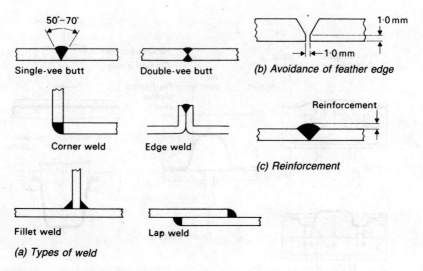

*(a) Types of weld*

50°–70°

Single-vee butt

Double-vee butt

*(b) Avoidance of feather edge*

1·0 mm

1·0 mm

Corner weld

Edge weld

Reinforcement

*(c) Reinforcement*

Fillet weld

Lap weld

**Fig. 7.32** Edge preparation

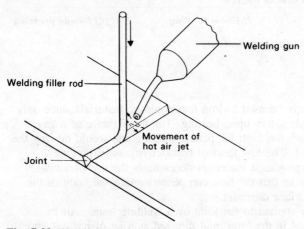

Welding gun

Welding filler rod

Movement of hot air jet

Joint

**Fig. 7.33** Welding plastics

in thermoplastic materials. A small root gap should be provided, no feather edges should be left, and the weld bead (reinforcement) should not be removed as it can increase the joint strength by up to 20 per cent. The technique of plastic welding is shown in Fig. 7.33.

## Solvent welding

Again, this process can only be applied to thermoplastic materials since, once cured, thermosets cannot be softened by solvents. When solvent welding, the edges or surfaces being joined, are softened by a suitable solvent 'cement' instead of by heat. The surfaces are pressed together after application of the solvent until evaporation is complete. The solvent has to be chosen to suit the material being joined. Often the solvent contains a small quantity of the parent material already dissolved in it to give the 'cement' gap-filling properties. To ensure rapid evaporation volatile solvents are required. Many of these solvents give off flammable and toxic fumes and great care is required in their use.

# 8 Heat treatment processes

## 8.1 Heat treatment

Heat treatment processes are used to modify the properties of materials by controlled heating and cooling cycles. The process chosen depends upon the material specification and the properties required. The temperature to which the material is heated depends upon certain *critical temperatures* at which chemical and physical changes take place within the material in the solid condition, and also the processing (e.g. cold-rolling) the material has received before heat treatment.

## 8.2 Recrystallisation

During the cold-working processes described earlier in this book, the grain of the metal becomes distorted. This distortion of the grain results in the metal becoming *work-hardened* and lacking in ductility. To prevent the metal cracking, its grain structure and ductility has to be wholly or partially restored. Internal stresses exist within the distorted crystals and, if the temperature of the metal is raised sufficiently, 'seed' crystals will form at the grain boundaries at points of high internal stress. The minimum temperature at which this occurs is called the *temperature of recrystallisation*. The more severe the cold-working, the greater will be the internal stress in the metal and the lower will be the temperature at which recrystallisation commences.

## 8.3 Annealing (plain carbon steels)

All annealing processes associated with plain carbon steels are concerned
with rendering the steel soft and ductile so that it can be cold-worked or
machined easily. Annealing is achieved by heating the steel to the
appropriate temperature for its carbon content and previous processing, as
shown in Fig. 8.1(*a*), and cooling it very slowly. This slow cooling is
usually achieved by turning off the furnace and allowing the furnace and
the work to cool down together. The annealing temperatures shown in

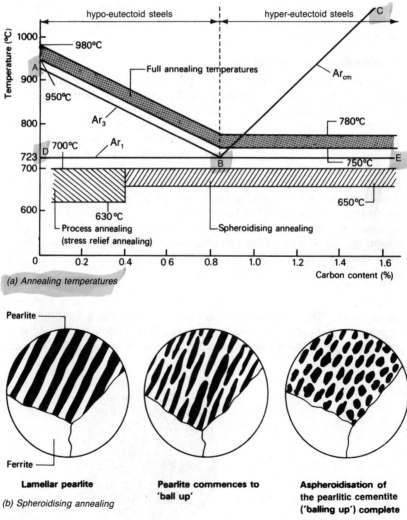

(a) Annealing temperatures

(b) Spheroidising annealing

**Fig. 8.1**  Annealing

Fig. 8.1 are related to the upper and lower critical temperatures of the iron-carbon phase equilibrium diagram as indicated by the lines ABC and DBE. (See *Engineering Materials, volume 1.*) There are three basic annealing processes applicable to plain carbon steels.

## Stress-relief annealing

This is also know as *sub-critical annealing, process annealing* and *inter-stage annealing*. The process is carried out at sub-critical temperatures as shown in Fig. 8.1(*a*). It only applies to the lower carbon content steels which can be cold-worked. This is because stress-relief annealing is a recrystallisation process and it depends upon the severity of the cold-working before annealing to trigger the recrystallisation process at subcritical temperatures.

## Spheroidising annealing

When steels containing more than 0.5 per cent carbon are heated to just below critical temperature, as shown in Fig. 8.1(*a*), the iron-carbide in the grain of the metal tends to 'ball up'. This is referred to as *aspheroidisation* and is shown in Fig. 8.1(*b*). No chemical changes occur in the steel; it is simply a surface tension effect. This process is usually applied to previously quench-hardened steels (see section 8.5) which already have a fine grain structure. This results in fine globules of iron-carbide (cementite) after aspheroidisation. After treatment the steel can be drawn and it will also machine freely to a good surface finish. Furthermore, steel which has been subjected to spheroidising annealing will quench-harden more uniformly and with less chance of cracking and distortion. As with any other annealing process, heating is followed by slow cooling.

## Full annealing

Steel which has been cast or forged will have cooled from very high temperatures. This leads to a coarse grain structure with a mesh-like appearance and poor mechanical properties. This mesh-like structure is referred to as a *Widmanstätten structure*, as shown in Fig. 8.2. To render

**Fig. 8.2** Widmanstätten structure

the steel usable, it has to be reheated to approximately 50°C above the upper critical temperature for hypo-eutectoid steels, and to approximately 50°C above the lower critical temperature for hyper-eutectoid steels. Again slow cooling is required after heating.

## 8.4 Normalising (plain carbon steels)

Annealing processes, and particularly full annealing, are intended not only to soften the steel but to give it maximum ductility for subsequent flow forming operations. This can lead to a poor surface finish as the metal tends to tear when machined. The normalising temperatures for steels are shown in Fig. 8.3. In the normalising process, cooling is much quicker than for annealing, resulting in a finer grain structure. This improves the machining properties of the steel at the expense of ductility. It is usual to remove the work from the furnace after heating and allowing it to cool down in freely circulating air, but away from draughts. Normalising is frequently carried out after rough machining large forgings and castings to remove residual stresses before finish machining. This avoids subsequent distortion of the finished work.

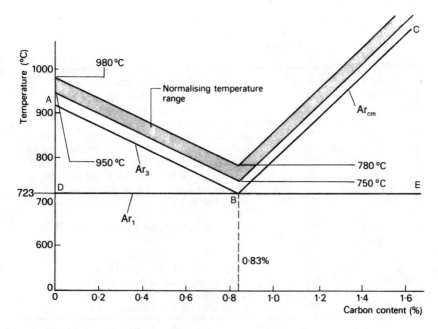

**Fig. 8.3** Normalising temperatures for plain carbon steels

## 8.5 Hardening (plain carbon steels)

If components made from plain carbon steels with a carbon content greater than 0.5 per cent are heated to the same temperature as for full annealing (Fig. 8.1) but, instead of being cooled slowly, they are quenched (cooled quickly) in water or oil, they will become hard and brittle. To reduce the brittleness the components have to be *tempered*. This involves reheating to the temperatures listed in Table 8.1 and again quenching. Although very much less brittle after tempering, there is some slight loss of hardness.

For a steel to quench harden, it has to be cooled more rapidly than its *critical cooling rate*. In a thick component, heat will be trapped in the centre of the component which will cool more slowly than the outer layers in contact with the quenching medium. In practice the centre of the component may not achieve its critical cooling rate. This leads to a variation in hardness across the section of the component as shown in Fig. 8.4. This variation of hardness is referred to as *mass effect*. Plain carbon steels have a high critical cooling rate, so thick sections cannot be fully hardened throughout. However, a 3 per cent nickel steel containing only 0.3 per cent carbon will harden uniformally across its section because it has a relatively low critical cooling rate. This latter steel is

**Table 8.1** Tempering temperatures

| Colour* | Equivalent temperature (°C) | Application |
|---|---|---|
| Very light straw | 220 | Scrapers; lathe tools for brass |
| Light straw | 225 | Turning tools; steel-engraving tools |
| Pale straw | 230 | Hammer faces; light lathe tools |
| Straw | 235 | Razors; paper cutters; steel plane blades |
| Dark straw | 240 | Milling cutters; drills; wood-engraving tools |
| Dark yellow | 245 | Boring cutters; reamers; steel-cuttting chisels |
| Very dark yellow | 250 | Taps; screw-cutting dies; rock drills |
| Yellow-brown | 255 | Chasers; penknives; hardwood-cutting tools |
| Yellowish brown | 260 | Punches and dies; shear blades; snaps |
| Reddish brown | 265 | Wood-boring tools; stone-cutting tools |
| Brown-purple | 270 | Twist drills |
| Light purple | 275 | Axes; hot setts; surgical instruments |
| Full purple | 280 | Cold chisels and setts |
| Dark purple | 285 | Cold chisels for cast iron |
| Very dark purple | 290 | Cold chisels for iron; needles |
| Full blue | 295 | Circular and band saws for metals; screwdrivers |
| Dark blue | 300 | Spiral springs; wood saws |

*Appearance of the oxide film that forms on a polished surface of the material as it is heated

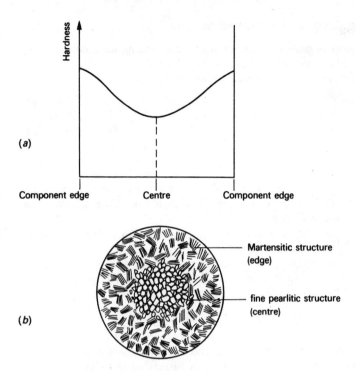

**Fig. 8.4** Mass effect (hardenability)

said to have good *hardenability*. Thus hardenability can be defined as the ease with which hardness is attained throughout the mass of the metal.

Lack of uniformity of structure and hardness in steels with a poor hardenability can seriously affect their mechanical properties. For this reason it is necessary to specify a maximum diameter or *ruling section* for which the stated mechanical properties can be achieved under normal heat treatment conditions. One reason for adding alloying elements such as nickel and chromium to steels is to reduce the mass effect and to increase the ruling section for which the required properties can be achieved.

## 8.6 Case hardening (plain carbon steels)

Sometimes components require a hard, wear-resistant case and a strong tough core. These composite properties are achieved by case hardening. The component is made from a steel which is easily processed and which will provide the properties required in the core. The case hardening process is as follows.

## Carburising

The component is heated in contact with a carburising medium so that it will absorb additional carbon into its outer layers. Various carbonaceous materials are used in the carburising process.

(a) *Solid media* such as bone charcoal or charred leather, together with energisers such as sodium and barium carbonates. The carbonates make up to 40 per cent of the total composition. The components to be carburised are packed into fabricated steel or cast iron boxes along with the solid carburising media which is in granular form. An airtight lid is sealed in place with fire clay and the boxes are heated to between 900°C and 950°C for up to five hours, depending upon the depth of case required. This should not exceed 2 mm as a thicker case will tend to flake off.

(b) *Fused salts* such as sodium cyanide together with sodium carbonate and varying amounts of sodium and barium chloride. Since sodium cyanide is a deadly poison and since it represents from 20 per cent to 50 per cent of the furnace content, stringent safety precautions must be taken in its use. The components are suspended in the fused salts in a gas or electrically heated salt bath furnace (see section 8.11). Large components are suspended individually from a bar lying across the pot or crucible. Copper wire must not be used as it will be dissolved by the cyanide and the component would drop to the bottom of the pot. Small work is suspended in baskets made from a non-reactive, heat resistant metal such as iconel. The advantages of using fused salts are:

   (i)  loading is quicker, easier and cheaper;

   (ii)  heating and carburisation are more uniform with less chance of distortion;

   (iii)  the components can be hardened by quenching in water straight out of the cyanide without further heat treatment. The cyanide 'cracks' off the surface of the components leaving them clean.

(c) *Gaseous media* are being used more frequently. These are based on natural gas (methane) which is a hydrocarbon gas. This gas is usually enriched by the vapours given off by heated oil which has been 'cracked' by heating it in the presence of a catalyst such as hot platinum. Gas carburising is carried out in both batch type and continuous furnaces. The components are heated up to 900°C to 950°C in an atmosphere of enriched natural gas. These gases are cleaned of moisture and carbon dioxide before being allowed into the furnace to avoid corrosion of the work. Since the gases are highly flammable, great care must be taken to avoid the build up of an explosive mixture of gas and air. Gas carburising is very clean and is used for the mass production of cases up to 1 mm deep.

## Heat treatment

The carburising process does not harden the steel, it merely adds carbon to the outer layers of the metal and leaves it in a fully annealed condition with a coarse grain structure. Therefore additional heat treatment is required to harden the case and refine the grain of the case and the core. The temperatures associated with this additional heat treatment are shown in Fig. 8.5. Before carburising, the steel — from which the components being case-hardened were made — had a uniform carbon content of 0.1 per cent. After carburising, the diffusion of carbon through the component is not constant, the carbon content of the case being about 1.0 per cent and the carbon content of the core being about 0.3 per cent.

(a) *Refining the core.* The metal is heated to a temperature of approximately 870°C which is just above the upper critical temperature for a 0.3 per cent steel, temperature [1] in Fig. 8.5. Quenching the carburised steel from this temperature will result in a fine grain, and tough core. At 0.3 per cent the carbon content of the core is too low to harden.

(b) *Hardening and refining the case.* The core-refining temperature is sufficiently high to cause grain growth in the case which has a carbon content of 1.0 per cent. Therefore the component is reheated to the hardening temperature for the case which is approximately 760°C, temperature [2] in Fig. 8.5. This temperature is too low to

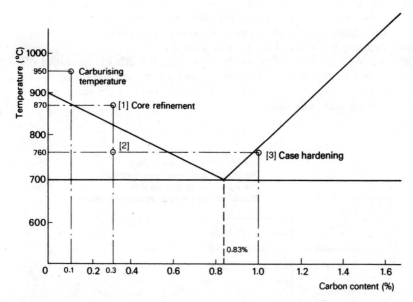

**Fig. 8.5** Case-hardening temperatures

cause grain growth in the core provided that the steel is heated quickly through the 650°C to 760°C range and is not soaked at the hardening temperature. The component will now have a hard, fine-grain case and a tough, fine-grain core.

(c) *Tempering*. Tempering at 200°C is advisable to relieve any quenching stresses which may be present.

The above procedure is used to give ideal results; however, in the interests of the speed and economy necessary under commercial conditions, the process is often simplified to a single heating and quenching from temperature [1] in Fig. 8.5. This can be satisfactory where the work is lightly stressed or where alloy steels are used which harden from lower temperatures and have less critical grain growth characteristics.

## 8.7 Localised case hardening (plain carbon steels)

It is not always desirable to case harden a component all over. For example, it is undesirable to case harden screw threads. Not only would they be extremely brittle, but any distortion occurring during heat treatment could only be corrected by expensive thread grinding processes. Various means are available for avoiding the local infusion of carbon during the carburising process. For example:

(a) heavily copper plating those areas to be left soft. This is suitable for pack-carburising and gas-carburising, but cannot be used with salt-bath carburising as the cyanide dissolves the copper;

(b) encasing the areas to be left soft with fire-clay;

(c) leaving surplus metal on as shown in Fig. 8.6. This is machined off between carburising and hardening and the infused carbon is removed with the swarf. Although expensive, it is the surest way of leaving local soft areas.

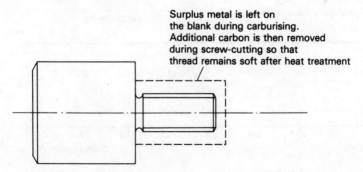

Surplus metal is left on
the blank during carburising.
Additional carbon is then removed
during screw-cutting so that
thread remains soft after heat treatment

**Fig. 8.6** Localised case-hardening

Localised case-hardening can also be achieved in medium and high carbon steels and some cast irons by rapid local heating and quenching. Figure 8.7(a) shows the principle of flame hardening (the Shorter process). A carriage moves over the component so that the surface is rapidly heated by an oxy-acetylene flame to the hardening temperature. The same carriage carries the water quenching spray. Thus the surface of

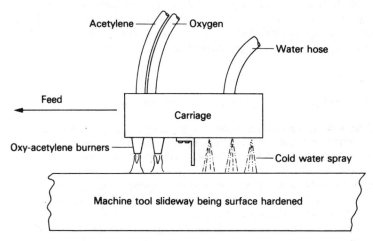

(a) Flame hardening (Shorter process)

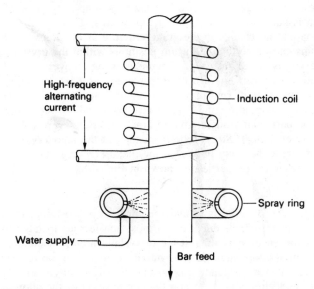

(b) Induction hardening

**Fig. 8.7** Surface hardening

the workpiece is heated and quenched before the core can rise to the hardening temperature. This process is widely used for the surface hardening of machine tool slideways. Figure 8.7(*b*) shows how the same effect can be produced by electromagnetic induction. The higher the frequency of the alternating current used, the shallower will be the case. This is because the higher the frequency, the nearer to the surface of the component will be the induced eddy currents which cause the heating. The heating coil is often made of tube which is perforated with fine spray holes so that it can be used for both heating and quenching. The coil can itself be formed to suit the contour of the component being hardened and this process is often used for the surface hardening of gear teeth.

## 8.8 Annealing (non-ferrous metals and alloys)

Unalloyed, non-ferrous metals such as pure copper and pure aluminium, together with many non-ferrous alloys such as the brasses and tin-bronzes, can only be hardened by severe cold-working. That is, they can only be *work-hardened*, and they do not respond to quench hardening heat treatment processes. However, they do respond to annealing processes and this is the only way in which they can be stress-relieved and softened after cold-working.

### Recovery

The minimum treatment for a cold-worked metal is simple stress relief. This treatment is performed at quite low temperatures. There is no recrystallisation and no change in the grain structure as a whole, but the individual atoms can move to equilibrium positions within the crystal lattice. This effect is called *recovery*. Treatment at the recovery temperature does not adversely affect the increased hardness and strength resulting from cold-working and may even enhance these properties. High ductility brass alloy consisting of 70 per cent copper and 30 per cent zinc was found to be particularly susceptible to cracking after severe cold-working (*season cracking*). Stress-relief annealing at the recovery temperature of 200°C not only prevented the metal cracking but improved its mechanical properties as shown in Fig. 8.8.

### Annealing

Where a cold-worked material is to undergo further cold-forming, it must first be annealed to restore its ductility. In most non-ferrous metals and alloys this is achieved by annealing at the recrystallisation temperature. The recrystallisation temperature is substantially higher than the recovery temperature and will vary depending upon the severity of any cold-working before annealing and also upon the composition of the alloy. Alloys tend to have a higher recrystallisation temperature than pure metals. Unlike ferrous metals, non-ferrous metals and alloys can be

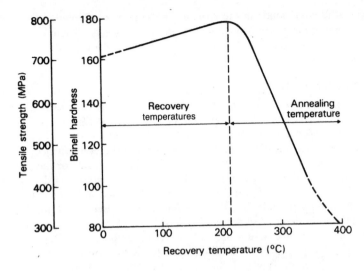

**Fig. 8.8** The effect of heat treatment on cold-worked 70/30 brass

quenched after recovery treatment or annealing since they do not quench harden. This speeds up the process, prevents excessive grain growth and improves the surface finish, since the rapid contraction of the metal strips any oxide film (scale) from the surface.

Recrystallisation annealing is equally applicable to low-carbon steels and was described as sub-critical annealing in section 8.3. In the case of steels, the cooling has to be very slow. The term 'sub-critical annealing', as used for low carbon steels, is not appropriate to non-ferrous metals and alloys since their heat treatment temperatures are not directly related to the critical temperatures of their phase equilibrium diagrams. The more common terms associated with non-ferrous metal and alloys are *process annealing* and *inter-stage annealing*. These names are derived from the fact that the annealing is carried out after cold-working processes, or between the stages of cold-working processes.

## 8.9 Solution and precipitation treatment

These heat treatment processes apply to a number of non-ferrous alloys, but especially to those aluminium alloys containing copper.

### Solution treatment

Although this is a process by which the alloy is softened and made more ductile ready for cold-working, it is not a recrystallisation process. The alloy is raised to a temperature of 500°C and quenched in water. The hard intermetallic compounds in the structure become a *solid solution* of copper in aluminium and it is from this that the process gets its name. All solid solutions tend to be soft and ductile and suitable for cold-working.

## Precipitation treatment

The solid solution produced by solution treatment is a *supersaturated* solution and as such is unstable at room temperature. On standing, particles of the copper-aluminium intermetallic compound $CuAl_2$ precipitate out and become finely dispersed throughout the component. These hard particles interfere with the 'slip-planes' in the grains of the metal and reduce the ability of the metal to deform, rendering it harder and more brittle. In this condition it cannot be cold-worked as it tends to crack. This hardening process is called *precipitation age hardening* and is a form of particle hardening. In some alloys, such as *Duralumin*, it is so pronounced that hardening occurs naturally at room temperature. This is referred to as *natural ageing*. Such alloys need to be solution treated . immediately before processing and kept under cool (refrigerated) conditions to delay the onset of precipitation. The process of precipitation can be accelerated by reheating the solution treated alloy in a furnace for several hours at 165°C. This is known as *artificial ageing*.

## 8.10 Requirements of heat treatment furnaces

The successful heat treatment of metals depends upon carefully controlled heating and cooling process. Therefore the requirements of a heat-treatment furnace are as follows.

## Uniform heating of the charge

The components to be heat treated may be placed into the furnace singly, or in batches, or passed through the furnace on some form of conveyor. Whatever the means of loading the furnace, these components are referred to as the *charge*. Uniform heating of the charge is necessary to prevent cracking and distortion of the component due to unequal expansion. Uniform heating is also necessary to ensure that the chemical and physical changes which occur in the metal during heat treatment processes are uniformly distributed through the charge.

## Accurate temperature control

Since the temperatures involved in heat treatment processes are critical, not only must heat treatment furnaces be capable of operating over a wide range of temperatures, they must be easily and accurately adjustable to the required temperature.

## Temperature stability

Not only is it essential for the temperature to be accurately adjustable but, once set, the furnace must remain at the required temperature. This can be achieved by ensuring that the mass of the heated furnace lining (refractory) is very much greater than the mass of the charge. Further, the furnace should have some form of automatic temperature control which measures the temperature of the furnace and controls the level of energy input.

## Atmosphere control

If the charge is heated in the presence of air the surface of the metal becomes heavily oxidised. The oxide film can become extremely thick and is then referred to as *scale*. Further, steels, may have the carbon content of their surface layers reduced by oxidation of the carbon. This is called *decarburisation*. Both oxidation and decarburisation can be avoided by controlling the atmosphere of the furnace, that is, the air is displaced in the furnace chamber by an inert gas (a gas which does not react with the metal). Alternatively the charge may be immersed in molten salts heated to the process temperature. Such salts may be chemically inert or they may react with the surface of the work in a controlled manner as in case-hardening processes.

The simplest form of atmosphere control is where the products of combustion of the burnt fuel replace the air in the furnace chamber. However this is not wholly satisfactory as contamination can occur from the sulphur in the fuel, the residual nitrogen from the combustion air, any residual oxygen present, and water vapour formed when the hydrogen content of the fuel is burned. Carbon dioxide present can react with the water vapour to form an acid which can corrode the work. The alternative, but more expensive solution, is to keep the products of combustion out of the furnace chamber and replace the air in the chamber with a mixture of inert and carefully controlled gases, specially generated for atmosphere control.

## Economical use of fuel

Fuel costs are the most important element in the operating costs of a furnace. Energy costs are continually rising over the long term and the economical use of fuel is essential both commercially and ecologically. To this end it is better to run a furnace continually on a shift basis than to repeatedly heat it up and cool it down. The energy required to keep heating a furnace up from the cold is much greater than that required to keep it operating on a continuous shift basis. Further, the repeated expansion and contraction of the furnace lining, when used intermittently, leads to cracking and early failure of the lining. Thus it is more economical for small- and medium-sized workshops to contract their heat treatment out to specialist firms, who can run their furnaces continuously, than to carry out their own heat treatment on an occasional, jobbing, basis.

**Low maintenance costs**

In order to keep maintenance to a minimum and preserve the refractory lining as long as possible, the furnace should not be used intermittently, nor should it be used beyond its maximum operating temperature even for a short time. Operating at excessively high temperatures also rapidly reduces the life of the heating elements in electric muffle furnaces and is wasteful of energy.

## 8.11 Types of heat treatment furnaces

### Semi-muffle furnace

The semi-muffle furnace shown in Fig. 8.9 is made in a variety of sizes, from small bench-top for tool-room and laboratory furnaces to very large furnaces for the batch treatment of large components. They may be gas or oil fired and the flame does not play onto the charge directly, but passes under the hearth to provide bottom heat. Bottom heat is provided by conduction and radiation from the hearth, whilst supplementary heating is provided by the circulation of flue gases and by radiation from

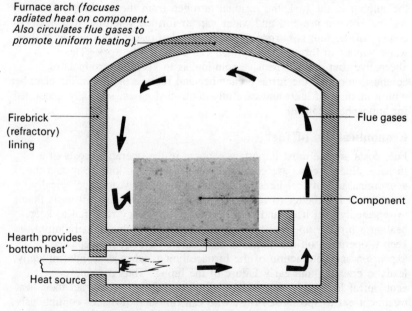

Furnace arch *(focuses radiated heat on component. Also circulates flue gases to promote uniform heating)*

Firebrick (refractory) lining

Flue gases

Component

Hearth provides 'bottom heat'

Heat source

**Fig. 8.9** Gas-heated semi-muffle furnace

the furnace crown. The combustion air is carefully controlled so that no excess oxygen is present in the flue gasses to cause oxidation. The flue gases are finally drawn off each side of the furnace door so that air entering at this point is immediately swept up the flue. Full atmosphere control is not possible with this type of furnace.

## Gas-heated muffle furnace

Figure 8.10 shows a gas-heated muffle furnace. The charge is completely separated from the combustion chamber by an inner chamber or 'muffle'. Thus the conditions for maximum economy of combustion can exist in the combustion chamber, whilst any desired atmosphere can be introduced into the muffle chamber.

## Electric resistance muffle furnace

Figure 8.11(a) shows a typical electric resistance muffle furnace. Since the electric resistance heating elements operate independently of the atmosphere in which they are placed, they may be installed directly into the muffle chamber. Figure 8.11(b) shows the construction of a typical electric-resistance heating element. This type of furnace is available in a wide range of sizes. Full atmosphere control can be provided and the use

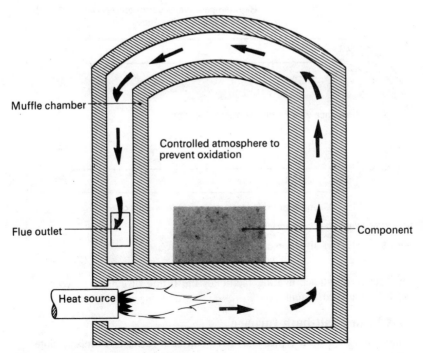

**Fig. 8.10** Gas-heated muffle furnace

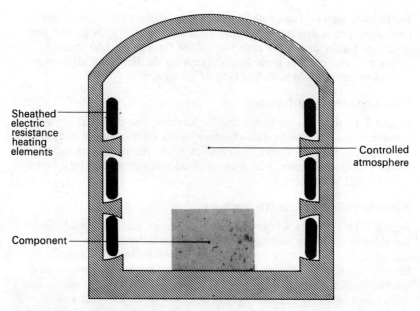

Sheathed electric resistance heating elements

Controlled atmosphere

Component

*(a) The electric resistance muffle furnace*

High-temperature & corrosion-resistant sheath — Inconel alloy tube

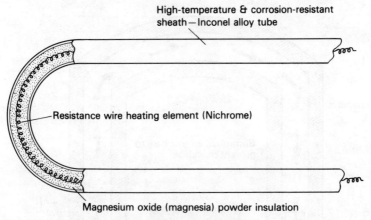

Resistance wire heating element (Nichrome)

Magnesium oxide (magnesia) powder insulation

*(b) Electric furnace heating element*

**Fig. 8.11** Electrically-heated muffle furnace

of electric resistance heating facilitates the fitting of automatic control systems and instrumentation.

## Gas-heated salt-bath furnace

Figure 8.12 shows a typical gas-fired salt-bath furnace. Points to note are:

295

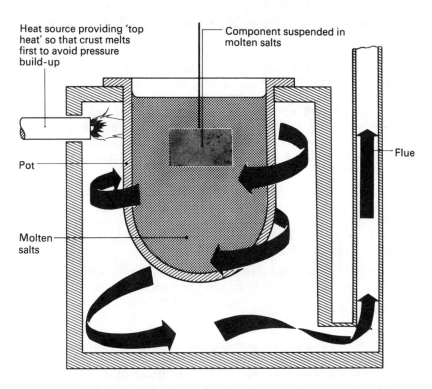

Heat source providing 'top heat' so that crust melts first to avoid pressure build-up

Component suspended in molten salts

Flue

Pot

Molten salts

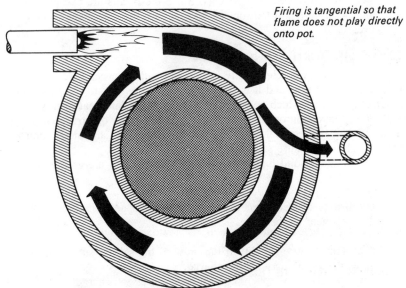

Firing is tangential so that flame does not play directly onto pot.

**Fig. 8.12** Gas-heated salt bath furnace

(a) *Tangential firing* so that the flame does not play directly onto the pot.

(b) *Top heat.* In the interests of safety, the salts must be melted from the top downwards. If heated from the bottom, the expanding salts could erupt red hot through the solid crust like a miniature volcano creating a very dangerous situation.

(c) *Pre-heating.* All work must be pre-heated to ensure that it is thoroughly dry. Failure to do this can result in an explosion which could throw the molten salts out of the pot. Suitable protective clothing including a face visor must be worn when using salt-bath furnaces.

The salts used are dependent upon the process being carried out, and all reputable manufacturers provide advice on the selection of suitable salts for various applications. It is usual to use an 'economiser' in the form of mica flakes floating on the surface of the salts to prevent loss through oxidation and fuming.

(a) *Nitrate-based salts* are used for low temperature applications such as tempering and for the solution and precipitation treatment of light alloys. Great care must be taken in their use for, if overheated, they can cause a serious explosion.

(b) *Chloride-based salts* are suitable for all applications above about 750°C, for example the annealing, normalising, and quench hardening of plain carbon and alloy steels.

(c) *Cyanide-based salts* are used for case-hardening small, low-carbon steel and alloy steel components. Since these salts are exceptionally and possibly fatally poisonous, special care must be taken in their use.

## Electrically heated salt-bath furnace

Figure 8.13 shows an electrically heated salt-bath furnace. Electrodes are immersed in the salts and it is the resistance of the salts to the passage of an electric current which converts electrical energy into heat energy. Since this conversion occurs within the salts, this type of furnace has a high efficiency. Electrical heating is readily adapted to automatic control where high temperature stability is required.

The advantages and limitations of salt-bath furnaces are as follows:

*Advantages*

(a) Uniformity of heating as the charge is enveloped in molten salt at the treatment temperature.

(b) Accurate temperature control.

(c) High temperature stability if the mass of the salts is substantially greater than the mass of the charge.

(d) No expensive atmosphere control required as the charge is enveloped in the molten salt.

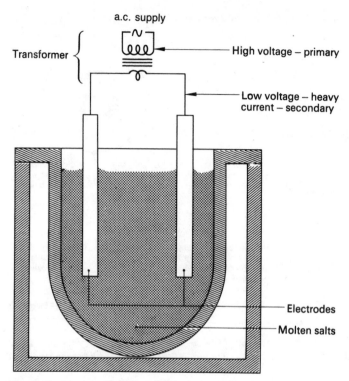

**Fig. 8.13** Electrically heated salt bath furnace

*Limitations*

(a) Only economical in fuel utilisation if run on a continuous basis.
(b) Regular maintenance required.
(c) Salt-baths are potentially dangerous in operation and in the salts used. A highly trained workforce is required.

## 8.12 Temperature measurement

### Thermocouple pyrometer

This is the most widely used temperature measuring device and is also used as the basis for automatic control systems. Figure 8.14(a) shows the principle of the thermocouple pyrometer. If the junction of two dissimilar metal wires — such as iron and copper — is heated, an electrical potential will appear across the ends of the wires dependent upon the temperature differential between the junction and the remote ends of the wires, and also upon the composition of the wires. If the wires forming

298

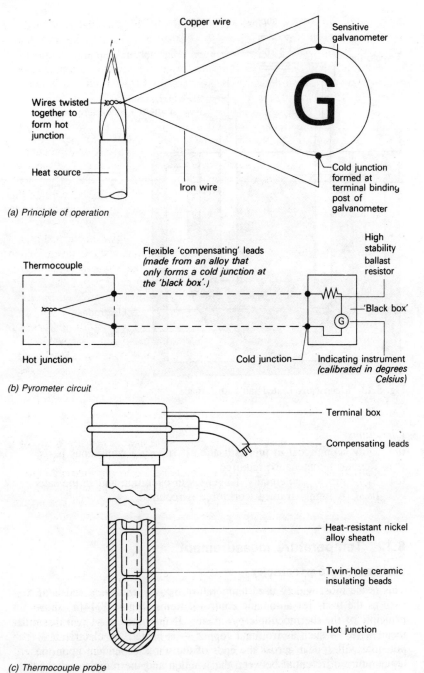

(a) Principle of operation

Copper wire

Sensitive galvanometer

Wires twisted together to form hot junction

Heat source

Iron wire

Cold junction formed at terminal binding post of galvanometer

(b) Pyrometer circuit

Thermocouple

Flexible 'compensating' leads
(made from an alloy that only forms a cold junction at the 'black box'.)

High stability ballast resistor

Hot junction

Cold junction

'Black box'

Indicating instrument
(calibrated in degrees Celsius)

(c) Thermocouple probe

Terminal box

Compensating leads

Heat-resistant nickel alloy sheath

Twin-hole ceramic insulating beads

Hot junction

**Fig. 8.14** The thermocouple pyrometer

the junction are part of a closed electric circuit, the potential generated will cause a small current to flow. In a circuit of constant resistance this current will, in turn, be dependent upon the magnitude of the potential. In the circuit shown in Fig. 8.14(a) the magnitude of the current will be indicated by the galvanometer. The connections between the dissimilar wires and the galvanometer form the cold junction.

Figure 8.14(b) shows the circuit for a practical thermocouple pyrometer. The component parts of the circuit are:

(a) The *thermocouple probe* (hot junction). This consists of a junction of two wires of dissimilar metals contained within a tube of refractory metal or of porcelain to protect the wires from chemical or physical damage. Porcelain beads are threaded over the dissimilar wire of the junction to insulate them and to locate them within the sheath, as shown in Fig. 8.14(c).

(b) The *indicating instrument*. This is a sensitive milliammeter calibrated in degrees of temperature so that direct readings can be taken. When the furnace is cold, this instrument should read ambient temperature or there will be a zero error. Since this instrument forms the cold junction, it should be mounted in a cool position unaffected by the heat of the furnace.

(c) The *ballast or 'swamp' resistor*. This is contained within the case of the indicating instrument. It is made from manganin wire whose resistance is unaffected by temperature change. The ohmic value of this resistor is made very large compared with the resistance of the instrument and with the external circuit. Thus it ensures accurate readings since it 'swamps' any variation of ohmic value in the rest of the circuit due to changes in temperature.

(d) The *compensating leads*. These are used to connect the thermocouple probe to the indicating instrument. They are made of a special alloy so that they form a cold junction at the indicating instrument but have no effect when connected to the thermocouple probe terminals. To avoid changes in calibration, the compensating leads must not be changed in length, nor must alternative conductors be used. The thermocouple, compensating leads and the indicating instrument must always be kept together as a set.

## Radiation pyrometer

The thermocouple pyrometer described above measures the temperature of the furnace atmosphere. This is not necessarily the temperature of the charge. Figure 8.15 shows a typical radiation pyrometer. This can be aimed at the furnace charge using the telescopic sight and it measures the temperature of the charge rather than the temperature of the furnace. The principle of this instrument is identical with the thermocouple pyrometer previously described. However, in the radiation pyrometer the radiant heat from the heated body is focused onto the hot junction by a parabolic mirror. This type of pyrometer is used in the following circumstances:

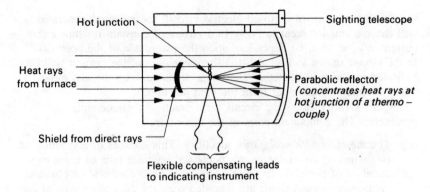

**Fig. 8.15** The radiation pyrometer

(a) where the temperature of the charge needs to be measured rather than the temperature of the furnace atmosphere;
(b) where the temperature of the furnace is so high that the normal thermocouple probe would be damaged;
(c) where the heated body is inaccessible.

## 8.13 Quenching media

The choice of quenching media depends upon the material being quenched and the rate of cooling which must be achieved. When quench hardening steels, the slowest possible rate of cooling which exceeds the critical cooling rate should be used to avoid cracking and distortion.

### Water

This is widely used as it is cheap, readily available, and has a high specific heat capacity. When heated it gives off no noxious fumes and is non-flammable. It can be used for quenching non-ferrous metals, case-hardening plain carbon steels, and quench hardening medium carbon steels where it exceeds the critical cooling rate.

### Quenching oil

This is a specially formulated oil. Lubricating and cutting oils must not be used. The cooling rate with oil is much lower and will only impart toughness to medium carbon steels. However it will quench harden high-carbon steels and is widely used for quenching alloy steels as the critical cooling rate for these latter steels is very much lower than for plain carbon steels. Quenching in oil is less likely to cause cracking as the cooling rate is lower than for water.

## Air blast

This can be used for quench hardening small components made from steels containing a very high percentage of alloying elements, for example, some high-speed steels.

## 8.14 The quenching bath

Where water or oil baths are used, the volume of the quenching bath should be sufficient to avoid undue increase in temperature when the heated work is immersed in it. Where the bath is used continuously, the quenching media should be circulated through a cooling system. The work should be constantly agitated in the bath to prevent a steam or oil vapour blanket forming around the work which would insulate it from the quenching medium. There should be a fume hood and extractor over the bath to draw off steam — in the case of water — and fumes in the case of oil. Where oil is used as the quenching media, an air-tight lid should be available so that the quenching bath can be sealed off instantly in the event of the oil overheating and igniting.

# 9 Finishing processes

## 9.1 Preparatory treatments (chemical)

The satisfactory application of finishing processes is in all instances dependent upon the careful preparation of the surface of the base material. Most component surfaces are contaminated with one or more of the following:

(*a*) oxide films resulting from reaction of the base material with atmospheric oxygen and moisture (e.g. the rusting of steel);

(*b*) metal salt deposits such as sulphates and carbonates of the base material as the result of acid rain attack (e.g. the *patina* on copper);

(*c*) soils in the form of grease, dust and dirt together with swarf and grinding wheel and polishing dross from machining and finishing processes;

(*d*) previous protective films (e.g. paint films which need to be stripped to provide a sound base for replacement).

Any of these contaminants which are present must be removed before finishing treatments are carried out.

### Acid pickling

Unless steels have been very thoroughly protected, rust will usually be present. Unfortunately rust will continue to spread under any decorative or protective coating and will eventually destroy the base metal. It will also lift the protective coating forming bubbles under the protective coating. This bubbling effect is often the first sign of 'body-rot' in a motor vehicle. Acid pickling in hydrochloric or sulphuric acid is used to remove rust and scale. The acid cannot distinguish between the oxide and the metal and will often attack the metal in preference to the oxide if the scale is thick. This results in uneven pickling and pitting of the metal surface. *Inhibitor* chemicals are usually added to the acid to prevent any attack on the base metal. Although expensive, the cost of the inhibitor is more than recovered by greatly extending the useful life of the acid. Untreated acid has to discarded when between 6 per cent and 10 per cent iron is present. It is essential to wash and neutralise the pickled metal before storage and treat it with a corrosion inhibitor such as lanolin or oil.

## Degreasing

The presence of greases and oils prevents wetting of the surface to be treated and must be removed before any pre-treatment or finishing processes is applied.

*Solvent degreasing.* Trichlorethylene or perchlorethylene are still widely used in vapour degreasing plants. The solvent is boiled and the vapours are condensed on cooling coils, the condensed liquid cascading down over the suspended components. Oil and grease removal is effective, but inorganic soils are only removed by the washing action of the condensed liquid.

Kerosene (paraffin) will disolve many oils and greases. Nowadays kerosene is blended with oil-soluble surface-active agents and becomes emulsifiable. Such systems have the advantage over vapour degreasing that soils and residues can be rinsed cleanly away from the metal surfaces by the detergent and flushing action of the liquid. Further, there is no toxicity factor to be considered, as is the case with chlorinated hydrocarbons.

*Alkali cleaning* is beneficial where degreasing is to be followed by electro-plating as any residual solvent film will lead to poor adhesion of the plating. Also, alkalis do not have the toxicity and flammability of the cholorinated hydrocarbons and kerosene. Alkali detergents range from washing soda and caustic soda to sophisticated blends of silicates, phosphates, carbonates and surface active agents. Phosphates and silicates are valuable detergents in their own rights, but become even more effective when a surface active agent is added. The surface active agent, (surfactant) performs a dual function: first, lowering the surface tension of the liquids so that they wet and penetrate the soils more efficiently and, second, the enhancement of the emulsification of oils and greases.

Alkali solutions are used at temperatures of about 80°C to 90°C. It is important that the components are adequately rinsed after alkali cleaning to avoid 'carry-over' into the plating baths, where the presence of alkalis would be highly undesirable. Alkali cleaning must not be used with aluminium and zinc based alloys unless a suitably buffered mixture is used, as these metals suffer from alkali attack.

## 9.2   Preparatory treatments (physical)

### Wire brushing

Wire brushing with a rapidly rotating coarse wire brush is used to dislodge loose debris and soils from structural steel work before painting or re-painting. The surface left by brushing provides a key for the first paint coat. Fine wire brushing is also used as a decorative finish on sheet aluminium.

### Shot and vapour blasting

Fine particles are blasted against the metal surface at high velocity using compressed air. This is used to descale structural steel work on site, as well as descaling smaller components under factory conditions. It is also used for cleaning and descaling sand castings. Although more expensive and labour intensive than acid pickling, particle blasting enhances the mechanical properties of materials, whilst acid pickling can detract from the mechanical properties of materials (see section 9.9).

### Flame descaling

This process depends upon the difference in expansion between the scale and the base metal when subjected to local heating. This technique is used for cleaning heavily rusted structural steelwork before maintenance painting. The steel surface is heated with an oxy-fuel gas torch fitted with a specially designed nozzle which gives a broad fan-shaped high intensity flame. The rapid expansion of the scale or rust compared with the relatively cool steel beneath it causes the scale and rust to flake off. Any entrapped moisture turns to steam and assists in the stripping process. For best results the prepared steelwork should be immediately painted with a primer containing a corrosion inhibitor whilst the metal is still warm (45°C).

### Abrasive finishing

This term covers a variety of manual and automatic processes similar to grinding. For rapid surface removal, finely-powdered aluminium oxide (emery) or silicon carbide is used. Unlike grinding, which uses a rigid abrasive wheel, the abrasive particles may be glued directly to a leather polishing wheel called a *stitched basil*, or an abrasive belt may be used as in *linishing* (Fig. 9.1(a)) or *back-stand* grinding (Fig. 9.1(b)). Belts have the advantages of lasting longer and cutting cooler because of the greater area of abrasive.

### Polishing

The manner in which a lustrous polished surface is produced is not fully understood, and there are currently two schools of thought. One is that polishing is an extension of the grinding principle but using very much finer abrasive particles. The other is that polishing produces a very high surface temperature in the metal. This causes the topmost layer of metal

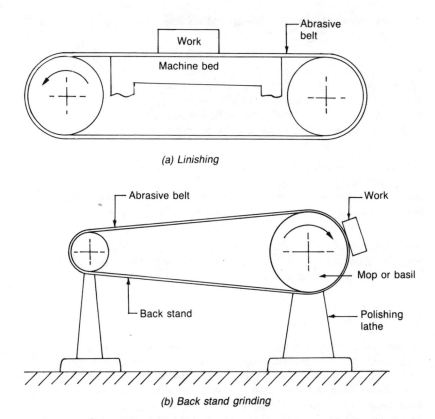

(a) Linishing

(b) Back stand grinding

**Fig. 9.1** Abrasive belt finishing

to melt and to be smeared out smooth by the polishing action to form a *Beilby layer*. Whichever is correct, in practice, polishing mops together with grease-based polishing compounds are used to achieve smooth, glossy polished surfaces with a high lustre. Polishing mops are made from linen, calico, cotton and sisal cloth. They are mounted on the spindles of polishing lathes and polishing takes place on the circumference of the rapidly spinning mops. There are three basic types of mop:

(a) *Loose fold mops* which are soft and flexible. They are used for the final polishing of contoured surfaces and are usually made from discs of calico cloth.

(b) *Stitched mops* are made from discs of cotton cloth and are spirally stitched to secure the discs together to make them more rigid. These mops are used for general and heavy duty manual grease mopping.

(c) *Bias type mops* are used for backstand contact wheels where greater flexibility is required than is possible with stitched leather 'basils' (see above). However, they are mainly used on automatic polishing machines.

*Polishing compounds* are available in bar form for manual application and in liquid form for automatic application. The compound consists of the abrasive particles suspended in a grease base which causes them to adhere to the mop. When the particles become dulled their temperature rises, the grease melts locally, the dulled grains are released and fresh grains are exposed. The abrasive used depends upon the material being polished. For example:

(*a*) Hydrated Silica (Tripoli) is used for non-ferrous metals and thermosetting plastics;

(*b*) Aluminium oxide (flour of emery) is used for ferrous metals;

(*c*) Chromium oxide is used for stainless steel and for the final buffing of chrome plated products.

*Note:* Because plated finishes are very thin, abrasive finishing and polishing must take place before plating. Only the lightest buffing should be necessary after plating to give the final lustre to the work.

## 9.3 Protective coatings

To retard the onset of corrosion and the eventual destruction of metallic components, assemblies and structures, various protective coatings are applied to insulate the base metal from the environment. The various mechanisms by which corrosion can occur are discussed briefly in *Engineering Fundamentals — F level*, and more fully in *Engineering Materials: volumes 1 and 2*. The coatings applied to metals may be protective, decorative or a combination of both. This section deals only with coatings which are protective.

### Galvanising

This is the coating of ferrous metals (usually low-carbon steels) with zinc. This process may be performed on sheet material or on finished goods. There are two processes. The sheet or finished goods may be cleaned, fluxed and dipped into molten zinc (*hot-dip galvanising*) or the zinc coating may be deposited on the base metal electrolytically (*electrolytic galvanising*). The hot dip process provides a thicker coating of zinc and better protection and is also 'gap-filling' and seals the joints of vessels designed to hold liquids. Electrolytic galvanising is not gap-filling, but the thickness of the coating and the amount of zinc used can be more closely controlled. Electrolytic galvanising is widely used as a pretreatment before paint finishing ferrous metal components.

### Sherardising

This, together with *calorising* and *chromising*, are the three *cementation* processes in common use. Sherardising consists of depositing zinc powder onto the surface of the components to be protected by placing the cleaned and dried components into a rotating barrel along with zinc powder at a temperature of about 370°C, which is just below the melting point of zinc. The time taken depends upon the thickness of the coat required and is usually about twelve hours. The zinc bonds to the surface of the ferrous workpiece by diffusion and forms a hard even layer of iron-zinc intermetallic compounds. The slight roughness of the surface provides an excellent key for subsequent painting processes.

## Calorising

This is a similar process to sherardising except that the work is heated in aluminium powder to between 850°C and 1000°C. Calorising is used to protect steel components from high temperature oxidation rather than against ambient temperature atmospheric corrosion. It also provides better protection at higher levels of humidity than sherardising.

## Chromising

This is also similar to the previous process, except that the work is heated in chromium powder, in an atmosphere of hydrogen, to between 1300°C and 1400°C. Because of the high temperatures involved this is an expensive process and is only used where a very high level of protection is required. The high temperatures tend to cause grain growth in the steel which impairs its mechanical properties.

## Chromating

Magnesium alloys rely upon the formation of a coherent oxide film to retard the effects of corrosion. Unfortunately, they do not respond to such processes as anodising (see section 9.4) and an alternative process called *chromating* has to be used. In this process the components made from magnesium alloy are dipped in a solution containing potassium dichromate together with chromic and phosphoric acid to form a hard oxide film on the surface. Unfortunately, this film is far from decorative and is a dark grey or even black. The oxidised surface is usually sealed with a coat of zinc chromate paint followed by a decorative paint of the required colour.

## Phosphating

This is the name given to a number of processes by which the surface of the base metal is chemically converted to complex metal phosphates, oxides and chromates. These processes originally went under the trade names of *Parkerising*, *Bonderising*, *Ganodising*, and *Walterising*. More recently these processes have been standardised under BS 3189. Nowadays, phosphating is virtually standard practice before the application of paint films. Conversion coatings are also used to improve the lubricity of bearings, and as a pretreatment for metals being formed by such processes as wire and tube drawing, deep drawing, and cold forging, where extreme pressure lubrication is required. As well as being applied to ferrous metal components, phosphate conversion processes can also be applied to zinc, zinc alloys, zinc-coated steels, aluminium and aluminium alloys.

## Metal spraying

Metal spraying is used for a variety of purposes. The most important is the coating of ferrous metal structures, which are too large to protect in any other way, with corrosion resistant coatings. Other purposes include building up worn shafts, and depositing surfaces which are wear resistant.

The process consists of spraying molten particles of metal onto a prepared surface. This surface should be free from grease and it should be slightly roughened to provide a key for the coating.

The metal coating is sprayed from a 'gun' into which it is fed in the form of wire or powder. Heat is provided by means of an oxy-fuel gas flame or by an electric-arc or by a plasma-arc inside the gun. The plasma-arc technique is reserved for high melting point metals. Compressed air is used to spray the molten metal onto the work. Some typical metal spraying applications are:

(a) *Zinc*. Used to rust-proof plain-carbon steels. The sprayed zinc coating is slightly porous, so it needs to be sealed by painting. Widely used in marine and structural applications, zinc is the most widely used deposit metal.

(b) *Aluminium*. Used to rust-proof plain carbon steels subjected to moist environments. Aluminium prevents scaling (oxidation) at high temperatures. It is increasingly used to protect car exhaust systems.

(c) *Copper*. Used to coat and to re-coat printing rolls used for high quality colour reproduction. It is also used to provide high electrical conductivity coatings where electroplated deposits are not thick enough to carry the required current. Additionally, copper is used for decorative coatings which provide a high level of corrosion resistance.

(d) *Brass*. Used for corrosion resistant decorative coatings and is cheaper than copper.

(e) *Bronze*. Use to build up bearing surfaces. The porosity of the spray deposited metal helps the retention of lubricants and improves lubrication.

(f) *Plain carbon steels*. Rebuilding worn bearing surfaces on shafts.

(g) *Hard facing materials*. Materials such as *Stellite* can be deposited on plain carbon steels and low-alloy steels to improve their wear resistance.

(h) *Stainless steel, (18/8)*. Extreme corrosion resistant coatings capable of operating at very high temperatures, for example, in chemical plant. Stainless steel is also used in architectural decoration.

## Cladding

In this process, a composite billet is made up of the base metal and the coating as shown in Fig. 9.2(a). As the metal is reduced in thickness by

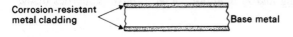

*(a)* **Section through clad metal composite**

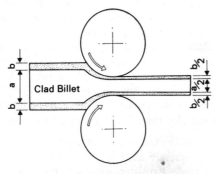

*(b)* **Proportional reduction of clad billet**

**Fig. 9.2** Cladding

rolling or drawing, as shown in Fig. 9.2(*b*), the thickness of the base and coating are reduced proportionally. A typical application of this process is the cladding of aluminium alloy with corrosion resistant, but weaker, high purity aluminium (*Alclad*).

## 9.4 Metallic decorative coatings

Decorative coatings usually provide some protection as well as enhancing the appearance of the product.

### Anodising

Aluminium and its alloys rely upon the formation of a self-healing, homogeneous, transparent oxide film on the surface of the metal to prevent corrosion. The process of anodising artificially builds up a thick, adherent layer of aluminium oxide that is resistant to atmospheric corrosion both for interior and exterior purposes even when subjected to the pollution of urban environments.

Components to be anodised are first cleaned and degreased by the use of chemical solvents, after which they are etched, wire brushed, or polished depending upon the surface texture required. The work is then made the *anode* of an electrolytic cell and a direct electric current is passed through the work. This is the reverse of the electro-plating process where the work is made the *cathode* of the cell. The electrolyte is a dilute acid selected according to the finish required. Finally, the surface is sealed, usually with boiling water or steam to improve the corrosion resistance of the coating and to minimise the absorptive properties of the oxide film.

## Electroplating

The components to be plated are made the cathodes (negative electrodes) of an electrolytic cell, as shown in Fig. 9.3. The electrolyte and the anode (positive electrode) will depend upon the metal being deposited. Briefly, when a direct electric current is passed through the cell the electrolyte becomes *ionised*. Metal ions are deposited upon the cathode (work) and the strength of the electrolyte is depleted. The anode may be *soluble*, in which case metal ions are dissolved from the anode to bring the electrolyte back up to strength. If the anode is *insoluble*, as in chromium plating, it only completes the circuit and makes no contribution to maintaining the strength of the electrolyte. Typical electro-deposits are:

(a) *Cadmium.* This is a white metal used to protect steel from atmospheric attack and is frequently used in the electrical and aircraft industries. Its low contact resistance reduces the risk of electrochemical corrosion where plated steel components and aluminium components are assembled together. Cadmium is toxic and should not be used where there is a possibility of contact with foodstuffs and drinking water. It is resistant to alkali attack and, for this reason it is preferred to zinc for marine purposes.

(b) *Copper.* The rich colour of this metal enables it to be used for

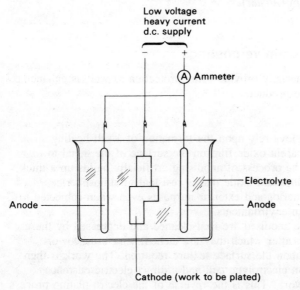

**Fig. 9.3** Electroplating

decorative purposes. It can be used directly with a polished or with an oxidised finish, in which case it is usually lacquered to prevent the formation of a 'patina' which would spoil its lustre and appearance. Alternatively it can be used as a 'base' prior to nickel plating. For example, zinc base die-castings are usually copper plated before nickel plating to prevent attack on the zinc by the nickel plating electrolyte.

(c) *Chromium (decorative and protective)*. The brilliant blue-white colour of chromium coupled with its resistance to tarnishing makes it an ideal finishing deposit over a nickel base. Only a thin film is required and this usually ranges from 0.00025 to 0.00075 mm in thickness. The chromium is not itself polished, but is applied over a brightly polished nickel base when a bright finish is required, or over a matt or semi-matt nickel base when a satin-chrome finish is required.

(d) *Chromium (hard)*. For engineering applications a thick layer of chromium is built up directly on to the component which is to be protected or reclaimed. This is a specialised process and differs from flash-chrome decorative plating in the techniques used. Deposits up to 0.4 mm thick can be built up where a component is to be sized by grinding after plating. The plated surface is resistant to abrasion and has anti-friction properties. For these reasons it is frequently used to protect the working faces of gauges and to build up and re-claim worn gauges.

(e) *Nickel*. This is widely used as an initial deposit before chromium plating. It is easier to process than chromium and gives a good corrosion-resistant finish. It can be polished and it has good *surface levelling* properties which causes it to build up in the hollows of the surface and improve the appearance of poorly polished and unpolished surfaces. For this reason it is widely used for the *barrel-plating* of unpolished small components. Unfortunately nickel has a yellowish tinge to its colour and tends to tarnish. For this reason it is frequently given a flash coating of chromium — a much more expensive metal — which has a more pleasing appearance and resists tarnishing.

(f) *Silver and gold*. These precious metals are highly corrosion resistant and are good electrical conductors. Gold, in particular, is widely used to protect the edge connectors of the printed circuit boards used in electronic equipment. Silver is used for plating switch contacts.

(g) *Tin*. This is used as a corrosion-resistant deposit on steel and non-ferrous metals. It is non-toxic and is widely used on food handling equipment. Tin-plate is produced in continuous strip plants where thin low-carbon steel strip is coated electrolytically with bright tin. Printed circuit boards and terminal tags are frequently tin plated to facilitate soldering.

(h) *Zinc*. See electrolytic galvanising in section 9.3.

## 9.5 Decorative coatings (plastic)

Plastic coatings can be both functional as well as being corrosion resistant and decorative. The wide range of plastic materials available for coating purposes provides the designer with a means of achieving:

(*a*)  abrasion resistance;
(*b*)  cushion coating (up to 6 mm thick);
(*c*)  electrical and thermal insulation;
(*d*)  flexibility over a wide range of temperatures;
(*e*)  non-stick properties;
(*f*)  permanent protection against weathering and atmospheric pollution subject to the inclusion of anti-oxidants and ultraviolet filter dyes.
(*g*)  reduction in maintenance costs;
(*h*)  resistance to corrosion by a wide range of chemicals;
(*i*)  the covering and sealing of mechanical joints, welds and porous castings.

There are many ways of applying plastic coatings to metal components, but two of the most widely used are as follows.

### Fluidised bed dipping

This technique is widely used with all fluidisable powders except for epoxy resins. Figure 9.4 shows a section through a fluidised bed dipping bath. The powder has a particle size of 60 to 200 mesh and is supported on a bed of air passing through the porous ceramic tile bed from the plenum chamber. The air lifts the powder, causing it to bubble up and drop back continuously. The effect is similar in appearance to boiling water, and the diffused powder offers little resistance to the immersed, preheated work. The plastic powder adheres to the heated work to form a homogeneous skin.

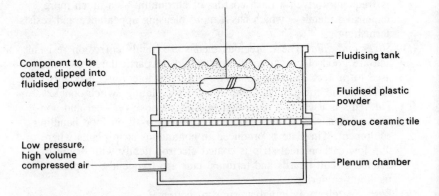

Component to be coated, dipped into fluidised powder —

Fluidising tank

Fluidised plastic powder

Porous ceramic tile

Low pressure, high volume compressed air —

Plenum chamber

**Fig. 9.4**  Fluidised bed dipping

## Liquid plastisol dipping

This process is limited to the use of a PVC plastisol. *Note*: a plastisol is a resin powder suspended in a plasticiser and no dangerous solvent is present. The process is similar to that described for fluidised bed dipping, except that the pre-heated work is dipped into a thixotropic (non-drip) liquid plastic instead of a powder.

## 9.6 Decorative coatings (paints)

Painting is widely used for the protection and decoration of metallic components and structures. It is the easiest and cheapest coating to apply with any degree of permanence. As with all applied coatings its success depends upon careful preparation of the work surface and pre-treatment.

Paints consists of a *binder* which sets to provide the protective film; a *pigment* to provide the required colour and other characteristics such as corrosion inhibition, and a *solvent* (thinner) which does not form part of the final paint film but gives the paint the required consistency during application and controls the drying process. A complete paint system consists of:

(a) *a primer* which acts as a corrosion inhibitor and provides a 'key' for the subsequent coats;
(b) *a putty* or filler which is used to fill surface blemishes in castings;
(c) *undercoats* which are used to build up the thickness of the paint film and to give 'body' to the final colour. 'Flatting-down' is essential between each undercoat and before the top-coat to provide a smooth surface where a high gloss is required (e.g. motor car bodywork).
(d) *a topcoat* or finishing coat. This gloss coat is not only decorative, it provides most of the corrosion and abrasion resistance.

There are four main groups of paints and these are described in *Engineering Fundamentals — F level* and in *Engineering Materials: volume 2*.

## 9.7 Paint application

### Brushing

This is the simplest and traditional method of applying paints to the work surface. Unfortunately it requires considerable skill, is labour intensive and, therefore, costly and the quality of the paint film is difficult to control.

### Spraying

This is one of the most versatile methods of coating surfaces with paint. Originally introduced for finishing mass produced motor cars, it is now used for large panels, structural steelwork and small components.

Conventional spraying uses compressed air to atomise the paint and to project it onto the surface of the component. It is a quick and relatively simple process requiring relatively low cost equipment. Further, it is versatile and can accommodate frequent colour changes. In the hands of a skilled operator, it can give consistently high standards of finish but paint and solvent wastage is high due to overspray and bounce. The process can be easily robotised to reduce labour costs and improve quality.

Airless spraying does not use compressed air to atomise the paint, but pumps it under pressure through a fine jet. This results in less overspray and bounce which, in turn, results in less hazardous spray dust than with conventional spraying. Therefore airless spraying is safer to use away from the spray-paint booth and it is widely used for site work and maintenance.

## Dipping

In this process the work to be coated is lowered into a bath containing the paint. The work is then removed and any surplus paint is allowed to drain off. The coated work is then passed through a stove to set and dry the paint. The whole process is usually automated with the work passing through the various stages suspended from a conveyor. Dip painting is highly productive and the labour costs are low, but close control is required for consistent quality.

## 9.8 The hazards of painting

The hazards of industrial painting fall into two main categories:

(a) explosion and fire hazards resulting from the use of flammable solvents and the formulation of flammable dust particles as the spray mist dries in the atmosphere;

(b) toxic and irritant effects due to the inhalation of paint mist (wholly or partially solidified) and solvent fumes.

These hazards are particularly related to spraying and stoving processes, but the storage of paints and solvents on a large scale also presents special problems. The local Health and Safety Inspector and the Fire Authorities should be consulted before painting on an industrial scale is undertaken.

It is essential when spray painting to provide an efficient means of extraction to remove the excess spray mist and solvent fumes. Spray booths serve the double function of removing the spray mist and fumes from the working area and then treating the exhausted air so that it is cleansed before being released back into the atmosphere. This prevents it becoming an environmental nuisance or hazard. The operator must wear full protective clothing and a respirator. Health problems are largely overcome by the increasing use of industrial robots for spray painting under factory conditions.

The main hazard associated with stoving ovens results from the use of unsuitable paints having volatile and flammable solvents, and from the accumulation of explosive dusts and gases in the fume extraction ducts. Stoving ovens and their extractors should have pressure release vents so that any explosion is carried upwards and away from the working area.

All electrical equipment associated with paint spraying booths have to be to Buxton Approved Standards for flame and explosion proof fittings.

## 9.9 Effects of finishing processes on material properties

All finishing processes have some effect upon the properties of the material being treated. This is a complex subject but some of the more important points are introduced briefly below.

### Mechanical finishing

Processes such as machining and polishing change the surface of the material mechanically. Positive rake machining leaves the surface in tension and this reduces the fatigue performance of the material, whilst negative rake machining leaves the surface in compression which improves the fatigue performance of the material. Many machining processes, and particularly grinding, cause local heating and thermal stressing of the surface layers of the material. This can lead to surface cracking and early failure of the material and most certainly will lead to a reduced fatigue performance. Polishing using a grease-based compound tends to leave the surface of the work in compression and, providing the work is not overheated, this can improve the fatigue performance of the material. Further, polishing removes surface discontinuities (incipient cracks) from which fatigue cracks can spread.

### Thermal effects

Many finishing processes are carried out above ambient temperatures and such processes can have the effect of impairing the mechanical properties. For example low-carbon steels become brittle when heated to 200°C for any period of time, yet many finishing processes are carried out at around this temperature. Similarly, aluminium alloys are particularly susceptible to processing at temperatures between 100°C and 150°C, yet this is the temperature for force drying paints.

### Chemical effects

Hydrogen is released in many finishing processes and this tends to be absorbed by metals and particularly by high strength alloy steels, causing a marked deterioration in the mechanical properties of the steel. The hydrogen absorbed by the steel can be driven off by heating the work to 200°C. However, as already stated, prolonged heating at this temperature can cause embrittlement in low carbon steels. Further, many deposited coatings seal the surface of the metal and prevent the hydrogen gas molecules escaping.

Chemical etching and polishing also reduce the fatigue strength of materials and, for this reason, particle blasting and mechanical polishing are preferable for high stressed components. Even a light vapour blast after chemical treatment is frequently all that is required to restore the mechanical properties of the metal.

## Surface alloying effects

The deposition of metals on metallic surfaces invariably results in chemical interaction at the interface. This usually results in some loss of fatigue strength. However the protection from corrosive fatigue often far outweighs the lowering of the mechanical fatigue performance.

# 10 Quality

## 10.1 Quality

Quality is the fitness of a product for the purpose for which it is required. This does not imply high cost and high precision. A wheelbarrow does not have to be manufactured to the precision of a machine tool, but providing it can be pushed easily, does not corrode away or rot, and it carries the load for which it was designed, then it is of suitable quality.

To ensure that the quality, or fitness for purpose, of a component or assembly has been achieved, then measurements must be taken to see if the design and manufacturing standards have been achieved.

## 10.2 Standards of length

For practical measurements there is a hierarchy of working standards. For example, in most engineering companies, inspection grade slip gauges would be used to check and measure work produced using workshop grade slip gauges, micrometers, verniers, etc. The inspection grade slip gauges could themselves be calibrated against a laser standard at the National Physical Laboratories and the company would receive a calibration chart. A large company might well have its own laser standard. The calibrated slip gauges could then, in turn, be used to check

**Table 10.1** Workshop standards of length

| Name | Range (in mm) | Reading accuracy |
|---|---|---|
| Steel rule | 150 to 1000 | 0·5 mm |
| Vernier caliper | 0/150 to 0/2000 | 0·02 mm |
| Micrometer caliper | 0/25 to 1800 | 0·01 mm |
| Slip gauges | 1·0025 to 327 | 0·0025 mm |
| | (105-piece set) | |

and calibrate the micrometers, verniers and other instruments and gauges in day-to-day use in the workshop.

It is usually assumed that any measuring device is ten times more accurate that the component feature which it is measuring. Table 10.1 lists some typical linear measuring instruments and the accuracy of measurement which can be achieved by them. The accuracy given is the reading accuracy. The measuring accuracy actually achieved will always be less than or equal to the reading accuracy and will depend upon the skill with which the measurement is made. All linear measurements are *comparative* measurements, that is, the component feature being measured is compared directly or indirectly with a standard of length, be it a rule or, for more precision measurements, slip gauges. However, these *working standards* are themselves based upon the *International Standard Metre* and the *International Yard* which is defined as 0.9144 metres. From 31 January 1964 the International Standard Metre became the British legal standard. The International Standard Metre is now defined as: *the length of the path travelled by light in a vacuum in 1/299 792 458 seconds.* This can be realised in practice through the use of an iodine stabilised helium-neon laser. The reproductivity is 3 parts in $10^{11}$, which may be compared to an accuracy of measuring the earth's mean circumference to one millimetre.

## 10.3 Measurement of length

### Engineer's rule

The steel rule is frequently used for measuring components of limited accuracy quickly. Figure 10.1 shows various ways of using a rule. To reduce sighting errors and increase the accuracy of measurement, the datum end of the rule should be aligned with the edge of a component by use of an abutment as shown. Another way of transferring measurements to or from a rule so as to reduce sighting errors is the use of calipers as shown in Fig. 10.2. The use of calipers requires considerable skill in achieving the correct 'feel'.

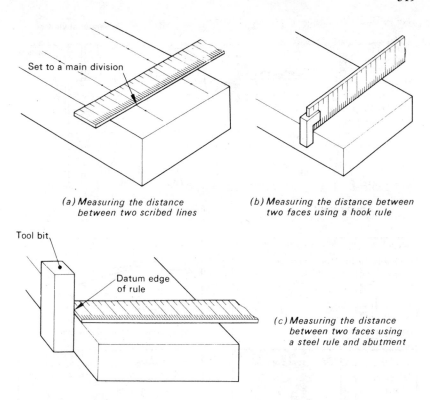

(a) Measuring the distance
between two scribed lines

(b) Measuring the distance between
two faces using a hook rule

(c) Measuring the distance
between two faces using
a steel rule and abutment

**Fig. 10.1** Use of a steel rule

## Micrometer caliper

This is one of the most familiar precision measuring devices used in the workshop and the inspection room. Figure 10.3 shows the construction of a typical micrometer, and names and describes the more important parts. The operation of a micrometer depends upon the principle that the distance moved by a nut along a screw is proportional to the number of revolutions made by the nut. Therefore by controlling the number of revolutions and fractions of a revolution made by the nut, the distance it moves along the screw can be accurately predicted. Figure 10.4 shows the scales for a metric micrometer with a screw which has a lead of 0.5 mm. The micrometer reading shown is as follows:

| | |
|---|---|
| 9 'whole' millimetres | = 9.00 |
| 1 'half' millimetre | = 0.50 |
| 48 hundredths of a mm | = 0.48 |
| | |
| Total reading | = 9.98 mm. |

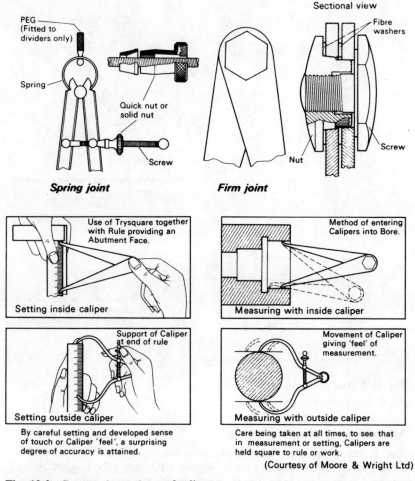

**Fig. 10.2**  Construction and use of calipers

## Internal micrometer

An internal micrometer is shown in Fig. 10.5(*a*). Its range is 50 mm to 210 mm. For any one rod the scale range is 20 mm. It suffers from severe practical limitations. For instance it cannot be adjusted readily once it is in a hole or slot and this adversely affects the 'feel' which can be obtained. Further, it cannot be used for small holes and slots. For cylindrical bores the *cylinder gauge* shown in Fig. 10.5(*b*) is a more satisfactory instrument. This employs a micrometer controlled wedge to expand three equispaced anvils until they touch the wall of the bore.

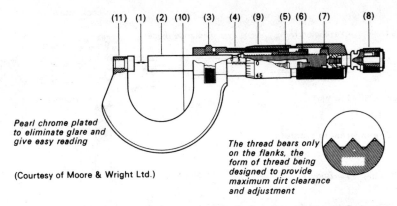

Pearl chrome plated
to eliminate glare and
give easy reading

(Courtesy of Moore & Wright Ltd.)

The thread bears only
on the flanks, the
form of thread being
designed to provide
maximum dirt clearance
and adjustment

(1) **Spindle and anvil faces** – Glass hard and optically flat, also available with **Tungsten carbide** faces

(2) **Spindle** – Thread ground, and made from alloy steel, hardened throughout, and stabilised

(3) **Locknut** – effective at any position. Spindle retained in perfect alignment

(4) **Barrel** – Adjustable for zero setting. Accurately divided and clearly marked. Pearl chrome plated

(5) **Main nut** – Length of thread ensures long working life

(6) **Screw adjusting nut** – For effective adjustment of main nut

(7) **Thimble adjusting nut** – Controls position of thimble

(8) **Ratchet** – Ensures a constant measuring pressure

(9) **Thimble** – Accurately divided and every graduation clearly numbered

(10) **Steel frame** – Drop forged. Marked with useful decimal equivalents

(11) **Anvil end** – Cutaway frame facilitates usage in narrow slots

**Fig. 10.3** Construction of a micrometer caliper

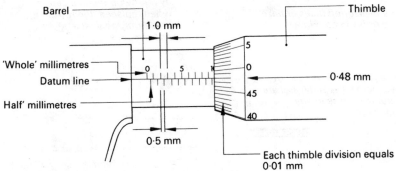

**Fig. 10.4** Micrometer scales (metric)

## Depth micrometer

A depth micrometer is shown in Fig. 10.6. It can be seen that it consists of a micrometer measuring-head together with a number of extension rods. The desired rod can be easily inserted by removing the thimble cap. When the cap is replaced the rod is held firmly against the positive datum

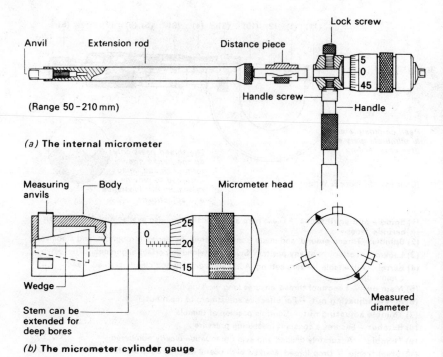

**Fig. 10.5** Internal measuring devices

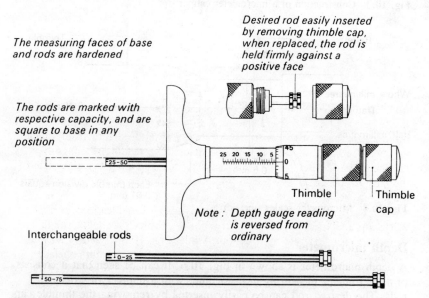

**Fig. 10.6** Micrometer depth gauge

face. The rods are marked with their respective measuring range and are perpendicular to the base at any setting. The measuring faces of the base and rods are hardened. Note that the scales of a depth micrometer give *reverse readings* when compared with the scales of a micrometer caliper or inside micrometer. Care has to be taken when using a depth micrometer as it is easy for the measuring force on the rod to lift the base off the work.

## Vernier caliper

Figure 10.7 shows a vernier caliper. Unlike the micrometer, the vernier caliper can take inside as well as outside measurements with the one instrument. Further, the vernier caliper reads from zero to the full length of its beam scale, whereas the micrometer only reads over a range of 25 mm. Unfortunately the vernier caliper is not as accurate as the micrometer for the following reasons.

(a) It is difficult to obtain a correct 'feel' due to its size and weight.
(b) The scales are difficult to read even with the aid of a magnifying glass.
(c) The reading accuracy is only 0.02 mm (micrometer 0.01 mm).

Figure 10.7(c) shows a typical 50-division vernier scale as used on a metric instrument. The zero mark of the vernier scale is just beyond the 32 on the main scale so the measurement is slightly in excess of 32 mm. The first pair of vernier and main scale graduations to come into line with each other is at 11 on the vernier scale. Since each vernier division is 0.02 mm, the total reading is as follows.

| | |
|---|---|
| 32 'whole' millimetres | = 32.00 mm |
| 11 vernier divisions of 0.02 mm each = | 0.22 mm |
| Total reading | = 32.22 mm |

## Vernier height gauge

In the vernier height gauge, shown in Fig. 10.8(a), the fixed jaw becomes the base of the instrument. This base is the datum from which the measurements and settings can be made. The reading obtained from the main and vernier scales represents the distance from the underside of the base to the upper side of the moving jaw (lower surface of scribing blade).

The height gauge can be used for a number of applications in the workshop and for inspection. Figure 10.8(b) shows the height gauge being used for accurate marking out, whilst Fig. 10.8(c) shows how it can be used to check the height of hole centres from a datum surface (where the holes are the same diameter) and the centre distance. If the scribing blade is used for the application shown in Fig. 10.8(c), the accuracy is limited to the skill of the operator. It is very difficult to obtain a satisfactory 'feel' due to the mass of the instrument and the

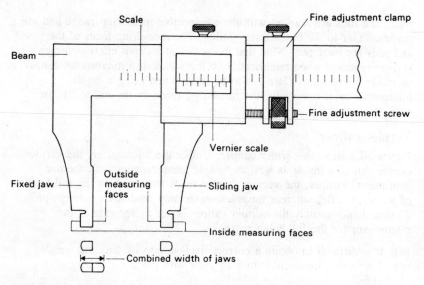

Scale

Beam

Fine adjustment clamp

Fine adjustment screw

Vernier scale

Fixed jaw

Outside measuring faces

Sliding jaw

Inside measuring faces

Combined width of jaws

*(a) The vernier caliper*

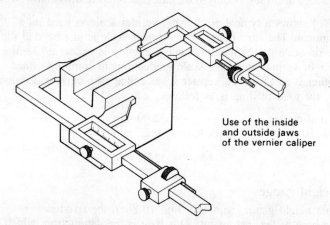

Use of the inside and outside jaws of the vernier caliper

*(b) Applications of the vernier caliper*

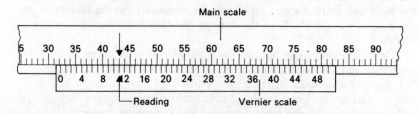

Main scale

Reading

Vernier scale

*(c) The vernier scale (50 divisions)*

**Fig. 10.7** Vernier caliper

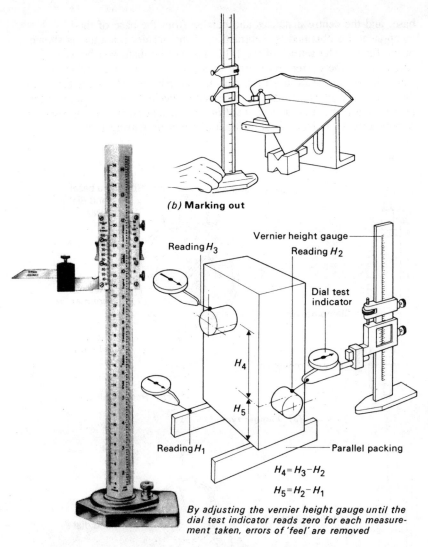

*(b)* **Marking out**

Reading $H_3$

Vernier height gauge

Reading $H_2$

Dial test indicator

$H_4$

$H_5$

Reading $H_1$

Parallel packing

$$H_4 = H_3 - H_2$$

$$H_5 = H_2 - H_1$$

*By adjusting the vernier height gauge until the dial test indicator reads zero for each measurement taken, errors of 'feel' are removed*

*(a)* **The vernier height gauge**   *(c)*   **Measuring the height of a surface**

**Fig. 10.8**  Vernier height gauge

friction between its base and the surface plate (datum surface) it is standing on. Note: a *datum* is a point, line, edge or surface which forms a common basis from which a number of measurements can be taken. As an aid to accuracy, a dial test indicator (DTI) can be used to ensure a constant measuring pressure (feel) as shown in Fig. 10.8(*c*). In this case, the readings obtained from the scales are not absolute distances from the base, and the centre distances and heights from the base of the component are obtained by subtraction of the vernier readings as shown in the figure. The setting of the DTI must not be disturbed between readings and the correct measuring pressure will have been achieved when the vernier scale has been adjusted so that the DTI reads zero with the stylus in contact with the surface being checked. In this example the DTI is said to be used as a *fiducial indicator*; that is, it is being used to remove errors of 'feel' by ensuring a constant measuring pressure.

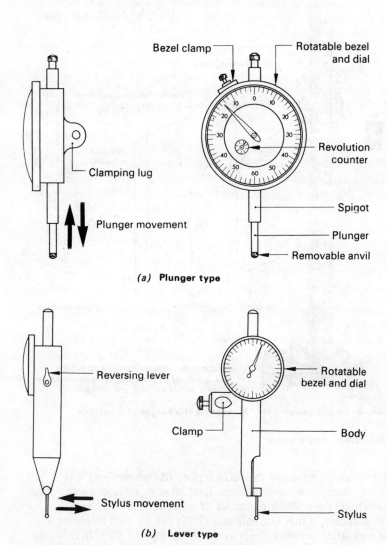

*(a)* **Plunger type**

*(b)* **Lever type**

**Fig. 10.9** Types of dial test indicators (DTI)

# Dial test indicator (DTI)

This instrument measures the displacement of its plunger or stylus and displays that displacement by means of a rotating pointer and calibrated dial. Figure 10.9 shows the two most popular types of this instrument normally used.

The *plunger type* instrument, shown in Fig. 10.9(*a*), relies upon a rack and pinion followed by a gear train to magnify the displacement of the plunger and rotate the pointer. This type of instrument has a long plunger movement and is fitted with a secondary scale to count the number of revolutions of the main pointer. Various dial markings and magnifications are available.

The *lever type* instrument shown in Fig. 10.9(*b*), relies upon a lever and scroll system of magnification. It has only a limited range of stylus movement; little more than one revolution of the pointer. It is more compact than the plunger type and is widely used for machine setting and inspection where the position of the dial makes it convenient to read.

## Slip gauges

These are blocks of high carbon steel which have been hardened and stabilised by heat treatment. They are then ground and lapped to very high standards of accuracy and finish as indicated in Table 10.2. The essential requirements of the lapped measuring surfaces of slip gauges are that:

(*a*)   the faces are parallel;
(*b*)   the faces are flat;
(*c*)   the faces are accurately the stated distance apart;
(*d*)   the finish is sufficiently high that two slip gauges may be 'wrung' together. That is they adhere to each other by molecular attraction.

Table 10.3 lists the sizes of the individual slip gauges in a standard 78 piece metric set. In addition, the set has two *protector slips* which are 2.50 mm thick and made from wear resistant steel or tungsten carbide. They are added to the end of the stack to protect the other gauge blocks from wear. The required dimension is obtained by wringing together various slip gauges. To obtain maximum accuracy, the following rules must be observed.

(*a*)   Use the minimum number of blocks.
(*b*)   Wipe the measuring faces clean.
(*c*)   *Wring* the individual blocks together.

If the slip gauges are left wrung together for too long they will form a cold weld and their measuring surfaces will be damaged. Therefore the gauge blocks must be separated, cleaned, wiped with petroleum jelly (vaseline) and returned to their case immediately after use. Figure 10.10 shows how a stack of slip gauges is built up to give a dimension of 39.9725 mm using the set listed in Table 10.3. The first slip selected is always the one giving the right hand digit or digits of the required

**Table 10.2** Accuracy of slip or block gauges [maximum permissible errors: 1 μm (micrometre)]

| Size of gauge (mm) | | Grade 2 | | Grade 1 | | | Grade 0 | | |
|---|---|---|---|---|---|---|---|---|---|
| Over | Up to and including | Flatness | Parallelism | Gauge length | Flatness | Parallelism | Gauge length | Flatness | Parallelism |
| — | 20 | 2·5 | 3·5 | + 5·0 − 2·5 | 1·5 | 2·0 | + 2·0 − 1·5 | 1·0 | ±1·0 |
| 20 | 60 | 2·5 | 3·5 | + 8·0 − 5·0 | 1·5 | 2·0 | + 3·0 − 2·0 | 1·0 | ±1·5 |
| 60 | 80 | 2·5 | 3·5 | +12·0 − 7·5 | 1·5 | 2·5 | + 5·0 − 2·5 | 1·0 | ±2·0 |
| 80 | 100 | 2·5 | 3·5 | +14·0 −10·0 | 1·5 | 2·5 | + 6·0 − 3·0 | 1·0 | ±2·5 |

Grade 2: General workshop applications.
Grade 1: Precision workshop (toolroom) applications.
Grade 0: Inspection.

*Not listed in table:*
Grade 'calibration': A reference standard for testing grades 2, 1, 0.
Grade 00: A reference standard used only by slip gauge manufacturers to test all other grades.

**Table 10.3** Slip gauge set

**Set No. 78**

| Range (mm) | Steps (mm) | Pieces |
|---|---|---|
| 1·01 to 1·49 | 0·01 | 49 |
| 0·50 to 9·50 | 0·50 | 19 |
| 10·00 to 50·00 | 10·00 | 5 |
| 75·00 and 100·00 | — | 2 |
| 1·002 5 | — | 1 |
| 1·005 | — | 1 |
| 1·007 5 | — | 1 |

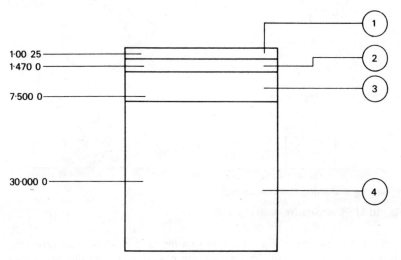

**Fig. 10.10** Building up slip gauges

dimension and the remainder are selected in sequence. If protector slips (2 × 2.5 mm) were to be used with the stack in Fig. 10.10, block number three would be reduced to 2.50 mm.

## Comparator

It has already been stated that all measurement is comparative. However, in engineering the term *comparative measurement* is reserved for the technique shown in Fig. 10.11. Here a plunger type DTI is used to determine the difference between the component size and a length standard; in this case a stack of slip gauges. Since the accuracy of a dial gauge decreases as the displacement of the plunger increases, the stack of slip gauges should be made as near as possible to the required dimension so that the plunger movement is as small as possible.

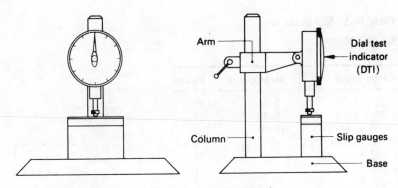

(a) **Dial gauge mounted on a simple comparator stand**

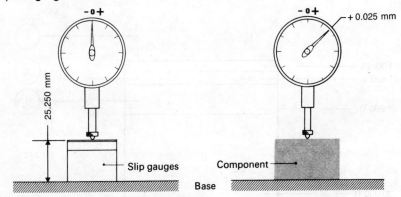

(b) **Setting and using the comparator**

**Fig. 10.11** Comparative measurement

It can be seen from Fig: 10.11(b) that the DTI is set to read zero when slip gauges totalling 25.250 mm are placed under the plunger. When the workpiece is exchanged for the slip gauges, the DTI indicates a reading of +0.025 mm. Thus the workpiece dimension is 25.250 + 0.025 = 25.275 mm. For more accurate measurement, pneumatic, electronic and optical comparators are used and these will be considered in *Manufacturing Technology: volume 2*.

## Cosine error

The measuring head of a comparator, be it a DTI or one of the more sophisticated devices mentioned above, only indicates the displacement of the measuring stylus. Whether or not this is the same as the error in the workpiece will depend upon how the measuring head is set. The most common error of setting is *cosine error* resulting from the axis of the measuring stylus being inclined to the datum surface from which the measurement is made. This is shown in exaggerated form in Fig. 10.12. The true deflection $D$ can only be measured along AB which is perpendicular to the datum surface. When the DTI is inclined along BC,

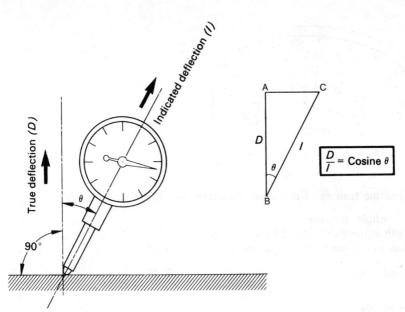

**Fig. 10.12** Cosine error

it indicates the stylus deflection $I$, and this indicated reading is greater than the actual error value, that is:

$$I = D/\text{cosine } \theta$$

where:  $D = $ *true deflection*
$I\ = $ indicated deflection

Thus for the DTI to indicate the actual error the DTI must be set *perpendicular to the datum surface*.

## 10.4 Measurement of angles

### Protractors

Simple protractors have a reading accuracy of only $\pm 0.5°$. However, by the addition of a circular vernier scale, as shown in Fig. 10.13, the reading accuracy can be greatly increased. The main scale is graduated in degrees of arc and the vernier scale has 12 divisions each side of zero. These are marked 0 to 60 minutes of arc so that each division equals 1/12 of 60, that is 5 minutes of arc. Thus the reading of a vernier bevel protractor equals:

(*a*)  the largest 'whole' degree on the main scale indicated by the vernier zero graduation; *plus*
(*b*)  the reading on the vernier scale in line with a main scale graduation.

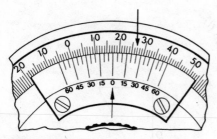

**Fig. 10.13** Vernier protractor scales

Thus the reading of the scales shown in Fig. 10.13 is:

| | |
|---|---|
| 17 'whole' degrees | $= 17°$ |
| Fifth vernier division (25 mark) is in line with a main scale graduation | $= 00°25'$ |
| Total reading | $= 17°25'$ |

## Sine-bar

There are no standards for angles. But all angles can be defined in terms of linear dimensions and therefore, ultimately referred back to the International Standard Metre. The *sine-bar* uses linear measurements to define angles to a high degree of accuracy as shown in Fig. 10.14. It can be seen from Fig. 10.14(*b*) that the sine-bar, slip gauges and datum surface form a right-angled triangle. The sine-bar itself forms the *hypotenuse* and the slip-gauges form the *opposite side* to the angle being measured.

Since  sine $\theta$ = (opposite side)/(hypotenuse)
Then  sine $\theta$ = (height of slip-gauges)/(centre distance of roller axes).
    = H/L

The centre distance of the contact roller axes is the 'nominal length' of the sine bar, normally 10 inches or 250 millimetres.

Figure 10.15 shows how the sine-bar is used to check small components mounted upon it. The DTI is mounted upon a suitable stand such as a vernier height gauge which is rigid and can provide a fine adjustment. The DTI is moved over the component at position 'A' in Fig. 10.15 and zeroed. The stand and DTI is then slid along the datum surface to the second position 'B' as shown and the DTI reading is noted.

*Method 1*

The height of the slip gauges is adjusted until the DTI reads zero at each end of the component. The actual angle can then be calculated using trigonometry as previously described, and any deviation from the specified angle is the error.

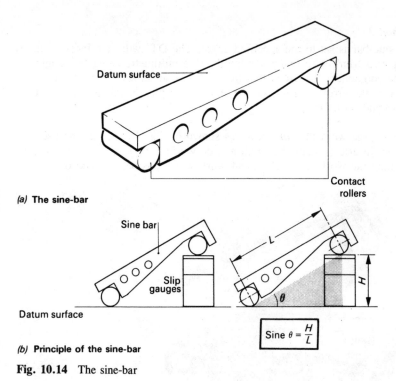

Datum surface
Contact rollers
(a) The sine-bar
Sine bar
Slip gauges
Datum surface
L
H
θ
Sine θ = H/L
(b) Principle of the sine-bar

**Fig. 10.14** The sine-bar

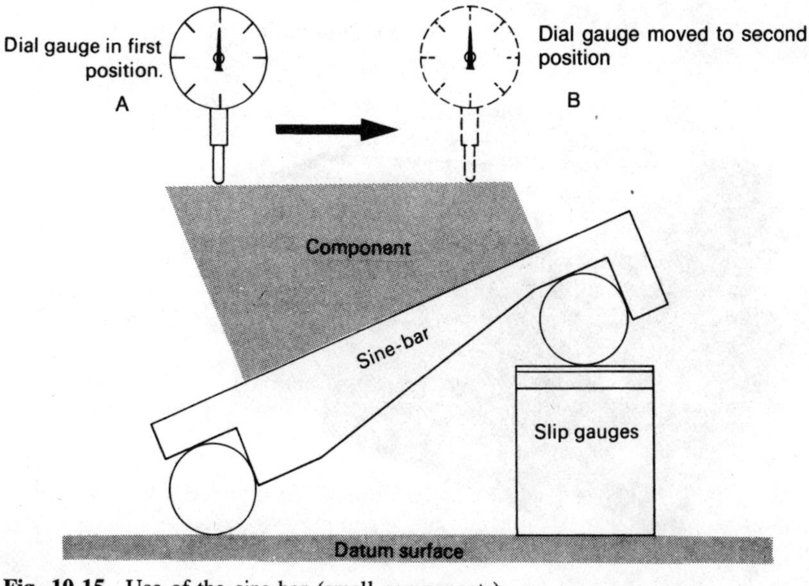

Dial gauge in first position.
A
Dial gauge moved to second position
B
Component
Sine-bar
Slip gauges
Datum surface

**Fig. 10.15** Use of the sine-bar (small components)

*Method 2*

The sine-bar is set to the specified angle. The DTI will then indicate any error as a 'run' of so many hundredths of a millimetre along the length of the component. Provided that the DTI was set to zero in the first position, the error or 'run' will be shown as a plus or minus reading at the second position.

For large work the *sine-table*, as shown in Fig. 10.16, may be used. This is, in effect, a sine-bar with a wide working surface and a T-slot for clamping the work. For cylindrical work which has been turned or

(*a*) **Sine-table**

(*b*) **Compound sine-table**

**Fig. 10.16** Types of sine-table

ground between centres or which can be mounted on a mandrel, *sine-centres*, as shown in Fig. 10.17, may be used. Further applications of the sine-bar and alternative methods of precision angular measurements using optical measuring instruments such as the auto-collimator or the angle-dekkor together with combination angle gauges will be considered in *Manufacturing Technology: volume 2.*

**Fig. 10.17**  Sine-centres

336

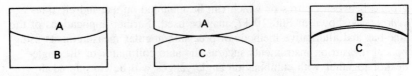

**Fig. 10.18**   Generation of a flat surface

## 10.5   Reference surfaces

The need for and use of a *datum surface* when measuring linear distances
and angles has already been introduced. Such a datum or reference
surface is of equal importance when determining straightness, flatness and
squareness. Recognising that an accurate reference surface was essential
for precision measurement as long ago as 1830, Sir Joseph Whitworth
devised the three-plate technique of surface generation, shown in Fig.
10.18. This is based upon the principle that it is impossible to devise any
combination of mating three surfaces together unless they are flat. The
two plates 'A' and 'B' can be scraped so that they mate together without

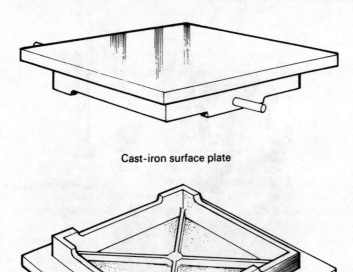

Cast-iron surface plate

**Fig. 10.19**   Surface plate

being flat. This out-of-flatness is shown up as soon as they are compared with a third plate 'C'. It is only by working the plates together so that they are fully interchangeable that three perfectly flat surfaces are generated.

Reference surfaces in engineering workshops and inspection rooms consist of surface plates and surface tables. The most accurate reference surface is the *toolmaker's flat*. This is a disc of hardened and stabilised steel some 200 mm diameter and with finely lapped surfaces. These surfaces should be finished so that slip gauges may be wrung to them, and when viewed through an optical flat it should show straight interference fringes.

Surface plates and surface tables are made from cast iron and their under surfaces are heavily ribbed for strength and rigidity as shown in Fig. 10.19. The working surfaces are planed for workshop use and hand scraped for inspection and reference use. They are stabilised by weathering or by heat treatment between rough machining and finishing. Plate glass and granite are also used for reference surfaces as they are extremely stable. They also have the advantage that, if accidentally scratched, they do not throw up a 'burr'. Unfortunately they do not have the anti-friction properties of cast iron and have a less pleasant 'feel' in use.

## 10.6 Straightness

Straightness is normally checked using a straight edge as a reference surface.

*Steel straight edges* are made up to 2 metres in length and may be rectangular in section or have a bevelled edge as shown in Fig. 10.20(a).

*Cast iron straight edges* are made from close-grained cast iron. After rough machining they are stabilised by weathering or heat treatment and then finish machined and scraped to a reference surface. They are made up to 3 metres long and are widely used for checking machine tool slideways. Cast iron straight edges are heavily ribbed and bow-shaped (camel-backed), as shown in Fig. 10. 20(b), to prevent distortion. When not in use they should be placed upon their feet which are provided at the *points of minimum deflection*.

Some confusion often occurs between the *Airey points* and the *points of minimum deflection*. The Airey points, shown in Fig. 10.20(c), are used for supporting length standards, such as combination length bars, so that the measuring ends are perpendicular and parallel and are drawn up into this position by the sag along the unsupported length of the bar. The points of minimum deflection are shown in Fig. 10.20(d). Slight sagging of the ends of the bar assist in drawing up the unsupported middle length of the bar. Thus all deflections are kept to a minimum, but the ends are not perpendicular nor are they parallel.

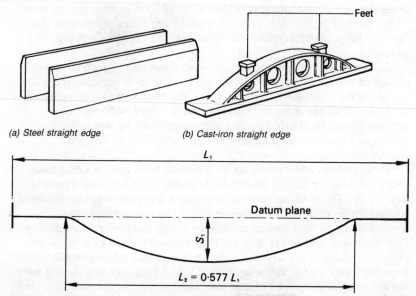

(a) Steel straight edge  (b) Cast-iron straight edge

**The sag $S_1$ that occurs in a bar supported at the airey points is so arranged that it pulls the ends of the bar up square with the measuring plane**

(c) Airey points

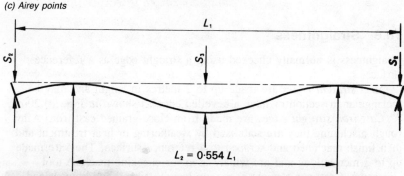

**For minimum deflection conditions, some sag $S_2$ at the ends of the bar is permissible to reduce the sag at the centre $S_3$. When $L_2 = 0.554 L_1$, $S_2$ and $S_3$ are at a minimum, and considerably less than $S_1$**

(d) Points of minimum deflection

**Fig. 10.20**  Straight edges

Just as it is not possible to make or measure a component to an *exact size*, neither is it possible to make it to an *exact shape*. When measuring both straightness and flatness, reference is made to an imaginary, perfect plane called the *mean true plane*. Figure 10.21 shows that it is a perfectly flat plane situated relatively to an actual surface so that the plus errors and minus errors are equally balanced above and below the plane.

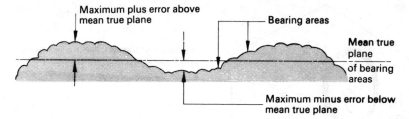

**Fig. 10.21** Mean true plane

In fairly coarse measuring situations, the deviation of a surface can be determined approximately as shown in Fig. 10.22. The irregular gap between the straight edge and the surface being tested can be determined by the use of a feeler gauge as shown.

Alternatively the cast iron straight edge may be used as a narrow surface plate. Engineer's blue, smeared on the straight edge, is transferred on contact to the high spots of the surface being tested. These high spots are hand scraped down until the pattern shows uniform bearing surfaces along the length being tested (see section 10.7).

Small components can be tested for straightness with a precision straight edge and light box as shown in Fig. 10.23. The light box provides a source of uniform illumination which is independent of the

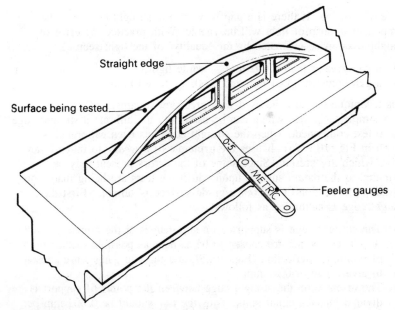

**Fig. 10.22** Use of a straight-edge—feeler gauge

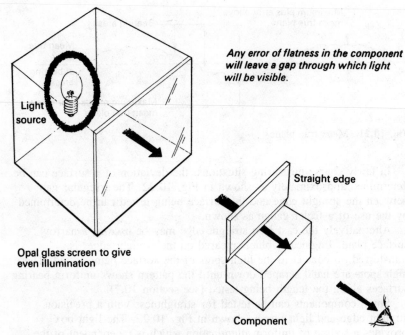

*Any error of flatness in the component will leave a gap through which light will be visible.*

Light source

Straight edge

Opal glass screen to give even illumination

Component

**Fig. 10.23** Use of a straight-edge–light box

angle of viewing. If there is a gap between the straight edge and the component, a strip of light will be visible. With practice the error of straightness can be estimated by the 'quality' of the light seen:

(a)  a gap greater than 0.002 mm — white light,
(b)  a gap between 0.001 mm and 0.002 — tinted light.

This technique can also be used with precision squares.

A simple technique which can be used both to calibrate a straight edge and to test components when the straight edge has been calibrated is shown in Fig. 10.24(a). It uses the principle of a *wedge* to magnify any errors which are present. Since some of the errors present may be attributed to the datum surface upon which the tests are being made, only a grade A inspection or reference grade surface is suitable. First the straight edge is calibrated as follows.

(a)  The straight edge is supported on slip gauges at the points 'A' and 'C'. These points are chosen to be as near as possible to the points of minimum deflection (Fig. 10.20) and slip gauges are chosen to give a rise of 0.02 mm.
(b)  The distance on the straight edge between the points of support is divided into ten equal parts. Thus the rise should be 0.002 mm per division.

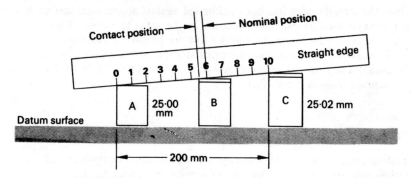

*(a) Use of the straight edge*

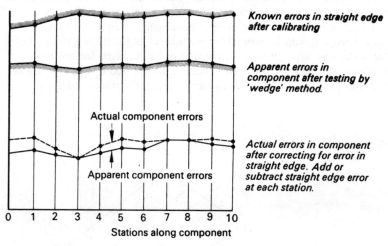

Known errors in straight edge after calibrating

Apparent errors in component after testing by 'wedge' method.

Actual errors in component after correcting for error in straight edge. Add or subtract straight edge error at each station.

*(b) Straightness test results*

**Fig. 10.24** Use of a straight-edge–wedge method

(c) Knowing the height at 'A' and the increase in height at each successive point along the straight edge, slip gauges can be used to test the height at each point and any deviation are noted on a calibration chart. For instance at point 6, the slip gauges 'B' should equal:

$$25.00 \text{ mm} + (6 \times 0.002 \text{ mm}) = 25.012 \text{ mm}$$

However, a slip gauge stack of this magnitude makes contact with the straight edge between points 5 and 6, showing that there is a hollow at this point.

(d) The slip gauges are now built up to the actual height at point 6. The difference between the actual height and 12.012 mm is the error at this point and is recorded on the calibration chart.

Once the straight edge has been calibrated against a reference surface it can then be used to test other surfaces by the same technique. The apparent errors for the surface under test are plotted graphically along with the known errors in the calibrated straight edge as shown in Fig. 10.24(*b*). The two sets of errors are then added algebraically to obtain the actual errors in the surface.

## 10.7 Flatness

Testing large areas for flatness requires sophisticated equipment and techniques. However, for surfaces of limited accuracy and size the following technique can be used.

The surface to be checked is marked out with a soft lead pencil, so as not to damage the surface, into a series of parallel bands as shown in Fig. 10.25. It is then checked using a bevel edge straight edge and feeler gauges. Errors should be plotted for each band as for testing straightness. If the surface is large enough, the wedge technique used for testing straightness can be used for each band lengthways and crossways. These results can then be fed into a computer set up for surface modelling and a

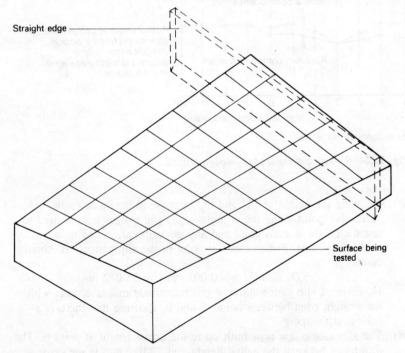

**Fig. 10.25** Testing for flatness — straight edge

magnified image of the surface can be produced. Care is necessary when checking for surface flatness with a straight edge. Reference to Fig. 10.25 shows that although the surface is 'winding' it will appear flat if measured parallel to the sides. Therefore additional checks should be made across the diagonals to detect errors of flatness due to winding.

Small surfaces can be checked against a reference surface. The surface to be checked is first carefully cleaned and any 'burrs' are removed with an oil stone. Engineer's blue is then smeared over this surface. The blued surface is then inverted over a reference surface (inspection grade surface plate) and gently moved in a series of small circles as shown in Fig. 10.26(a). This will transfer the blue to the high spots of the scraped reference surface, lightly and uniformly. Any attempt to apply 'blue' directly to the reference surface usually results in a poor distribution

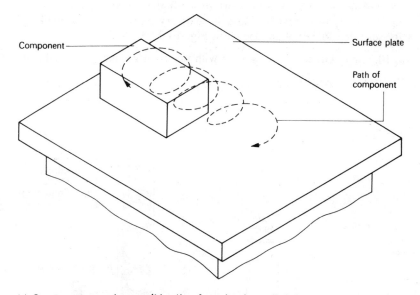

*(a)* **Component moved across 'blued' surface plate in small circles**

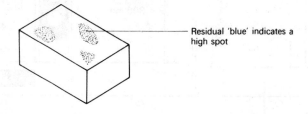

*(b)* **'blue' is transferred to high spots on component**

**Fig. 10.26** Testing for flatness — reference surface

leading to a false interpretation of flatness. The surface to be checked is now cleaned of blue and once more brought into contact with the reference surface with the same rotary motion. Residual 'blue' will now be transferred back to any high spots on the surface under test. These high spots may be broken down by hand scraping, and the checking process repeated. The sequence of checking and scraping is repeated until the surface under test has a uniform pattern of small closely spaced high spots over its whole area.

## 10.8 Squareness

As well as straightness and flatness, the engineer is concerned with *perpendicularity* or squareness. Although sophisticated optical equipment and techniques are available for work of the highest precision, small components can be checked using a standard *try square*. Some examples of try-squares to BS 939 are shown in Fig. 10.27.

Fig. 10.27(*a*)  Grade 'B' try square with precision ground, hardened and tempered blade.

Fig. 10.27(*b*)  Grade 'AA' (reference) try square for sizes up to 300 mm blade length. Both the stock and the blade are hardened

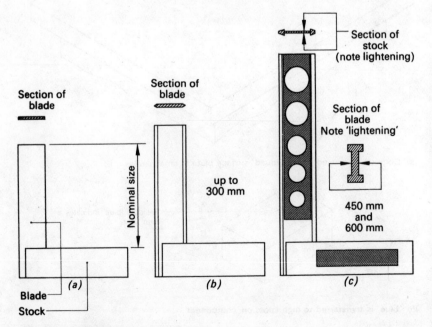

**Fig. 10.27**  Engineer's try square

and precision ground. The bevel edges are left 'glass hard'.

Fig. 10.27(c)   Grade 'AA' (reference) try square for sizes from 450 mm to 600 mm in length. The stock and blade are both hardened and precision ground. Again, the bevel edges of the blade are left 'glass hard'. The stock and the blade have been designed in conjunction with the National Physical Laboratories to provide maximum rigidity with minimum weight.

Although not a British Standard specification, many inspection rooms favour a *cylinder square*, as shown in Fig. 10.28, when working from the datum surface of a surface plate or table. The cylinder square is

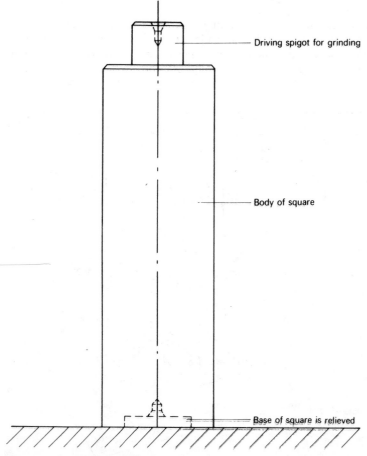

**Fig. 10.28**   Cylinder square

346

usually made from through-hardened or case-hardened steel with the body and the base ground at the same setting on a precision cylindrical grinding machine. The advantages claimed for this type of square are its stability when standing on a datum surface, and the fact that it makes *line contact* with a flat surface.

Figure 10.29 shows applications of a try square for testing perpendicular surfaces. In Fig. 10.29(*a*), the stock is placed against the edge AB of the component and slid gently downwards until the blade comes into contact with the edge BC. Any lack of squareness between edges AB and BC will allow light to be seen between BC and the try square blade. It is not always convenient to hold a large component and try square up to the light and Fig. 10.29(*b*) shows an alternative technique. A surface plate is used as a datum and the squareness of the component is checked with a feeler gauge. Alternatively, a light box may be used for a visual check of any gap between the component and the try square blade.

A more accurate method of testing squareness is the use of a *squareness comparator* as shown in Fig. 10.30. The DTI is set to zero with the comparator in contact with a known squareness standard, such as a grade AA try square, as shown in Fig. 10.30(*a*). When the comparator

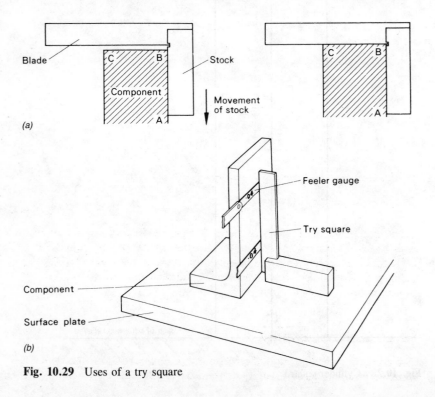

**Fig. 10.29** Uses of a try square

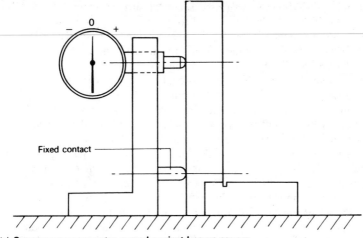

(a) **Squareness comparator zeroed against known square**

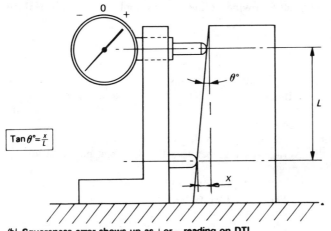

$$\boxed{\text{Tan}\,\theta° = \frac{x}{L}}$$

(b) **Squareness error shows up as + or − reading on DTI**

**Fig. 10.30** Squareness comparator

is brought into contact with the component being checked, as shown in Fig. 10.30(b), any error is indicated as a plus or minus reading on the DTI. Since the centre distance between the fixed contact and the DTI plunger is known, the angular error may be calculated using trigonometry.

## 10.9 Surface texture

The marked improvement in the reliability of engineering mechanisms over the post-war years is largely due to developments in the understanding and techniques of assessment of surface texture (finish). It is no use specifying close dimensional tolerances to a process whose inherent surface roughness lies outside that tolerance, as shown in Fig. 10.31(a). The tolerance and the surface finish of the manufacturing process must be matched, as shown in Fig. 10.31(b).

The life (which is inversely proportional to the rate of wear) of mating surfaces, such as shafts and bearings, is also dependent upon surface finish. A rough surface with large peaks and valleys will have less contact area and will wear more quickly than a smoother surface. Even two surfaces having the same roughness index can have different wearing characteristics. Figure 10.31 shows two surfaces having the same roughness index, that is the same height peaks and the same depth valleys with the same spacing. It is obvious from the appearance of these surfaces that the one shown in Fig. 10.31(c) will wear less quickly than the one shown in Fig. 10.31(d) under the same conditions of service.

BS 1134 discusses fully the assessment of surface texture, but some fundamental principles will now be considered. Reference to Fig. 10.32 will help to explain the following definitions, as applied to surface texture assessment.

**Real surface** is the actual physical surface separating the component from surrounding space.

**Effective surface (measured surface)** is the close representation of a real surface obtained by instrumental means.

**Effective profile (measured profile)** is the contour which results from the intersection of the effective surface by a plane conventionally defined with respect to the geometrical surface.

**Irregularities** are the peaks and valleys of a real surface.

**Spacing** is the average distance between the dominant peaks on the effective profile.

**Surface texture.** Those irregularities with regular or irregular spacing which tend to form a pattern or texture on the surface. The texture may contain the following components.

(a) *Roughness.* The irregularities in the surface texture which are inherent in the production process but excluding waviness and errors of form.

(b) *Waviness.* That component of surface texture upon which the roughness is superimposed. Waviness may result from such factors as machine or work deflections, vibrations, chatter, and heat treatment or warping strains.

**Lay** is the direction of the predominant surface pattern, ordinarily determined by the production method used. Surface measurement is usually carried out at right angles to the lay.

**Sampling length** is the length of profile selected for the purpose of making an individual measurement of surface texture.

**Reference line** is the line chosen by convention to serve for

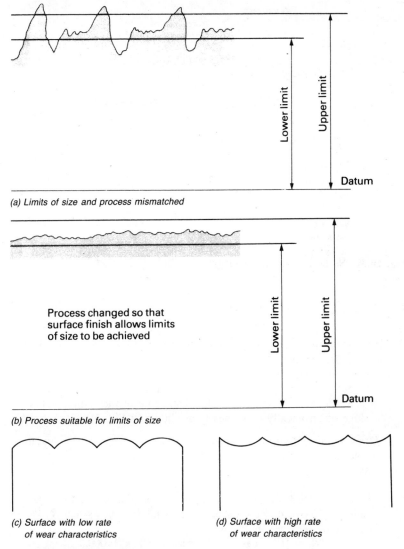

(a) Limits of size and process mismatched

Process changed so that
surface finish allows limits
of size to be achieved

(b) Process suitable for limits of size

(c) Surface with low rate
of wear characteristics

(d) Surface with high rate
of wear characteristics

**Fig. 10.31** Surface characteristics

quantitative evaluation of the roughness of the effective profile. The preferred methods of grading surface texture currently employed are the:

(a) arithmetical mean deviation ($R_a$), previously known as the centre line average (CLA) height index;

(b) average peak to valley height index ($R_z$).

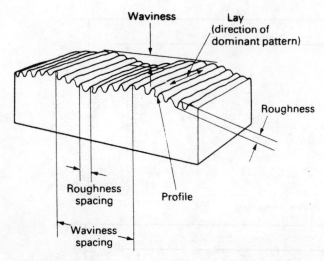

**Fig. 10.32** Surface texture terminology

## Determination of $R_a$ values

$R_a$ is the universally recognised parameter of roughness. It is the arithmetical mean of the departures of the profile from the mean line. It is normally determined as the mean results of several sampling lengths $L$ and is shown in Fig. 10.33.

When determining $R_a$ values from graphical recordings of surface texture it is necessary to determine the centre line of the sample. This can be done electronically or manually as shown in Fig. 10.33(a).

(a) Draw a line AB so that it grazes the deepest valley and lies parallel to the general course of the record over the sampling length $L$.

(b) Measure the area $P$ (shaded) with a planimeter. Thus:
$$H_m \text{ (mean height)} = P/L$$

(c) The centre line CC can now be drawn in parallel to the line AB at a height $H_m$ above it. Reference to Fig. 10.33(b) shows that $R_a$ values can now be obtained as follows:
$$R_a = [(\Sigma \text{ areas } r + \Sigma \text{ areas } s)/L] \times [1000/V_m]$$
where: $R_a$ = arithmetical mean deviation in microns (0.001 mm)
$\quad L$ = sampling length in millimetres
$\quad r$ = areas of peaks in square millimetres
$\quad s$ = areas of valleys in square millimetres
$\quad V_m$ = vertical magnification
$\quad \Sigma$ is a mathematical symbol meaning 'the sum of'.

Finally, the overall value of $R_a$ for the entire traversing length can be determined by taking the mean of successive values of the sampling lengths. Table 10.4 relates roughness grade numbers ($N$) to $R_a$ values and

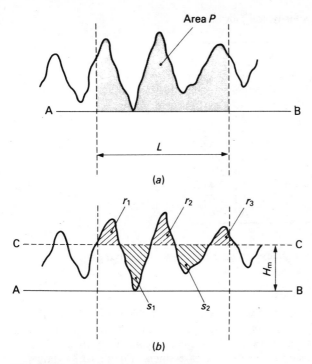

**Fig. 10.33** Determination of $R_a$ values

**Table 10.4** Roughness grade number

| $R_a$ value (mm) | Roughness grade number |
| --- | --- |
| 50 | $N12$ |
| 25 | $N11$ |
| 12·5 | $N10$ |
| 6·3 | $N9$ |
| 3·2 | $N8$ |
| 1·6 | $N7$ |
| 0·8 | $N6$ |
| 0·4 | $N5$ |
| 0·2 | $N4$ |
| 0·1 | $N3$ |
| 0·05 | $N2$ |
| 0·025 | $N1$ |
| 0·0125 | — |

**Table 10.5** *N* values for typical processes

| Process | *N* value |
|---|---|
| Casting, forging, hot rolling | $N11-N12$ |
| Rough turning | $N9$ |
| Shaping and planing | $N7$ |
| Milling (HSS cutters) | $N6$ |
| Drilling | $N6-N10$ |
| Finish turning | $N5-N8$ |
| Reaming | $N5-N8$ |
| Commerical grinding | $N5-N8$ |
| Finish grinding (tool room) | $N2-N4$ |
| Honing and lapping | $N1-N6$ |
| Diamond turning | $N3-N6$ |

Table 10.5 relates roughness grade numbers to some typical manufacturing processes.

### Determining $R_z$ values

The $R_z$ value is also known as the ISO 10-point height parameter. It is measured over a single sampling length and is itself an average of several positive and negative peak values; it is a useful parameter when only a short length of surface is available for assessment. Figure 10.34 shows how $R_z$ values are determined graphically. The five highest peaks and the five deepest valleys are conveniently measured from an arbitrary datum line $A' \dots B'$ drawn parallel to the centre line AB for a chosen length $L$, so that:

$$R_z = [(p_1 + p_2 + \dots p_5)/5 - (v_1 + v_2 + \dots v_5)/5]$$

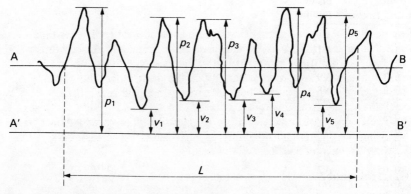

**Fig. 10.34** Determination of $R_z$ values

It was shown in Fig. 10.32 that most machined surfaces consist of a number of irregularities superimposed upon each other. If a very short length of surface is tested, it will be seen that only the roughness will register and the $R_a$ value will be low. However, if a longer length is tested both the roughness and the waviness will register and the $R_a$ value will be higher. Therefore, for comparative purposes, the test length must be standardised. Sample lengths currently in use are 0.25 mm, 0.80 mm, and 2.50 mm. These are referred to as cut-off wavelengths and the most frequently used is 0.80 mm.

Various methods of surface texture assessment have been derived, but the most commonly used involves electronic magnification as in the Taylor-Hobson *Talysurf*. Basically this instrument uses a device similar to the pick-up on a record player which is drawn over the surface under test and the signals produced by displacement of the stylus are amplified and printed out on a paper tape.

Figure 10.35($a$) shows a typical set of electronic surface texture assessment equipment. It can be seen that it consists of a traverse unit and an amplifier/recorder unit. The amplifier contains electronic filters which enables different parameters of the surface texture to be studied. The traverse unit may also be mounted on a column and base plate as shown in Fig. 10.35($b$) to facilitate setting up. Figure 10.36 shows a typical print out for a ground surface. In this example the vertical magnification is ×20 000; the horizontal magnification is ×100, and one division represents one micron (0.000 001 metre). The $R_a$ value for this example is 0.2 micron approximately.

## 10.10  The cost of quality

Quality has already been defined as 'fitness for purpose' and must be considered at every stage of manufacture.

### Design quality

The designer has a very considerable influence on quality. It is at this stage that such attributes as dimensional, geometrical and surface finish tolerances are set, appropriate British or International Standards are invoked and materials are chosen. The design must reflect the requirements of the customer both in performance and reliability. Generally it can be assumed that reliability increases as quality increases. However, care must be taken not to 'over engineer' the product since increasing the quality and reliability usually results in increasing the material, production and inspection costs.

### Material quality

The adoption of standard specifications for materials and 'bought in' components leads to improved product quality and reliability and reduced

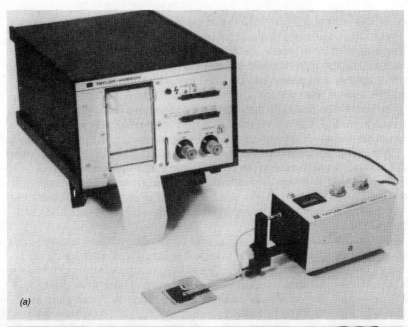

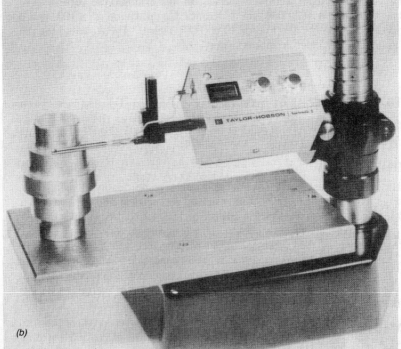

**Fig. 10.35** Electronic surface texture assessment equipment

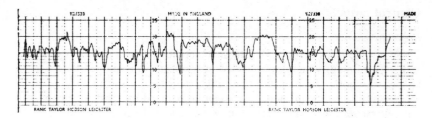

**Fig. 10.36** Typical surface texture traces

waste during production. However, it is essential that materials and components bought from outside sources are sampled and inspected before being issued for manufacture. Traditionally this was done on the purchaser's premises, but modern practice puts the responsibility on the supplier and most large manufacturers will only purchase from suppliers whose quality control satisfies, and is regularly audited by, the purchaser who specifies the quality standards and the method of testing.

## Production quality

This is sometimes called manufacturing quality. The dimensional accuracy which can be expected from various production processes has been summarised in section 6.6, and the surface finish which can be expected from various production processes has been summarised in Table 10.5. The accuracy which can be expected from various measuring devices has been summarised in Table 10.1. The quality of production indicates the degree to which the processing reflects the design requirements. Generally it can be expected that the greater the precision to which the product has to be manufactured, the greater will be the manufacturing costs. To some extent consistency of manufacture has been improved by the adoption of automation and computer controlled machine tools, which remove the chance of human error resulting from lack of concentration and fatigue, as discussed in chapter 5.

## Product quality

This is the combination of design quality, material quality and production (manufacturing) quality and is a measure of how well the products 'fitness for purpose' satisfies the customers requirements.

## Cost of quality

The cost of quality control is made up of the following elements:

(a)  control costs:
    (i)   prevention costs,
    (ii)  appraisal costs;
(b)  failure costs.

## Control costs

### Prevention costs

These are the costs associated with such activities as quality management and staff training, which are intended to inculcate working practices and attitudes to work which ensure that only products of a satisfactory quality are produced. Although faulty work can be rejected by rigid inspection, this represents waste, unnecessary expense, and reduced profitability. Prevention costs should be less than, and preferable to, the costs of such waste which should be eliminated at source.

### Appraisal costs

These are the direct costs of sampling, inspection and testing of raw materials, 'bought in' components, work in progress, and the finished product to ensure 'fitness for purpose', and the prevention of products which are below the specified quality reaching the market and damaging the reputation of the manufacturer.

## Failure costs

The cost of failure and the resulting waste has already been introduced under the heading 'prevention costs'. Generally the number of failures varies inversely with the cost of quality appraisal (inspection) and these cost elements can be expressed graphically as shown in Fig. 10.37.

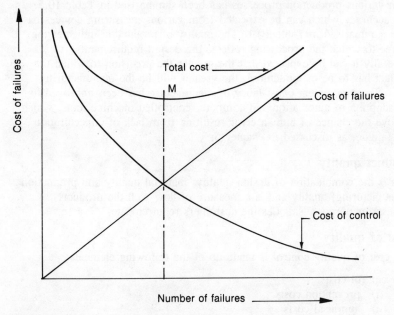

**Fig. 10.37** Cost of quality

The cost of failure represents such factors as, the cost of spoiled material, the cost of wasted production time, the cost of rectification, the cost of customer compensation, the cost of replacement and the loss of customer loyalty. However, reducing the failure rate increases the cost of quality control. Quality appraisal is expensive and if the failure rate is to be reduced to zero then total inspection of all material, and every component at every stage of manufacture, coupled with extensive testing of the final assembly would be required. This would raise the cost of the product to a level which the market would not support. This is a good example of prevention being better than cure and is the reason why 'prevention costs' are a worthwhile investment. Ultimately there has to be some compromise between quality and what the customer will pay.

Figure 10.37 showed the relationship between cost of failure and cost of quality control. The *total cost of quality* is the adding together of these two cost elements. It can be seen that this cost is a minimum at the point 'M'. Thus it would appear that this is an acceptable compromise between quality control costs and failure costs. However, in practice, such a simple decision is not possible and consideration must also be given to such factors as 'good-will' (customer loyalty), and safety. For example, a zero failure rate has to be aimed for in those components of motor vehicles and aircraft upon which human life depends. Statistical methods are widely used in quality control and these are considered in *Manufacturing Technology: volume 2*.

# 11 Manufacturing relationships

## 11.1 The need for information flow

The free flow of information between the departments of an engineering company is essential to the well-being of that company. In a small company consisting of the proprietor and two or three employees this is no problem. However, in large companies, information flow becomes more complex and companies have failed when the channels of information flow have broken down. In a large company it is impossible for one person to solve all the problems and make all the decisions, so the responsibility for decision making and management has to be devolved. As soon as this happens the organisation of the company breaks up into specialised departments. Unfortunately as specialisation increases, the range of interests narrows until, ultimately, the specialist success of the department becomes an end in itself. This leads to selfish decision making which is independent of its effect on other members of the company. As has already been stated, such a lack of cooperation and the consequent breakdown in the free flow of information spells doom for the success of the company. The traditional method of showing the interrelationships between the various departments in a company, which is still widely used, is the hierarchical line management 'tree' as shown in Fig. 11.1. Such hierarchies of managers are common in companies and, although the titles of the roles have changed, this structure has been derived from older institutions such as government offices, and the military. This was largely inevitable since, at the time of the industrial

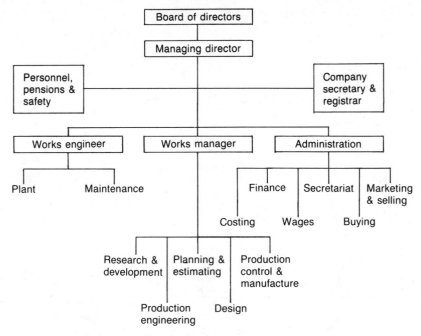

**Fig. 11.1** Company organisation chart (hierarchical)

revolution and the growth of the factory system, the only persons with large scale organisational experience came from such institutions.

In such a system a 'top' manager is responsible to some governing body such as a board of directors. This manager (chief executive) transmits the decisions of the board down through the lines of communication to the next level of management, who are immediately responsible for the implementation of those decisions within their departments and, depending on the size of the company, this devolvement continues down the line to lower layers of management. However, the primary lines of interdepartmental communication essential for cooperation and success are not clearly defined, and it is all too easy for departmental demarcations to develop with the breakdown in information flow mentioned earlier. Obviously a more flexible and less bureaucratic structure is not only desirable but even essential for the success of a company.

An alternative method of organisation is shown in Fig. 11.2. Here, the policy forming board of directors forms the 'hub' of the circles. Their decisions are passed out radially to the departmental heads along radial lines and feedback follows the same routes. The concentric circles show the levels of management. Thus the radial lines represent the traditional, hierarchical system of line management whilst the circular lines indicate interdepartmental information flow.

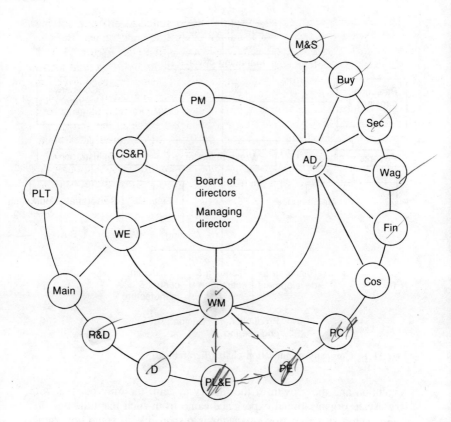

PM    = Personnel management
CS&R  = Company secretary & registrar
WE    = Works engineer
WM    = Works manager
AD    = Administration
PLT   = Plant
Main  = Maintenance
R&D   = Research & development
D     = Design
PL&E  = Planning & estimating
PE    = Production engineering
PC    = Production control
COS   = Costing
Fin   = Finance
WAG   = Wages
Sec   = Secretariat
Buy   = Buying
M&S   = Marketing & selling

**Fig. 11.2**  Company organisation chart (circular)

The circular system of organisation is best suited to problem solving. It is used widely in Japan and firms with Japanese connections. Because of its success, it is now increasingly adopted in the UK. Figure 11.3 shows that the problem is at the 'hub' of the circle and the radial arrows indicate the concentration of each of the departmental representatives on the problem. The peripheral arrows represent the interchange of ideas between departments. Secondary information flow can take place across the circle as required, as indicated by the arrow between the shop foreman and the production engineer. This type of organisation is often used to solve quality problems with the appropriate management and shopfloor workers sorting out the problem on equal terms. Although this circular or 'round table' approach implies parity between the persons present, inevitably one of the group has to act as 'ring master' to ensure an equal input opportunity for everyone present.

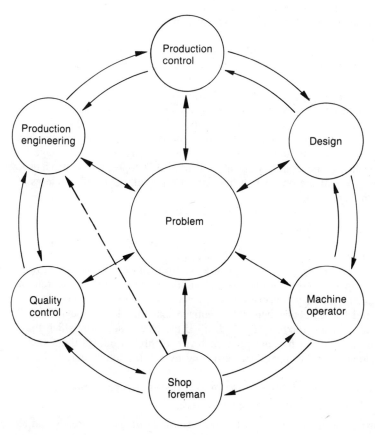

**Fig. 11.3** Round-table problem solving

Matrices and flow charts are also appropriate for more complex organisational problems such as the organisation of large-scale projects involving many companies, for example the Channel Tunnel.

## 11.2 Departmental functions, marketing and sales

The primary functions of marketing and sales are often confused. *Marketing* is essentially a research operation. The question any company should regularly ask itself is: 'are we in the right business'? If the answer is no, it should ask the question: 'what business should we be in'? For example, a number of prosperous steam locomotive manufacturers went out of business because they had failed to change to alternative products when British Rail started to change over to diesel and electric locomotives.

They failed through lack of *market research*. The organisation of marketing and its relationship with selling varies between those companies selling a standard product and those companies fabricating 'one-off' products to order.

A company making a standardised product, or a range of such products, needs to watch market trends very carefully. Every product has a life cycle. A slow down in sales growth is a warning signal. It may mean that greater effort in selling is required or that the life of the product is in decline. A positive falling off in sales volume is a very clear signal that, despite the efforts of the sales force, the end of the product life cycle is in sight. Too many companies persist with a product beyond its useful life and even sell it at a loss. Long before this stage has been reached a successful company will have developed a new product to take the place of the one which has passed the peak of its life cycle as shown in Fig. 11.4.

Market research plays a vital role in the development of new products. Apart from providing the data necessary to decide whether a new product or a new market is required, it can help to decide what the new product should be and whether it has a viable market. New products arise in a variety of ways. They can arise from information brought back to the company by its salesmen; they can arise from planned research and development, or they can even arise by accident. Stainless steel was discovered by accident when it was noticed that samples of nickel-chromium ferrous alloys which had failed the experiment for which they had been formulated had not gone rusty when thrown out on the scrap heap. However no company can last long by relying upon such accidental discoveries.

Thus the responsibilities of the market research department can be summarised as:

(a) providing the company with up-to-date data of market trends and customer requirements;

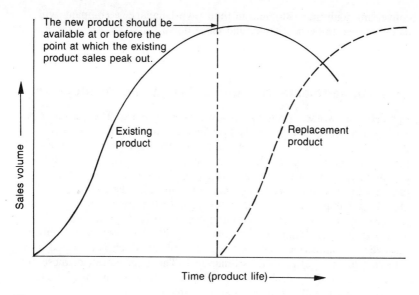

The new product should be available at or before the point at which the existing product sales peak out.

Existing product

Replacement product

Sales volume

Time (product life)

**Fig. 11.4** Product life cycle

(b) providing the company with information about the product development, marketing strategies and pricing strategies of its competitors;

(c) providing the company with information about the life cycle of its existing products so that new products can be developed before the existing products cease to be marketable and profitable;

(d) making a preliminary assessment of ideas for new products;

(e) making a detailed study of the viability of a new product before large sums are spent upon research and development, and also upon the purchase of capital equipment and tooling.

In addition to these research and advisory functions, the marketing department is also responsible for 'softening up' the ground for the sales force by planning the publicity surrounding the launch of a new product. In contrast to marketing, selling has two main functions:

(a) the procurement of the orders and contracts from customers, upon which the financial prosperity of the company depends;

(b) the feed back of information on customer's requirements, information concerning the effectiveness of promotional material, and customer satisfaction with distribution, servicing and product reliability.

No matter how well researched the market, no matter how well developed the product, without a knowledgeable and enthusiastic sales force in the field, trained in modern selling techniques and capable of conversing with the customers in their own language, a company will quickly cease to be profitable, and close down.

## 11.3 Departmental functions, design and development

For better or worse, 'progress' is always taking place. The customer is always demanding better quality products at a lower price. However, these two requirements are often incompatible and a compromise has to be reached by providing value for money. One customer may prefer to pay more for, say, a luxury car, whilst another customer may prefer to pay less for a volume production car. In both cases the customer will expect the car purchased to represent 'state of the art' technology within its class and to reflect current styling trends. In fact appearance and styling (industrial design) is now not only applied to consumer durables but even to commercial and industrial equipment which is expected to be 'pleasing to the eye' as well as functional. The achievement of these aims is the function of the design and development department working closely in collaboration with the marketing department.

## 11.4 Departmental functions, production planning

The method of production of any new product must be carefully planned. Production planning requires the answer to such questions as: 'is the product to be built within the confines of existing plant'? If the answer is yes then the production departments and the design team must get together to ensure that not only is it possible to manufacture the new product on the existing plant, but it can also be manufactured profitably on the existing plant. This involves consultation with the financial departments.

However, if the answer to the original question is no then new questions arise such as:

(a) How much can be spent on new plant?
(b) What new plant is necessary to satisfy the demands of the new product?
(c) Will the anticipated market and sales volume warrant the use of automated plant (e.g. CNC machines and robots), and has the company got the expertise to use such equipment effectively?
(d) Is a compromise required between the demands of the design team and the practical requirements of production?

Again interdepartmental information flow and consultation is necessary if the correct decisions are to be made and a working compromise reached.

## 11.5 Departmental functions, estimating and costing

Estimating and costing are closely associated with production planning. In fact, they are often an extension of the work of the planning engineer. At each planning stage, the production time and the material quantities involved must be estimated and costed so that the economic viability of the process can be assessed. The cost of a new product is determined in two stages.

### Estimating

This, as the word implies, is the assessment of the time taken to produce a new product based on experience and historical data. There are essentially two techniques.

(*a*) Comparison of the new product with a previous, similar product for which actual production times are known. The experience of the estimator is then used to make allowance for any differences.

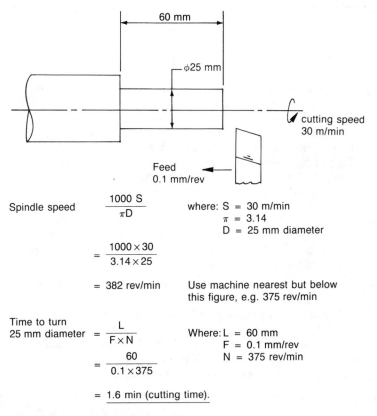

Spindle speed $\dfrac{1000\,S}{\pi D}$  where: S = 30 m/min
$\pi$ = 3.14
D = 25 mm diameter

$= \dfrac{1000 \times 30}{3.14 \times 25}$

= 382 rev/min  Use machine nearest but below
this figure, e.g. 375 rev/min

Time to turn
25 mm diameter $= \dfrac{L}{F \times N}$  Where: L = 60 mm
F = 0.1 mm/rev
N = 375 rev/min

$= \dfrac{60}{0.1 \times 375}$

= 1.6 min (cutting time).

**Fig. 11.5**  Calculation of cutting time

366

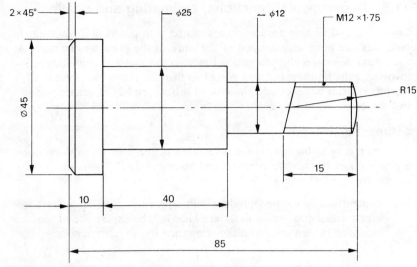

2 × 45° — ⌀25 — φ12 — M12 × 1·75

⌀45

R15

15

10   40

85

Dimensions in millimetres. Material: Free-cutting mild steel.

**Fig. 11.6** Typical turned part

(*b*) The new product is broken down into its constituent elements and the estimated time is synthesised as follows.

  (i) *Productive time* can be calculated from the cutting parameters for each machining operation. For example, the time taken to turn a diameter on a component can be calculated as shown in Fig. 11.5. More problematical are operations which are performed manually. Estimates of manual operation times can be calculated from tables of *observed times* produced by the *work or time study* engineer.

  (ii) *Non-productive time* consists of such operations as loading and unloading components, removing swarf from the machine, and changing tools. Such times are also calculated from tables of observed times.

The total 'floor-to-floor' production time for a component is the sum of the productive and non-productive times. A typical turned component is shown in Fig. 11.6 and the comprehensive planning sheet showing the estimated times for producing the component on a capstan lathe is shown in Fig. 11.7. It is immediately apparent that the times can be much more accurately estimated if the component is produced on a CNC lathe as there are no variable human elements to take into account.

## Costing

Once the process times and the material quantities have been estimated, the product can be *costed*. To arrive at the *direct labour cost* it appears

# A.N. ENGINEERING CO. LTD.

PLANNED BY:
CHECKED BY:

DRG NO | MACHINE | MATERIAL | QUANTITY | DATE REQUIRED | SPECIAL FEATURES

| 1 OPERATION NO | 2 OPERATION | 3 TOOLING | 4 TURRET OR X SLIDE | 5 SPEED m/min | 5 SPEED rev/min | 6 FEED RATE mm/rev | 7 LENGTH OF CUT mm | 8 CUTTING TIME (MIN) | 9 NON PRODUCTIVE TIME (MIN) |
|---|---|---|---|---|---|---|---|---|---|
| 1 | Feed to stop | Bar stop | T | – | – | – | – | – | 0·100 |
|  | Index & lock turret | – | – | – | – | – | – | – | 0·100 |
|  | Change speed | – | – | – | – | – | – | – | 0·085 |
| 2 | Turn 25 mm diam. | Roller tool box | T | 50 | 600 | 0·25 | 75 | 0·5 | – |
|  | Index & lock turret | – | – | – | – | – | – | – | 0·100 |
|  | Change speed | – | – | – | – | – | – | – | 0·085 |
| 3 | Turn 12 mm diam. | Roller tool box | T | 50 | 1250 | 0·25 | 35 | 0·112 | – |
|  | Index & lock turret | – | – | – | – | – | – | – | 0·100 |
| 4 | Radius end | End turning box | T | 50 | 1250 | Manual | – | 0·08 | – |
|  | Index & lock turret | – | – | – | – | – | – | – | 0·100 |
|  | Change speed | – | – | – | – | – | – | – | 0·085 |
| 5 | Rough thread | S/O Die head | T | 10 | 250 | 1·75 | 15 | 0·035 | – |
| 6 | Withdraw, re-set die head, finish | S/O Die head | T | 10 | 250 | 1·75 | 15 | 0·035 | – |
|  | Index to stop & lock | – | T | – | – | – | – | – | 0·080 |
| 7 | Recess | Parting tool | X | 30 | 250 | Manual | – | 0·200 | 0·150 |
| 8 | Chamfer | R.H. 45° chamfer tool | X | 30 | 250 | Manual | – | 0·200 | – |
| 9 | Part off | Parting tool | X | 30 | 250 | Manual | – | 0·350 | – |
| 10 | Break bar end ready for next cycle | L.H. 45° chamfer tool | X | 30 | 250 | Manual | – | 0·150 | – |
| | TOTALS | | | | | | | 1·562 | 0·985 |

cycle time 1·562 + 0·985 = 2·547 minutes per component

**Fig. 11.7** Comprehensive planning sheet

368

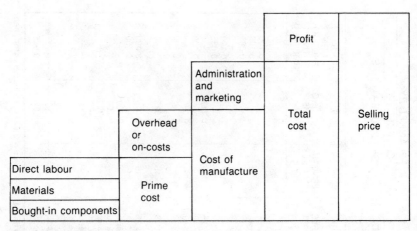

**Fig. 11.8** Cost structure

that the cycle time arrived at in Fig. 11.7 has only to be multipled by the appropriate rate of pay. However this is too easy and once again the experience of the planning engineer is called upon for the following reasons:

(a) the operator will not maintain a constant rate of production but will tire towards the end of the shift;
(b) allowance must be made for the operator to attend to personal needs from time to time;
(c) allowance must be made for the machine to be adjusted from time to time, to compensate for tool wear or accidental tool breakage.

These factors are usually taken into account by adding a contingency factor to the estimated cycle time. Finally, other factors such as material costs, overhead expenses, and profit margins must be taken into account to arrive at the final selling price as shown in Fig. 11.8. Thus the process of costing and estimating involves cooperation and consultation between the production planning engineers (cycle time), the personnel department (wage rates) and the cost accountants (overheads and profit margins).

Note that costing and estimating is not the same as *cost control*. Cost control is used to ensure that production costs do not get out of step with the original estimates and costing upon which the initial selling price was based. Cost control is considered in *Manufacturing Technology: volume 2.*

## 11.6 Departmental functions, production control

Whilst production planning is largely a technical function, production control is largely an administrative function. Once the product has been accepted for production, the tooling is in place and the materials have been purchased, the production control department takes over. Basically its responsibilities are to ensure that:

(a)  the right components are produced at the right time to satisfy the customer's delivery requirements,
(b)  the plant is uniformly loaded so that neither 'bottle-necks' occur nor expensive capital plant stands idle,
(c)  stocks of work between operations are kept to a minimum,
(d)  only minimum 'buffer' stocks of finished work are kept to ensure prompt delivery. This is particularly important towards the end of the life cycle of a product.

Thus it is important that the production control department works closely with the sales department to ensure that delivery promises to customers are kept. It is also important that the production control department works closely with the marketing department to ensure that stocks of old products are run down in line with withdrawal of the product, and that stocks of any new product are available ready for its launch.

## 11.7  Departmental functions, inspection and quality control

The importance of quality control and its achievement has already been considered in Chapter 10. Increasingly, consumers are expecting improved quality at minimum cost in a never ending search for 'value for money'. Quality control is paramount in the achievement and maintenance of the 'good-will' and customer loyalty upon which the success of a company depends. All successful companies are continually striving to improve quality to internationally acceptable standards. 'Good-will' takes years to build up and only minutes to lose through lack of attention to detail.

## 11.8  Departmental functions, maintenance

The maintenance of the plant and premises in good condition is essential if the manufacturing and commercial departments of a company are to maintain a high level of operating efficiency. Maintenance falls into two categories:

(a)  Routine or *preventative* maintenance, that is, the regular servicing of the plant and premises so that major problems are avoided. For example, it is better to paint the window frames of the building regularly than disrupt the work of an office whilst a rotten frame is replaced. Again, a major plant breakdown can cause loss of production, late delivery, and a very angry customer.

(*b*) Major repairs or refurbishment. The best of preventative maintenance schemes cannot prevent occasional major breakdowns. Further, from time to time plant has to undergo major refurbishment. Either of these occurrences require the closest cooperation between the departments concerned so that disruption is minimised and the least possible production time is lost.

## 11.9 The organisation of a new product

Having considered the various departmental functions, the need for a free flow of information between those departments and some organisational systems to ensure that flow of information, it is now necessary to consider the information itself.

For a number of years, Messrs A. Locksmith Ltd., have been manufacturing car door locks for the motor trade. They have specialised in locks for the lower cost end of the volume car market. For some time their design department has been working with their customers to develop a new range of locks providing greater security against theft. Market research has established the need for a range of similar high security locks which can be fitted to existing vehicles in place of the original locks. The information required to make the manufacturing decisions for such a project will now be briefly considered.

### Economic information

Having shown the need for the improved lock, market research must answer a number of fundamental questions in order to justify the expense of a detailed design study. This basic economic information would be as shown below.

#### Quantity

(*a*) Does the anticipated demand justify the cost of tooling up to manufacture such a range of locks?
(*b*) Does the anticipated demand justify the cost of production?
(*c*) Will the range cover all previous cars or only a limited number. If the latter, which cars?

#### Make/buy

(*a*) What parts will be made and what parts will be cheaper to buy in from specialist firms?
(*b*) Has the plant sufficient capacity to make all these replacement locks in addition to its current production?
(*c*) If the answer to (*b*) is no, can part or the whole of production be contracted to outside suppliers?

#### Delivery date

By when is delivery required? Does the launch date need to coincide with a trade show? And can this date be achieved without interfering with other work?

*Marketing*

Can any inducement be given to the motoring public to buy these locks? For example, could the cost of fitting be wholly or partially offset by insurance premium rebates?

## Design information

*Purpose*

The design team need to be given a clear brief as to what they are to design and the purpose of the design. Lack of precise and detailed information can lead to much wasted time and unsatisfactory designs.

*Size & shape*

Since these proposed locks are to replace existing locks they will need to be the same size and shape. This information can be obtained from a number of sources. These include the company's own records since it is an established manufacturer of car locks; the British Standard Institutions publications for the motor trade; the manufacturers of the cars for which the improved replacement locks are going to be made.

*Accuracy*

This needs to be no greater than is necessary to ensure the locks can be easily assembled and that they will work satisfactorily over their projected life span. As has been mentioned previously in this book unnecessarily close tolerances only lead to increased cost and result in the product being 'over engineered'.

*Materials*

These need to be closely specified to ensure 'fitness for purpose'. They need to have adequate properties for the duties the components made from them have to perform. It would be uneconomic to specify a high duty alloy steel where a plain carbon steel would be adequate.

*Treatment*

Any heat treatment process for components subject to wear needs to be specified.

*Finish*

Any decorative or anti-corrosion finishes need to be specified.

## Plant information

This is required during the planning and design stages to ensure that the product can be made without having to resort to the purchase of expensive items of capital equipment.

*Range*

Is the range of processes available adequate to ensure that as many components as possible can be manufactured within the existing plant so that investment in new plant is minimal?

## *Capacity*

Can the new product range be manufactured within the capacity of the existing plant or will it have to be sub-contracted to outside suppliers?

## *Availability*

Will plant capacity be available at the time that the new product is to be put into production?

## *Capability*

Is the plant capable of producing components of the required quality?

## *Batch/Flow*

Is batch production to be used so that the new product can be manufactured between batches of current products, or is flow production to be used in which case a new production line will need to be organised?

## *Maintenance*

Will the plant be over-utilised? Will the additional loading on the plant interfere with the planned maintenance programme and lead to breakdowns and disruption of production?

# Manufacturing information

Once the design has been accepted; once any problems concerning plant availability and suitability have been resolved and the decision to manufacture has been made, the following information will be required so that production can commence.

## *Batch size*

This will determine the method of manufacture and the sophistication of any special tools required.

## *Special tooling*

As well as the product design, the drawing office will need to issue drawings for any special tooling such as jigs, fixtures and press tools. 'Lead time' must be allowed for the manufacture of this equipment.

## *Software*

If CNC machine tools and robots are to be used, then part programmes will need to be written for the various components.

## *Quality*

Inspection and quality control is an expensive but important element of the manufacturing process. Since the new products chosen for this example are a range of improved locks for the motor industry, it is most likely that the car firms concerned will set their own standards based on the British Standard Recommendations for quality control. Since large batches of similar products are being made, statistical quality control techniques can be used to reduce inspection costs.

## Treatments

The need for heat treatment, and protective and decorative finishes have already been discussed. Such treatments are often contracted out and arrangements will have to be made with suitable sub-contractors as well as quality control systems to ensure this outwork is up to standard.

# Industrial engineering

## Method study

This is concerned with finding the best way of doing jobs, particularly manual operations. Each selected area of work must be observed by specialist method study engineers and their observations recorded and analysed. They must then develop the most efficient way of doing the job so as to ensure fast and consistent results with a minimum of operator fatigue. They must install the new method and ensure that its use is maintained and that the workers concerned do not revert to less efficient methods out of personal preference.

## Work measurement

The main objective of work measurement is to achieve *standard times* for jobs. Standard time is the time it takes a trained worker to carry out a job at a specified level of performance. Standard times are used for costing purposes, production plannning and determining manning levels.

## Planning and scheduling

Planning and scheduling are necessary to ensure that all the parts arrive at the next stage of production without shortages causing hold ups or the creation of excessive stocks of work in progress. Without proper planning and scheduling, the even loading of plant and the smooth flow of production would not be possible and delivery schedules would not be met.

# 12 Exercises

## Chapter 1

1. Prepare a design specification for a simple component of your own choice and explain how this specification influences the manufacturing processes to be used in terms of: geometry; quality; materials; machine or equipment process capability; and cost.
2. The component shown in Fig. 12.1 consists of a number of geometrical surfaces. Identify these surfaces and specify a suitable machining process for the production of each surface.
3. The unit manufacturing cost for producing a particular component by hand is £5.00. Using a machine reduces this cost to £3.00 but the machine costs £1500.00. Draw a break-even graph and determine the minimum number of components which have to be manufactured before the cost of a machine can be justified.
4. List the advantages and limitations of sand-casting compared with pressure die-casting.
5. List the advantages and limitations of forging and finish machining compared with machining from the solid for the cluster gear shown in Fig. 12.2.
6. (a) Compare and contrast the processes of drawing solid rod and drawing tube on a draw bench. Use sketches to illustrate the principles in each case.
   (b) With aid of sketches show how small diameter wire is drawn on a multiple die machine and explain how the machine

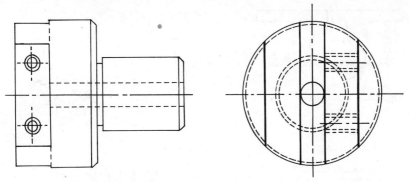

**Fig. 12.1**

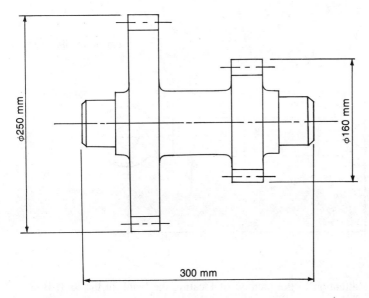

φ250 mm

φ160 mm

300 mm

**Fig. 12.2**

compensates for the increase in length of the wire as its
diameter is progressively reduced at each stage.

7. Explain with the aid of sketches how the brass door-bolt section
shown in Fig. 12.3 is produced by a combination of hot-extrusion
and cold-drawing.

8. (a) Sketch a simple blanking tool, naming the more important
features, for producing the blanks for the bracket shown in
Fig. 12.4. Take into account the grain orientation of the strip
so as to avoid cracking occurring during the bending process.

   (b) Sketch a simple piercing tool for piercing the fixing holes in
the blank for the bracket shown in Fig. 12.4. Pay particular

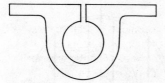

**Fig. 12.3**

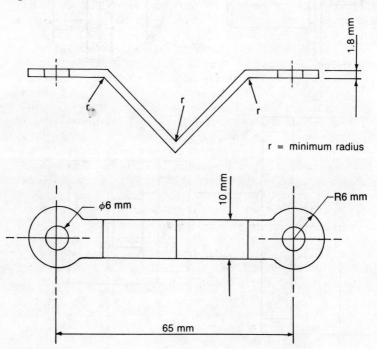

r = minimum radius

**Fig. 12.4**

attention to the method of locating the blank in the tool. Both holes are to be produced at the same time. Name the more important features of the tool.

(c) Sketch a simple press bending tool, naming the more important features, for forming the bracket shown in Fig. 12.4. Pay particular attention to the method of locating the pierced blank in the tool.

9. Discuss the types of component and plastic moulding materials for which the following moulding processes are most suitable: flash moulding; transfer moulding; injection moulding; and extrusion moulding.

10. State *two* applications of chemical machining and explain why chemical machining is the most appropriate process in each instance.

# Chapter 2

11. With the aid of sketches show how the fundamental metal cutting wedge is applied to the following metal cutting tools so as to provide rake and clearance angles: lathe parting-off tool; twist drill; thread cutting tap; slot milling cutter for a horizontal milling machine; power hacksaw blade; cold chisel.

12. Describe the influence which the workpiece material has on the selection of cutting angles for a given cutting tool and also upon the type of chip produced.

13. (a) With reference to manufacturers' manuals, describe the essential differences between a P15 carbide tool insert and a K30 carbide tool insert. Give an example where it would be appropriate for each to be used, with reasons for your choice.

    (b) With the aid of sketches show the difference between positive rake and negative rake cutting and discuss the advantages and limitations of each technique.

14. Show with the aid of sketches what is meant by the terms *orthogonal* cutting and *oblique* cutting. Describe the effect of these tool geometries on the cutting action of a single point lathe tool in terms of the $d{:}f$ ratio and chip thickness.

15. Discuss the factors which influence the choice of cutting speed, rate of feed and depth of cut when setting up a machine for a given job.

16. Calculate the time taken, to the nearest second, to complete a cut using a slab milling cutter under the conditions set out below.

    | | |
    |---|---|
    | Diameter of cutter | 100 m |
    | Number of teeth | 8 |
    | Feed per tooth | 0.05 mm |
    | Cutting speed | 30 m/min |
    | Length of cut | 250 mm |

17. Describe with the aid of sketches:

    (a) the difference between the formation of continuous and discontinuous chips;

    (b) what is meant by a *built-up edge* on a tool and how it may be avoided;

    (c) the function of a chip breaker.

18. The life of a lathe tool is 3 hours when it is cutting at 80 m/min. Given that $Vt^n = C$, calculate the highest cutting speed which will give a tool life of 8 hours. Take $n = 0.15$.

19. (a) Discuss the factors which have to be considered when selecting an abrasive wheel (grinding wheel) for a specific application.

    (b) Explain what is meant by 'arc of contact' and how this affects the grade of wheel chosen.

20. List the main functions of a cutting fluid and discuss the factors which have to be considered when selecting a cutting fluid for a particular application.

## Chapter 3

21. With the aid of sketches describe:
    (a) the difference between restraint and location as applied to work-holding on machine tools;
    (b) the difference between frictional and positive restraints as applied to work-holding on machine tools.

22. With the aid of sketches explain:
    (a) what is meant by the *six degrees of freedom* as applied to work-holding on machine tools;
    (b) how these freedoms may be restrained when work is held:
        (i) between centres on a lathe;
        (ii) in a three-jaw self-centring chuck on a lathe;
        (iii) in V-blocks on a drilling machine;
        (iv) in a machine vice on a vertical spindle milling machine.

23. Figure 12.5 shows a component which is to be set up for milling the slot A. The surfaces PQRS have been previously machined and may be used for location purposes.
    (a) With the aid of sketches show how a single component could be located, aligned and clamped on a milling machine table for the production of the slot.
    (b) Sketch a suitable milling fixture for machining the slot in a batch of components, naming the main features of the fixture.

24. Figure 12.5 shows a component in which the holes marked B are to be drilled and reamed. The surfaces PQRS have been previously

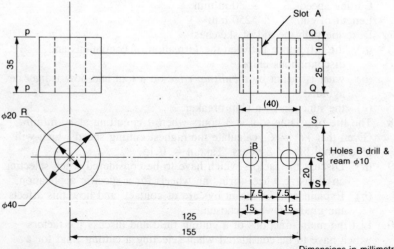

Dimensions in millimetres

**Fig. 12.5**

machined and may be used for location purposes. Sketch a suitable drilling jig naming the main features.

25. Figure 12.5 shows a component in which the slot A is to be milled and the holes B are to be drilled and reamed. With the aid of sketches show a suitable method of work-holding on a CNC milling machine so that both the slot and the holes may be produced at the same setting for a small batch of components.

26. Discuss the advantages and limitations of magnetic chucks as work-holding devices on grinding machines.

## Chapter 4

27. With the aid of sketches explain the difference between *generating, forming* and *copying* surfaces when machining.

28. Discuss the essential requirements of a machine tool and explain how these are met with in a typical vertical milling machine.

29. List the essential requirements of machine tool beds and columns and discuss how these requirements are met with in a typical centre lathe.

30. (a) With the aid of sketches compare and contrast the power transmission systems of a centre lathe and a milling machine and suggest reasons for any differences.

    (b) Discuss the advantages and limitations of belt drives compared with gear drives as applied to the transmission systems of machine tools.

31. Discuss the advantages and limitations of the following types of slideways: dovetail slideways; inverted-V slideways; hydrostatic slideways.

32. With the aid of sketches, develop the fundamental geometrical movements and alignments of *two* of the following: horizontal spindle milling machine; vertical spindle milling machine; centre lathe; column type drilling machine; cylindrical grinding machine; surface grinding machine.

33. (a) Discuss the advantages and limitations of plain bearings compared with anti-friction (ball and roller) bearings for machine spindles.

    (b) Sketch a typical machine spindle and its bearings and indicate how your design allows the spindle to expand without distortion or misalignment as its warms up.

34. (a) Compare and contrast the advantages and limitations of the following machine tool positioning systems: lead screw and nut; rack and pinion; hydraulic piston and cylinder.

    (b) State the advantages of using a recirculating ball screw and nut rather than a conventional lead screw and nut on CNC machine tools.

35. (*a*) Explain why it is bad practice to use the same mechanism (e.g. lead screw and nut) for both positioning and measuring in a machine tool, and suggest how this may be avoided.

    (*b*) List some causes of misalignment resulting from lack of care and attention when setting up a workpiece on a machine tool.

## Chapter 5

36. Despite the fact that CNC machine tools are more complex and costly than conventional machine tools they are being used increasingly in manufacturing industry. Discuss the reasons why this should be so.

37. Figure 12.6 shows outline diagrams of a number of machine tools. Redraw these diagrams and add and label the X, Y, and Z axes.

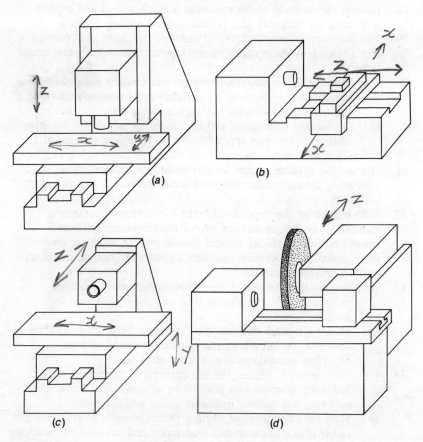

(a)

(b)

(c)

(d)

**Fig. 12.6**

38. Explain the essential differences between *point-to-point* control systems and *continuous path* control systems.

39. With the aid of sketches explain the difference between *open-loop* and *closed-loop* control systems, and list the advantages and limitations of each system.

40. Discuss the relative merits and limitations of the following methods of data input: conversational manual data input; punched tape data input; magnetic tape data input; direct numerical control.

41. (a) Explain what is meant by the following terms used in programming: character; management word; dimensional word; block; preparatory code; miscellaneous command; modal command.

    (b) A typical letter address format could be:
    N4 G2 X4,3 Y4,3 Z4,3 I4,3 J4,3 K4,3 F3 S4 T2 M2
        (i) State whether this format is in inch or metric units and state the reason for your choice.
        (ii) Explain what this format means.

42. (a) State what is meant by the term *canned cycle*.
    (b) State the advantage of using canned cycles.
    (c) With the aid of sketches show the sequence of a typical canned cycle.

43. Explain why CNC machine controllers are provided with *tool length offset* and *cutter diameter/tool nose radius compensation*, and why it is important that the machine operator is fully trained in the use of these facilities.

44. Prepare an operation planning sheet listing the tooling, spindle speeds, and feed rates for machining the component shown in Fig. 12.7. Use this data to prepare a part programme for machining the component from the solid on a vertical spindle CNC milling machine. Specify the controller and the machine for which the programme has been written.

45. Prepare an operation planning sheet listing the tooling, spindle speeds, and feed rates for turning the component shown in Fig. 12.8. Use this data to prepare a part programme for machining the component from a solid blank on a CNC lathe. Specify the controller and the machine for which the programme has been written.

## Chapter 6

46. Discuss the effects of design, batch size, and component accuracy on the assembly process.

47. Explain the meaning of the following terms using sketches if necessary.
    (a) Selective and non-selective assembly.
    (b) Maximum and minimum metal condition.

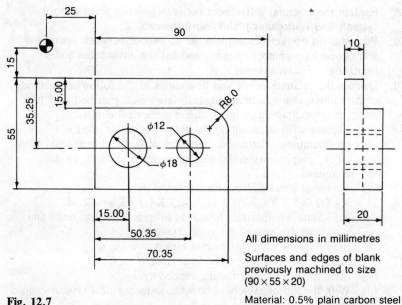

**Fig. 12.7**

All dimensions in millimetres

Surfaces and edges of blank previously machined to size (90 × 55 × 20)

Material: 0.5% plain carbon steel

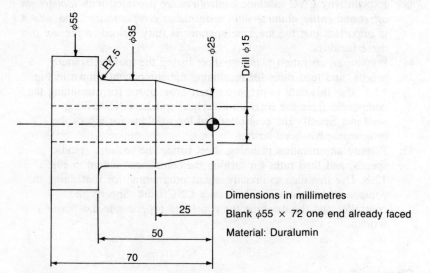

Dimensions in millimetres

Blank ⌀55 × 72 one end already faced

Material: Duralumin

**Fig. 12.8**

    (c)  Hole basis and shaft basis systems.
    (d)  Clearance, interference and transition fits.
48.  Explain the meaning of the following terms using sketches if necessary.
    (a)  Limits of size.

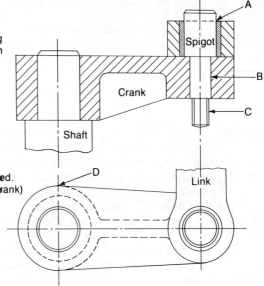

A — Easily removed retaining
device causing minimum
overhang

B — Device to prevent the
spigot rotating in the
crank

C — Screwed fastening
with locking device

D — Device to fix crank
rigidly to shaft, yet
allow crank to be removed.
(Hint: consider bicycle crank)

**Fig. 12.9**

- (b) Tolerance.
- (c) Minimum clearance (allowance).
- (d) Unilateral tolerance and bilateral tolerance.
- (e) Fundamental deviation and fundamental tolerance.
- 49. (a) With reference to the Primary Selection of Fits (BS 4500), calculate the dimensions for a shaft and hole combination specified as: 25 mm H8/f7.
  - (b) With reference to the Standard Tolerances (BS 4500) and the recommended relationship between process and standard tolerance, select suitable processes for manufacturing the shaft and hole specified in part (a) of this question.
- 50. (a) Explain, with the aid of sketches, the principles of:
  - (i) a mechanical compression joint;
  - (ii) a thermal compression joint.
  - (b) Name a suitable application for each of the above types of joint giving reasons for your choice.
  - (c) State the essential properties of the materials selected for the inner and outer elements of a compression joint.
- 51. Figure 12.9 shows a simple engineering assembly. Specify suitable fastenings to be used at positions A, B, C and D, giving reasons for your choice.

## Chapter 7

52. Describe, using sketches if necessary, suitable applications for the following cutting equipment or processes:

(a) guillotine shear;
(b) portable nibbling machine;
(c) oxy-acetylene flame cutting torch;
(d) universal cropping and notching machine.

53. With the aid of sketches describe suitable applications for the following forming equipment:
   (a) folding machine;
   (b) press brake;
   (c) bending rolls.

54. With the aid of sketches describe *three* precautions which must be taken in order to achieve a satisfactory joint when using screwed fastenings to secure together rolled steel sections (RSJ or BSB).

55. Figure 12.10 shows a section through a typical riveted joint using a snap head rivet. Calculate the hole diameter and the shank length of the rivet to ensure a satisfactory joint.

56. (a) When soft soldering, describe what precautions must be taken to ensure a sound joint.
   (b) Explain why a flux must be used when soft soldering and explain the difference between a passive and an active flux and state under what circumstances each would be used.

57. (a) Describe the essential difference between hard soldering (brazing) and soft soldering, and describe the four basic conditions upon which a successful brazed joint depends.
   (b) Explain, with the aid of sketches, how a collar may be brazed onto the end of a shaft using preformed spelter and electric induction heating.

58. With the aid of sketches describe the essential principles of the following joining processes:
   (a) oxy-acetylene welding;
   (b) manual metallic-arc welding;
   (c) spot welding.

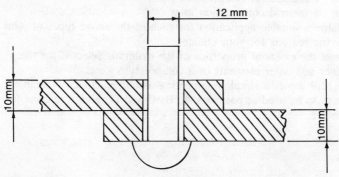

**Fig. 12.10**

59. Describe in detail the safety precautions which must be taken when:
    (a) oxy-acetylene welding;
    (b) manual metallic-arc welding.
60. (a) List the advantages and limitations of adhesive bonding for metal components compared with soldering, brazing and welding.
    (b) Explain, with the aid of sketches, how bonded joints may fail.
    (c) Describe the precautions which must be taken to ensure a sound bonded joint.
61. Describe, with the aid of sketches, how plastic materials may be joined by:
    (a) heat welding;
    (b) solvent welding;
    (c) adhesive bonding.
62. Describe, with the aid of sketches, how sheet plastic materials may be fabricated by heat bending, vacuum forming, blow forming, and pressing techniques.

## Chapter 8

63. Describe what is meant by *recrystallisation*, and how this phenomenon can be exploited when softening work-hardened, non-ferrous metals.
64. (a) With reference to plain carbon steels describe the process of:
    (i) sub-critical annealing;
    (ii) spheroidising annealing;
    (iii) full annealing;
    (iv) normalising.
    (b) State an appropriate application for each of the above processes giving reasons for your choice in each instance.
65. Describe in detail how a component made from a plain carbon steel containing 1.0 per cent carbon may be quench-hardened. Pay particular attention to the hardening temperature, the rate of cooling, and the precautions which must be taken to avoid grain growth, distortion and cracking.
66. Describe in detail how the component shown in Fig. 12.11 may be case-hardened whilst leaving the thread and hexagon head soft.
67. With reference to 'Duralumin' aluminium alloy describe how:
    (a) it may be softened by solution treatment;
    (b) natural age hardening may be delayed;
    (c) it may be precipitation age hardened by an artifical ageing process.
68. List the essential requirements of a heat-treatment furnace and explain how these requirements are met in:
    (a) an electrically heated muffle furnace;
    (b) a gas heated salt bath furnace.

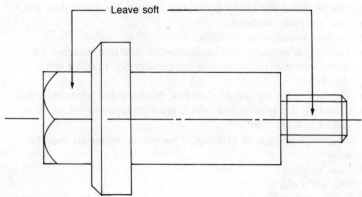

**Fig. 12.11**

69. (a) Describe in detail the general precautions which must be taken when using salt bath furnaces.
    (b) Describe in detail the particular precautions which must be taken when using nitrate-based salts for tempering and cyanide-based salts for carburising.
70. Describe the principles of the thermocouple and how they are applied to:
    (a) the thermocouple pyrometer;
    (b) the radiation pyrometer.

## Chapter 9

71. Describe one chemical and two physical preparatory treatments which may have to be carried out before the application of decorative or corrosion resistant finishes to metal components.
72. Describe suitable applications for the following finishing processes, giving reasons for your choice.
    (a) Galvanising (hot-dip).
    (b) Sherardising.
    (c) Chromating.
    (d) Phosphating.
73. (a) Describe the process of metal spraying.
    (b) Describe *three* typical applications of the metal spraying process giving reasons for your choice.
74. Describe the principle of *anodising* and explain how it protects aluminium and aluminium alloy components.
75. (a) Describe the principle of *electroplating*.
    (b) Explain why:
        (i) zinc alloy die-castings should be copper plated before nickel plating;

      (ii)  steel components are usually nickel plated before chromium plating.

76.  Discuss the advantages and limitations of plastic coating metal components compared with electroplating.

77.  Describe a complete paint system and explain the need for the various coats which have to be applied.

78.  Compare and contrast the processes of *spraying* and *dipping* as methods of applying paint films to metal components and fabrications.

79.  Describe the hazards associated with industrial painting processes and explain how these may be overcome.

80.  Describe briefly how finishing processes affect material properties in terms of: mechanical finishing; thermal effects; chemical effects; surface alloying effects.

## Chapter 10

81.  Define *quality* as applied to manufactured products and explain the importance of quality control in today's industrial environment.

82.  List the following measuring instruments in descending order of accuracy and state a suitable application for each instrument giving reasons for your choice: steel rule; slip gauges (inspection grade); laser standard; micrometer caliper.

83.  (*a*)  Write down the micrometer caliper readings shown in Fig. 12.12.

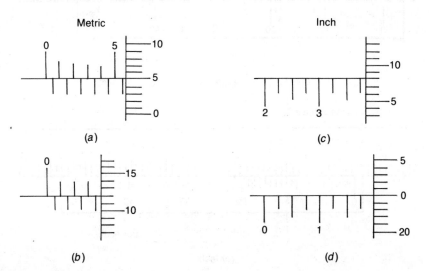

(*a*)                    (*c*)

(*b*)                    (*d*)

**Fig. 12.12**

    (*b*)   Explain the difference between *reading accuracy* and *measuring accuracy*.

84.  (*a*)   Write down the vernier caliper readings shown in Fig. 12.13.
     (*b*)   List the advantages and limitations of a vernier caliper compared with a micrometer caliper.

85.  Figure 12.14 shows a component being checked with a vernier height gauge using a DTI as a fiducial indicator. From the data given calculate the distance between the hole centres and the centre distance of hole B from the datum surface C.

86.  Figure 12.15 shows a turned component. List the measuring instrument most appropriate for checking each dimension during the machine process, giving reasons for your choice in each instance.

87.  (*a*)   With the aid of a sketch explain the principle of a *sine-bar*.
     (*b*)   Calculate the included angle of taper of a taper plug gauge supported between *sine-centres* if the centre distance between the contact rollers is 500 mm and the height of the slip gauge stack is 25.025 mm.

88.  (*a*)   State the precautions which should be taken when assembling and dismantling a stack of slip gauges in order to ensure maximum accuracy and minimum wear.

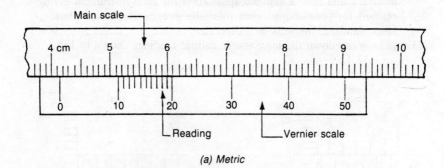

*(a) Metric*

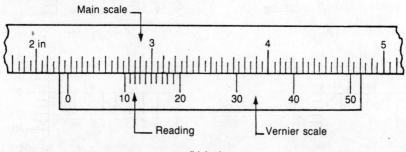

*(b) Inch*

**Fig. 12.13**

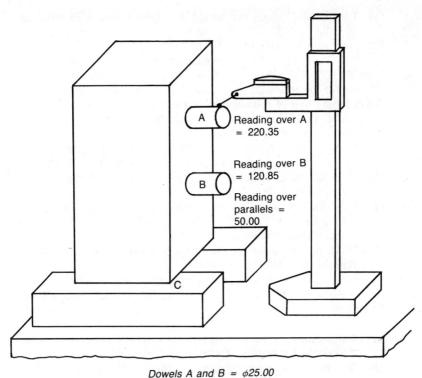

Dowels A and B = $\phi25.00$
Dimensions in millimetres

**Fig. 12.14**

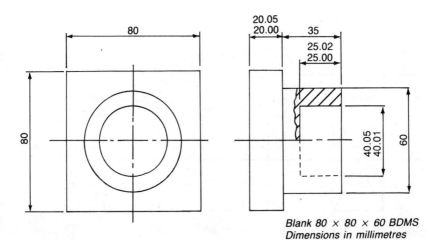

Blank 80 × 80 × 60 BDMS
Dimensions in millimetres
Open dimensions ± 0.5

**Fig. 12.15**

(b) List the slip gauges that would be required from a 78 piece set to build up a 25.7925 mm stack:
    (i) without using the 2.50 mm protector slips;
    (ii) using the 2.50 mm protector slips.

89. With the aid of sketches show how a dial test indicator (DTI) may be used for the following applications: as a comparator gauge; to detect lobing (out of roundness); to detect eccentricity in a turned component; to set the fixed jaw of a machine vice perpendicular to the T-slots in a milling machine table.

90. (a) Compare the advantages and limitations of a try square with a cylinder square as a workshop standard of perpendicularity.
    (b) With the aid of sketches show how a squareness comparator is set and used.

91. (a) Describe how a straight edge may be used to check flatness over a large area and state what precautions should be taken to detect errors of winding.
    (b) Describe how a surface plate may be used to check the surface flatness of a small component.

92. Comment upon the effect that developments in the understanding and in the techniques of assessment of surface texture (finish) have had on the quality of engineering products since the Second World War.

93. (a) Differentiate between 'roughness', 'waviness', and 'lay' when describing the texture of a machined surface.
    (b) The machining symbols shown in Fig. 12.16 also specify the $R_a$ value of the surface texture. In each instance select a suitable manufacturing process capable of producing such a surface and explain how the process has been selected.

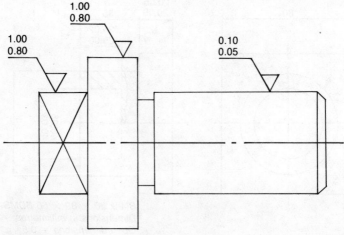

**Fig. 12.16**

94. With the aid of sketches explain the essential difference between $R_a$ and $R_z$ values when specifying surface texture.
95. Briefly describe the total cost of quality in terms of *control* costs and *failure* costs.

## Chapter 11

96. Discuss the importance of the free flow of information between the departments of an engineering company and draw up a management structure diagram for any company with which you are familiar.
97. Compare and contrast the problems which can arise in information flow in a very large company and in a very small company.
98. Differentiate between the *marketing* and *sales* function in a manufacturing company.
99. Discuss the functions of the following departments and their interrelationship in any engineering company with which you are familiar: design and development; production planning; costing and estimating; production control; production engineering/manufacture; inspection/quality control.
100. You have had an idea for a new product and, after taking professional advice, have decided to go into business on your own to manufacture it. You have adequate financial backing to set up a small- to medium-sized plant. Discuss the organisation of the introduction of the new product so as to ensure the success of the venture.

# Index